*Paul Henissart*

# NARROW EXIT

KU-094-471

**ARROW BOOKS**

Arrow Books Ltd
3 Fitzroy Square, London W1

An imprint of the Hutchinson Publishing Group

London Melbourne Sydney Auckland
Wellington Johannesburg and agencies
throughout the world

First published in Great Britain by
Hutchinson & Co (Publishers) Ltd 1974
Arrow edition 1976
© Paul Henissart 1973

CONDITIONS OF SALE: This book shall not, by way of trade or otherwise, be lent, re-sold, hired out or otherwise circulated without the publisher's prior consent in any form of binding or cover other than that in which it is published and without a similar condition being imposed on the subsequent purchaser. This book is published at a net price and is supplied subject to the Publishers Association Standard Conditions of Sale registered under the Restrictive Trade Practices Act, 1956

Made and printed in Great Britain
by The Anchor Press Ltd
Tiptree, Essex

ISBN 0 09 913240 0

D.L's BOOK SHOP
57, ELM ROW,
EDINBURGH

55ρ

He felt ashamed of his earlier suspicion of Kheli. The two thugs in the Citroen were certainly not carrying out his orders. The colonel might be mistrustful and overprone to spy on whoever encroached upon his territory, even a member of an offically friendly Service, but he did not resort to murder. Was it Gauthier? That was more likely, for he now realized that Preston suspected something. But just what Gauthier did not know and he had hardly had time to organize a murder attempt.

Who, then, did?

*This book is for Sylvie,*
*again*

## Author's note

While the setting of this book is Tunisia—
and therefore real—all of the characters
and incidents are imaginary.

# Contents

*Tunis? A nest of spies.*

— A Swiss Consul

# PART ONE

*I didn't come here for the climate.*
> —Ferenc Molnár (during a New York heat wave)

*We want our men to be honest, devoted, loyal and patriotic. In other words, we want them to be human.*
> —Isser Harel, former Chief, Israeli Secret Services

CHAPTER ONE

# The Qiryat

Ha Qiryat—which in Hebrew means "the city" or "the agglomeration"—is an administrative complex that rises behind a barbed-wire fence about one mile northeast of Tel Aviv, beyond the sluggish Yarkon River. The buildings are located in a suburb that was settled by German Protestants from Swabia, who migrated hopefully to Palestine during the nineteenth century. They planted trees in the sand, laid out wide asphalted streets and built sturdy homes; but in spite of their industry the venture failed. Some of the immigrants returned to Europe after the First World War, while the rest, reading the handwriting on the wall, hastily packed up in 1945. La Moshava Germanith, the suburb's present name, recalls their brief occupancy. The compound served during World War II as a police camp, then government ministries were temporarily situated there before being transferred to Jerusalem. Today, one of the two-story buildings is the headquarters of Ha Mossad, or The Institution—which is another name for the external arm of Israeli Intelligence.

Max recognized the other two men the General had summoned to his office.

He had seen them once or twice in the café on Dizengoff Street where members of The Institution informally meet for late-afternoon coffee and gossip, and so gained an inkling of what they were up to. One was tall and burnished like beaten copper; rawboned, he carried his six feet well; there was something casual and loose about his movements that no European Jew could or would affect; yet he lacked a sabra's proprietary air of belonging. An American, thought Max with less than joy.

The other was spare, alert and undersized, as functional and compact as a tiny gold coin.

The General indicated the Arab-looking individual, "Noah Black . . . and this is Marston"; he did not pronounce the trim little man's first name. (In the weeks ahead, Max never learned it, and felt no need to: some men are built so of one material, entire and plain, that it seems one name suffices to distinguish them from the race in general. But in Marston's case, the single name was also a professional label, like the *noms de scène* French character actors use.)

Max found the appearance of both men, especially the bigger, heavier one, slick and unreassuring. He swayed forward on the balls of his feet, making no attempt to conceal his suspiciousness as he surveyed the room. He was a stout, medium-sized man of forty with a wrestler's exaggeratedly powerful shoulders and a weather-reddened bull neck on which no collar ever rode securely. His hair was black, springy and twisted like licorice, but bald patches were beginning to spread out across his dry rotund skull. His prominent jaw was set at an unruly angle; one had the impression that if a hook were set in the tough folds of skin he would thrash and fight back for hours, like a giant game fish. Although he held the rank of reserve captain, these days most of his time was spent in the citrus groves outside Natanya, where he farmed ten acres, or forty *dunam*, of fertile red soil on the Sharon Plain.

"Levanon," said the General, "why are you standing? Sit down for God's sake and listen carefully."

The office was austere: detailed wall maps of Egypt, Syria, Jordan and Lebanon, three telephones, a blackboard, a decrepit-looking typewriter, a sagging divan and four cheap factory-made straight-backed chairs comprised the sum of furniture and equipment. In one corner, a metal space heater radiated an illusion of warmth—it was a frisky January day, but The Institution practiced occasional surprising economics. Beyond the tightly shut window, the blue cloudless sky of the Middle East gleamed realistically.

In spite of the chill, Max sweat. He had never grown accustomed to the weather in this country.

"We want to lay our hands on Salah Al Houaranni; this is the reason why you are here," the General announced brusquely, in his blunt South African accent. "Not to kill him," he added swiftly, addressing Max, "although he deserves it. For all his rubbishy talk of being the 'incarnation of Palestine's soul,' he is our biggest problem at this point. We want to bring him to trial and expose him for what he really is—an unhinged bloody fanatic whom even most Arab leaders are afraid of. The hospital raid up north last month was bad enough, but according to our reports he has far worse things up his sleeve."

On occasion, the General's face resembled a battleground on which Time had fought a major engagement and obtained a definitive victory. He had a shock of prematurely snowy hair and the fine numismatic profile of a Bourbon princeling or a Sioux chieftain. Like Max, he was careful about the climate—even in good weather he wore a gray hand-knitted pullover sweater over his khaki shirt; a shabby loose garment, ill-fitting and faded, it complemented the combs of stiff gray bristles that sprang out from his temples like the feathers of an aging bird of prey.

"We have determined there is no practical possibility of neutralizing Al Houaranni anywhere in the Middle East without accepting disproportionate casualties. We could try to suborn one of his followers, but with no assurance of results. We tried in Damascus and lost a valuable man. For years Al Houaranni has not, as a matter of principle, traveled outside the Middle East. It now turns out he will make a trip in three weeks to Tunis."

The General leaned back and smiled wintrily. "We could believe there was at least one Arab nation—Tunisia—that tolerated our existence, not happily but realistically. Al Houaranni's trip is intended to change all this." His clear blue sinless eyes settled insistently upon the three men for a second; it was this swift frank moment of examination Max would remember later, when his troubles began in earnest. "Al Houaranni will be in Tunis for two days. We want you to cut him out from his bodyguards, grab him, turn him over to us. Is this clear? The objective is simple—the operation itself is not."

He paused for a moment, for effect. He hoped the assignment was beginning to seem plausible and just, to assume solidity and weight in their imagination, like a distant point on the horizon whose true dimensions they could not suspect; but he was unsure whether he had achieved this goal. Max kept his eyes on the rectangle of immobile blue sky beyond the window; he consciously avoided glancing at the other two men, whom he already considered as accomplices. They are vulnerable, too, he thought. He could hear their steady, contained breathing. Neither of them spoke. But the salivating of their arid throats was almost painfully audible.

"Each of you has worked with us before. The mission calls for general experience and special skills for which you have been screened. It also requires an ability to work together harmoniously, and I am not kidding about this. But above all" —and here, improbably, the General's broad, wicked nose flared out at them menacingly; he was really as unpredictable as a rogue elephant—"with all your heart you must want this operation to succeed because you are convinced of its need and rightness. Belief!" He flapped his reddened hair-strewn hand on the dusty desk. "I am asking for belief from grown men. Sometimes I succeed in evoking it. Just by looking at you, I can tell that you are conscientious and disciplined—and perhaps not averse to a little flattery? I could ask for more— Jewish Supermen—but would I get them? The record here informs me that each of you is brave, but how can I really know that? When you do not even know yourselves. Listen to me: on this mission you are going to need more than bravery—enthusiasm will be your most reliable armor because, believe me"—his voice dropped with unintended effect— "there will come times when you wonder whether what you are doing is right."

"Why are you saying such a thing?" The outraged words

escaped from Max before he could clamp his overbig mouth shut. He found himself staring into the General's concerned eyes.

Simultaneously the other two men stirred nervously. It was as though the operation's scope had all at once demonstrated a nasty life of its own.

The General said accusingly, "Al Houaranni will even try to convert you. It won't surprise me; he knows his business as a demagogue. I don't want him to succeed."

"Wouldn't killing him, therefore, be more effective?" Black's loud voice, with its nasal drip of affectation, intruded into the room harshly. He had lustrous smooth dark hair cut and combed into precise waves, somber, resentful eyes and a chin that practically screamed of sullenness. Max recalled that in the café on Dizengoff, Black was known as Na Hazaorath, the "boy of splendor" (which means playboy), and he thought: He can't be real.

"Operationally, you are right: it is always easier to kill a man than kidnap him," the General snapped in rebuke, while his face remained stony. "However, we are not interested in assassination—or in creating a martyr. I am not sure myself that we should resort to kidnapping. But who has time for complete answers? The man's methods are dangerous; a decision had to be taken."

Max shifted his bulk slowly, to minimize an effect of top-heaviness that he tended to produce these days, and spoke for the second time. "Here is the only moderate government in the Arab world—do we want to undermine it? What is going to be the consequence for the Tunisians? You know that no Arab government can survive a new Eichmann-style kidnapping."

"Eichmann! A figure from the past. God, how I am bored with that opportunist who proved nothing in life or death. Al Houaranni is more important to us than Eichmann ever was," the General cut him short. "May I point out, Levanon, that your question is a little too artful? We are aware that the Tunisian government's mere existence serves a useful purpose . . . although we have no illusions about its ability to be a moderating influence in the Arab world. But we are talking about a president who is old and a government that is under systematic attack; if it is due to collapse, nothing we do will stop it. There's another point *you* haven't raised. We have a root problem at home: people—women, mothers, *voters*— are becoming fed up. Al Houaranni had a fantastic scheme to blow up the Wailing Wall. We nicked it in time; militarily, it made no sense, it would have been smarter to ambush the guard force of a *moshava*—but psychologically, how much effort would have been needed for us to recover? Are we going to present Al Houaranni's commandos with the opportunity to do damage simply because we are hypnotized by what may happen to the Tunisian government? Let me add, I would never approve a mission simply to flatter home opinion—in our field, it is always a fatal miscalculation." Candor did not become the General; his voice grew airy and bogus, and one understood how he had outlasted three changes of Cabinet and two prime ministers notorious for their foxiness.

"The question had to be raised," Max said.

"Of course; you were perfectly right. To get back to Al Houaranni: there are two reasons for his trip. His ostensible purpose is fund-raising; but the Tunisians have never shown much enthusiasm for annihilating us, and still less for giving

19

generously to the Palestinian cause. Undoubtedly, he will attempt a little tactful blackmail. The Tunisians are not what you might call overjoyed to have him as their house guest, but what can they do? The government prefers to tolerate an unwanted guest rather than expose itself to opposition criticism. There is a second, unofficial, reason for the journey which he is not publicizing. . . . He will make contact with disaffected elements. Certainly he will try to stir up trouble; in a way, it's become his specialty."

"In short," Max said, "he can't stay away."

"He has what he considers sound reasons for breaking his rule about never leaving the Middle East."

"Sound enough to run serious risks?" Marston asked.

"He will be in Tunis for the shortest feasible time—forty-eight hours," the General said. "I would tell you there is no hope whatever of seizing him under normal circumstances. The circumstances, however, are not normal. Al Houaranni's liking for intrigue makes him vulnerable—the mission is aimed at exploiting this weakness."

Max waited for the other two men's reaction. He expected Black to utter some comment, but the American remained silent, as did Marston. If the background facts were designed to instill belief, the General was making a serious psychological error. From experience Max knew that external factors, the so-called objective situation, weighed little in the decision to volunteer; the deepest motivations lay entombed under accumulated layers of mistakes and wrong turnings. Perhaps—it was more likely—the decision sprang out of a man's simple need to volunteer for hazardous duty at some time in his life? If the mission failed . . . Max had a fleeting image of three bodies laid out in a messy row on anonymous ground; if some detail went awry, gossip would circulate in the *moshava*, and the General would make sure that he was shunted away from this sort of work for good; and if it succeeded, in The Institution's austere tradition, he would receive a spattering of shy thanks which would soon be forgotten. Therefore, why volunteer in the first place? Long ago he had studied a good deal of philosophy and history, and sought to apply complicated theories to the maze of life; nowadays, at Emek Hefer, between sunup and sunset, he had limited time for reading; in the evening he drank whiskey and listened to records. He associated his periods of eager reading with youth. Then, he had assembled a number of certitudes for winter, like a squirrel's hoard of nuts, and now the need to probe and inquire seemed less acute.

The General brushed the folder on his desk with his fingertips tentatively, although he knew its contents (he did his homework in a downstairs study of his house, in predawn silence, long before his family was up). "Each of you has seen a copy of the operational timetable. This plan—Operation Flood—is the work of Emir, the Resident in Tunis. All our departments have gone over it with a magnifying glass for conceptual errors, and made deletions and additions." He paused. "It's not foolproof: a fool can carry it out and bungle it. However, in its revised, present state, it's an intelligent, professional piece of work that embodies and reflects the Resident's ideas. He's laid a very firm foundation for you to act upon."

"Why are you trying so hard to reassure us?" Max asked aloud.

Before he could get a reply, Black interrupted; and if the tone was respectful, he couldn't purge his voice altogether of its brash New York assertiveness. "The key person in Flood is the Resident—we get in and out successfully only if Emir's end holds up."

Max smiled faintly. The same thought had occurred to him. Black, he decided, had the soul of an agent, who thoughtfully limned out areas of future disappointment, so that Intelligence directors had no legitimate basis for reproach. It was not a bad quality.

"Emir is a remarkable man." The General's voice assumed a remote, impersonal tone, and Max noted that he ignored Black's specific criticism. "So much the better for you if he is the keystone. He has one vital quality I'm sure you'll appreciate—a capacity for enduring."

The way the General advanced that piece on the board, it had all the earmarks of a booby trap. "Enduring," in the General's ambiguous voice, cracked like a two-edged weapon. His own career, tacking and turning about in shoals of deceptiveness, prejudiced them against him. If this was the price one paid for enduring, it was high. Not that the three men in the room took what he said on faith—already a good, firm operational cement was established between them of strictly limited trust: once set, it was virtually impossible to sunder.

The General spoke again of Emir. "He has been in his current post for fourteen years. He has French nationality, and his wife is French. He operates on every level of Tunisian society. Money is, thankfully, not his motivation; he started out as an idealist, and as far as I can tell, he still manages to be one, in spite of all we do to discourage him." His aging, firm hand described a vague, deprecatory gesture, which was meant to include Government and Parliament.

"You have only to be with Emir a quarter hour to understand what sort of man he is. I could do with a few more with his ability and dedication."

He considered Max for a moment in distracted silence. "Your North African experience was limited to Tunisia, am I correct?"

Max's bald dome shone briefly as he nodded, and the General turned his attention to Black. "During the summer of 1963 you put into Tunis on a sailing boat out of Malta while on a cruise—"

"We stayed no more than two days."

"Then they're unlikely to have a photograph of you, except as part of a group. Marston, is this up to date? In 1961 you spent two months in Tunis with an older, widowed sister who wanted you to settle down and help run her travel agency. You rejected the idea, primarily out of lack of confidence in her business judgment. She ran the place under her married name and is now deceased; the agency was sold. You have never returned there since."

"I was right—she didn't know how to run it." Marston glared at the palms of his hands, as though challenging the fortune lines he saw.

The General, satisfied, said, "We don't want to think head shots of you are floating about in their files. You will fly in under identities we're establishing. Later, of course, they'll spot inconsistencies, but by that time you'll be out of the country. At the start, it's essential none of you has a record of previous political or criminal involvement: we looked for three men who had been in Tunisia, spoke Arabic and were unknown to the Tunisian Sûreté."

Max was fascinated by the General's method. Field command of an armored brigade had shaped his approach to tactical problems: first he outlined the objective, then only— often much later, and sometimes not at all—got around to inventorying the means needed to attain it.

"Marston, how long have you been driving a taxi?"

"Four years, sir."

"And during military service?"

"Every class of vehicle from command car to weapons carrier."

"Then you won't have any problem. I want to impress one final point on all of you: Tunis represents the *only* opportunity of neutralizing this madman. We are sending you out as a three-man commando instead of the usual four. Three will do the trick, and there is no purpose in risking a single extra life." This was added with calculated chilliness, for the General had a good grip on them now. He concluded briskly, "What happens, you will want to know, if you can't get near Al Houaranni? You will return here with no one the wiser, after spending a few days' holiday at official expense; it's as simple as that. There will be plenty of questions before you leave, but I think we've answered a few essential ones. I want to see you a minute, Levanon."

Black promptly rose, assessing the room's occupants out of dark, distrustful eyes before he departed. Marston's chair scraped; the little man left in stumpy disapprobation, as though he were quitting a dentist's office.

"What do you think of them?"

"Marston will do. Black may be a problem."

"Don't underrate Black. In spite of his manner, he's a first-rate officer. He speaks Arabic as well as you or I, he can handle weapons, he's tough and loyal. What's the matter with you, Levanon—are you becoming a snob? You're too intel- ligent to fall for this sabra nonsense. Our best people are not always native-born."

"I saw American volunteers in '56. Is this one going to demand ice cream in the middle of the desert too?"

"Does he look the sort? No one is fobbing a playboy off on you. I have every confidence that Black will shape up to your exacting standards; but if you're worried, say so now. I can still find a replacement—"

"No," said Max. "I object to his personality. Operationally he can be an asset."

"A replacement may involve other drawbacks, you know. When I play poker I discard cards, but this is not poker and we are not gambling only money."

"Black will do."

"Marston will be a useful man," the General said indiffer- ently. "Marston is excellent."

Max looked at the faraway sky. Why did he dare say that about believing? The question throbbed like a rudely awak- ened optical muscle behind his eye. The source of his outrage was close by and obvious: it was the General's dangerous ability to stir conviction in men. This was how he dispatched them into a topsy-turvy world of his own devising. It was a world that need not exist save for his unreasonable sense of duty. Flood was a case in point. A day ago, it had had no tangible existence except within a flat contingency folder, yet now they already believed wholeheartedly in it, accepted the fact that in several weeks they would be sweating with bloody holy terror under a prosaic sky quite similar to the pure unmoving rectangle beyond the window. Max knew that all too soon the unreal schemes the General elaborated in this gray square room were translated into reality; he had been subjected to his salesmanship before. In two or three weeks he would find himself deep in another world, the reverse of this one, the other side of the coin that gave this face its reality. He felt a swelling of his stomach muscles, and knew that as long as he possessed an imagination, the reaction was uncontrollable. He wished suddenly that there were more time to prepare and foresee, although in one tough kernel of his mind he acknowledged that if unlimited time were put at their disposal they would get nothing done. He also knew that no Intelligence operation is ever undertaken on the basis of a limitless fund of time.

He considered the General's old, embattled face and waited for him to speak.

"I wanted to see you about Emir." The General again placed his fingertips on the folder on the desk, as though it contained an intricate message that could be interpreted only by touch. "You can count on the Resident. He is utterly devoted, for reasons so complex that I can't begin to enumerate them. And he's never made a serious mistake so far."

"Let's hope he doesn't start now."

"I mean, he does not overestimate his capacities," the General replied irritably. "He misevaluates information that his sources give him. Who doesn't? But he keeps his sense of proportion. Emir doesn't panic—and he doesn't glow with dangerous enthusiasm either." The contradiction with what he had said earlier passed unnoticed.

Max shifted his weight again in the rigid, uncomfortable chair. To judge by the grimace the General made, silence was the wrong attitude.

"It's been years since I saw him. In those days he was a

26

strange fellow whom you could ask to do the most hair-raising things. He won't return, he's stayed out unusually long; we only agree because of the quality of the information. Naturally we've run controls on him to make sure he hasn't shifted allegiance, but in this respect everything is all right. If he walked in through the door now, no one would recognize him, except—perhaps—me." His voice carried an abrupt scratchy undertone of pain, like a record that has been damaged in one essential passage; for once, Max was treated to the bleak spectacle of the General being clumsy. "To be honest, sometimes I'm afraid we've lost contact with Emir as a man. Quite possibly, Emir has lost contact with himself as a man. It won't be the first time it's happened. It's the price he's paid, and we're involuntarily responsible."

"It doesn't affect your confidence in him—"

"All the more so, if you see what I mean." The General drew in his shoulders augustly and said with contempt, "The work is all he has left, the damn fool. I doubt it would do any good to recall him. What can we offer a man like that—a desk, a flat in Ramat Aviv, a season pass for the Philharmonic Orchestra? I admire his wife," he added irrelevantly, and rose.

"Emir will remain in place long after your group has come and gone, I want you to remember this. There will be tremendous fallout after Al Houaranni's disappearance, and we want Emir's cover protected at all cost—no matter what you do, this must receive priority. As officer in charge, you will contact him by telephone upon arrival—it will be your sole direct contact. Here are his address and telephone number in Tunis; you are not to divulge this material to your men. It is to be committed to memory."

Max accepted the slip of paper the General handed him (which he would later destroy) and waited for the final piece of information to click into place.

"As for Emir's name, I suppose that I must give you it too," the General said reluctantly. He went to the blackboard, quickly wrote out two words in chalk and stepped back. Then, with an astonishing, God-like gesture, he vigorously rubbed out the name, looked at the faint remaining imprint and wiped it out too with a damp cloth.

For a moment the name on the blackboard had read Alex Gauthier.

## CHAPTER TWO

# The Resident

GAUTHIER looked forward to lunch on most days. As *envoyé permanent* of an influential and liberal Paris morning newspaper, he ate during the week with men whose conversation was accurate or wildly inventive, or both, informative, chatty and sometimes discerning—Tunisian ministers, subsecretaries and their zealous aides, boastful fellow correspondents, hungry young attachés with a fondness for Franco-Tunisian cooking; or he returned to his house in Carthage and shared with Anne-Marie, his wife, and Marc, his son, a meal prepared by the maid—bland or oily, depending upon her versatile mood; or he remained alone in his office and munched a pizza and green salad brought up from the ground-floor café-restaurant. All of these arrangements suited Gauthier, who paid little attention to food, enjoyed company but could do without it, and at times yearned for a midday break relished in solitude. At irregular intervals throughout the month, however, his routine changed. He drove away from the center of the city and met men whom he did not invite into his home and did not necessarily greet if he encountered them on Tunis' streets. No women belonged to his network; he flatly refused to employ a woman agent. The Qiryat had grumbled at first—for form's sake, he suspected —then condescendingly let the matter drop.

He arrived a quarter hour early at the restaurant in La Goulette. A case officer—a Resident Director, still more so— is expected to reconnoiter a meeting place before an agent's arrival. An agent can unknowingly be under surveillance and lead a hostile Service to a rendezvous. An agent can make mistakes. An agent can betray. Long ago, Gauthier had developed a hard-bitten attitude toward the presumptuous rules of the support staff in the homey atmosphere of Secret Service headquarters. If his instinct dictated a reason for breaking the regulations, he unhesitatingly broke them. In the present instance, however, he believed that it was a wise precaution to turn up first. The agent with whom he had an appointment was the most unreliable of men.

Lusty, raucous and incurably lower class, Tunis' waterfront district of La Goulette—unkempt collection of ramshackle stucco cottages, matchbox houses and would-be villas on a sand bar nine miles north of the city, upon which generations of Corsican civil servants, Jews, Maltese and Arabs have left their combined stamp of squalor—is famed for its sea food. The offshore waters teem with fish, and offer a rich Mediterranean choice of mullet, red mullet, mackerel and sea perch. There are other specialties besides—cow's neck, couscous *bkaila*, which is prepared with a black sauce, and cheese crepes. Lucullus, Venus, Monte Carlo, Chez Bichi, Maurice's and other establishments compete along the two principal thoroughfares. In summer, crowds of diners, men in shirt sleeves and women in frail silk sheaths, stroll in the warm, tingling dark and inspect the day's catch laid out on ice-filled counters. There is no point in comparison shopping, as prices chalked up on blackboards outside each place vary only slightly.

The blue sky came down on La Goulette with a flash, like the blade of a guillotine. As he advanced along the street, the familiar lingering odor—legacy—of cheap frying oil, oranges, coffee and open sewers assailed Gauthier. Here was the street scene that so enraptured tourists in season but which merely reflected a desperate ennui. There was little complexity in Arab commerce: it boiled down to simple transactions that put a premium on rhetoric and mutual confidence. A beggar trotted after him with cupped hands and exclaimed beseech-ingly, if tritely, "May thy day be made of honey, O Sidi!" Gauthier stepped nimbly past him. "*Tu es riche et tu ne me donnes rien?*" Affecting surprise, the man turned away, disconsolate. "Cursed be the ship that brought thee to this shore!" he howled from a safe distance.

Language, thought Gauthier, is the only ornament of the poor.

He sat down at Maurice's, choosing a table that faced the municipal garden, where a fountain and three scraggly palmet-tos await better times. It was quarter to one. He smoked a cigarette and examined the menu. He was a broad-shouldered, bronzed man, tall and erect, with curly straw hair and a cast of Scandinavian austerity to his full, serious features. At forty, the lines around his thin, disdainful nose curved away like scimitars. He was occasionally taken for a Norwegian banker or a Dutch nobleman; or for a northern Frenchman, which was fairly close to the truth; but then people suspected he must have a pint of dour Flemish blood coursing obsti-

31

nately through his veins. Women thought of him as stand-offish and intimidating, certainly not much fun, and suspected he might be difficult to handle; but when he abruptly displayed a sharp, swift, lopsided grin, when his eyes grew bluer and clearer, and the scimitars glittered, they amended their impression.

A lank waiter with a long, ragged chin approached. "What do you want?" he asked curtly, as Arabs will when they cannot anticipate a response. "Food? Fish? Wait! You will eat a *complet de poisson* for not much money." Gauthier lifted his glacier-blue eyes, and something bright, like specks of flint, crumpled the waiter's bravado style, caused him to grin feebly and move away without a further word.

Gauthier had chosen this restaurant at his last meeting with Ben Larbi. In winter the restaurants of La Goulette that stay open put up stiff drapes and turn on the central heating to ward off the snapping chill. Tunisians are highly sensitive to cold and dark, and must be induced to stray far from home as soon as the season heels over and the sun fails to thaw the breath of cold morning air. Many of the waiters at Maurice's were from the south, and when the wind blew from the east, out of the Mediterranean, with its taste of winter dark and alien force, they became pensive and fell homesick for their blue savage skies. "Nothing good comes from the east," they said, "neither the wind nor the people." In this, they reflected the Maghreb Arab's distrust of Mishrak, the sunrise lands from Syria to the Gulf of Oman. In this season, trade was slack; only one other table was occupied—by a fat, stolid woman with oily ringlets and a brave Sicilian mustache who was arguing with her husband. By the time the man he was

32

waiting for stepped quickly in through the door, Gauthier had concluded that the rendezvous was clean.

With a brief nod Ben Larbi extended a reluctant hand, then sat down and eyed Gauthier across the tablecloth accusingly. He was slight, sleek, well oiled and feline, like an ocelot.

"I had no desire to come at all——"

"Then it is to your credit that, for once, you are on time."

"There is a limit"——he bared his teeth briefly——"to what even I can do."

Gauthier considered him in silence, as he had studied the waiter. When his eyes turned pale, further comment was seldom necessary.

Ben Larbi looked at the menu in Gauthier's hand. "As you can imagine, I am not very hungry. But to keep your expenses from being ridiculously low, I shall have a lobster cocktail, then a *salade tunisienne*, after that I shall see. At any rate, a bottle of Sancerre. I need a glass of wine."

"During Ramadan?"

"This restaurant is run by Jews, and only Europeans can afford lunch here."

"Come off it. The owner is from the same place you are." Then he added, to needle his agent, "It's still a form of cheating."

As though the light were too intense, although in fact they sat in aquarium pallor, Ben Larbi frowned at the ceiling. His effeminate face grew almost playful. "If that were all I had on my conscience!"

It was the final week of Ramadan, when Moslems' nerves are ready to snap after the month-long observance of fasting and sexual abstinence during the daylight hours. Gauthier

33

knew the rich in Tunis didn't give a damn about the rules; they lapped Scotch steadily, long before sundown, and as for sex . . . the siesta and *coucheries* were interwoven as closely as threads in a Kairouan rug. But Ben Larbi, for all his social climbing, did not belong to this spoiled milieu. Like many others, he practiced Ramadan without believing, to affirm his superior status as an Arab. Not that he'd followed the precepts to the letter—there had been two bad lapses, which meant two days of atonement after the feast of Ain Seguir, when everybody else resumed a normal existence. This prospect visibly added to his irritability.

Gauthier settled down to the *complet de poisson*—grilled fish, a fried egg and fried potatoes—he had ended by ordering, with a half bottle of Sidi Rais rosé wine, which Tunisians unjustly disdain; it looked and tasted like warm stone, and he fancied it. At first, Ben Larbi ate finickily; with Europeans he affected dainty table manners. But halfway through lunch the habits of early boyhood overcame him, and he hunched over his food, rapidly stuffing tomatoes, onions and sardines into his mouth, while washing the whole down with glassfuls of Sancerre, as though he could never get enough to eat and drink. The white wine had the merit of dissolving his original sourness, for suddenly he became talkative.

"I am terribly unhappy about this assignment," he said. "For once, a man is coming to Tunis who is capable of acting and forcing the West to pay attention to our collective problem, and you are bent on destroying him. It's part of your typical inhuman sense of irony to force me to contribute to this crime. If it involved any of these mediocre Arab leaders, believe me, I would have less scruples; they bore me with their narrow ambitions. Generally speaking, politics are not my field. Women have the sense to interest themselves in what is real and not this wretched, never-ending squabble for money and influence."

"I'm glad you've developed an admiration for women."

Ben Larbi displayed his amusement for just a second; he leaned forward and laid his hand lightly on Gauthier's wrist; he couldn't resist the desire for contact. "To show you my good faith, I attended last night's meeting."

"Well, have they changed their minds?"

"Of course not; we made a final review of arrangements. It wasn't easy; I have to be extremely careful—"

"Why? You're part of their gang."

"We distrust one another far more than outsiders. It's all being organized in the smallest possible circle, to prevent betrayal. Don't you understand that?" He reflected somberly and added, "Why they trust *me*, I don't know. They are very worried because Al Houaranni's arrival is viewed as a unique opportunity they simply cannot afford to squander." He dabbed his black hair back into place and frowned again. "Why aren't you satisfied with the information I get you from the Ministry? You are making me run unnecessary risks. If this operation goes wrong, do you realize that you'll lose on two counts? We'll both have to run for it—if we are lucky."

Gauthier looked at him without blinking.

Ben Larbi was becoming excited. "I don't want any part of this stupidity: To help your dirty *Yhoud* friends in Tel Aviv," he hissed.

A neat touch, Gauthier thought, was the conscience-stilling peroration about Jews; in this way, with characteristic spinelessness, Ben Larbi sold out his own side while abusing the other. Gauthier let the silence dwell to his advantage, then said, "I think I can get you slightly more for expenses." He caught Ben Larbi's flickering glance of assessment, and specified, "Two hundred dinars supplementary costs."

"Why do you think two hundred dinars will change my mind?"

"Because I know how you will spend them." Gauthier suddenly felt fed up with the meal, the restaurant and, above all, with Ben Larbi—there was no fire behind the man, it was all cold, mean calculation. Ben Larbi disgusted him. He felt as though he had inhaled too much perfume in a sweaty bedroom. "You have contracted to do this work," he reminded him.

"I would rather go to prison."

"There are no *taffar* in the block for political inmates." Gauthier used the word for aggressive homosexuals. In his dealings with this agent, he had never employed the word before. Pronounced matter-of-factly, without inflection, it anchored the conversation with its dull realism. A flatly delivered insult carries the most contempt.

"Let's cut out the nonsense. Did you bring the documents?"

Then Ben Larbi said, "Three hundred dinars. I desperately need the money."

"Stop it."

"I don't even know what you're up to."

"Ignorance is a security measure on *your* behalf."

"You are confronting me with an appalling problem of conscience—"

"Which you will resolve in your usual manner."

36

"You know, this time blackmail won't work."

Carefully, Gauthier watched the other man's set face for revolt. "Very well. You are unable or unwilling to fulfill your commitment, and I have a lot of work waiting at my office. *Andiamo?*" He made a gesture to call the waiter, and as he had expected, Ben Larbi's resistance collapsed in one swift, ignominious movement.

"Wait! I have the password, the meeting place, the transport arrangement and the final time schedule."

With method Gauthier chose his first cigarette since lunch; he blew a pale circle of smoke away from his guest's face, but studiously avoided offering him the pack.

"The password is *el Hayeb*, which means 'life.' Al Houaranni will be taken in a car without markings to a villa in Mutuelleville, where he will meet the Inner Committee. The meeting will take place between six and seven in the evening. It cannot last beyond seven-fifteen, because he must be back in Tunis to attend a reception at the Moroccan Embassy. If he remains away more than an hour from his hotel, he risks arousing the government's suspicion. I do not see why you are so disagreeable today."

"Have you the police passes?"

Ben Larbi picked up the menu and then laid it down. "I shall have only coffee so as not to abuse your generosity," he said.

Gauthier's fingers felt the flat Manila envelope inside the menu and descended it beneath table level. This was the vulnerable moment, he knew. Danger flickered here on the thin line between play-acting and reality which he had crossed so many times that he could hardly tell anymore where it lay.

He drew breath profoundly, as a man does who has been swimming alone for a long time in the middle of the sea, then his fingers moved the envelope toward his pocket.

"I have changed my mind," Ben Larbi said. "I shall have brandy too."


Two years before, this *attai*, this queer, had started to pass official documents to him under the impression that they were being paid for by the French Intelligence Service. Their first meeting had taken place in the bar of the Tunisia Palace Hotel. It was surprising, Gauthier had discovered, how relatively easy it was to identify potential recruits among intellectuals and at a ministerial level in the government; it was far more difficult to recruit officers and students; still more difficult to win the cooperation of minor-rank bureaucrats whom he needed to carry out simple tasks—like leaving a door unlocked—that required no special knowledge or perception. Ben Larbi was employed as a clerk-typist in the Files Section on the fourth floor of the Interior Ministry. Ben Larbi gathered the impression that the husky blond Frenchman knew more than his European colleagues about the real situation inside the country. After several further encounters and a series of carefully sown hints, he realized that Gauthier's curiosity went beyond legitimate inquisitiveness. Ben Larbi knew that he was being sounded out and measured for a role. Far from causing panic, this realization pleased him. At the Ministry he earned fifty dinars a month—about one hundred dollars—which he eked out with thirty dollars from the Police des Étrangers, which is a cover for the Secret Police, on whose behalf he kept an eye on foreigners he met. Thus, while Gauthier was cultivating him, he had a motive for reciprocating the interest. Ben Larbi was not averse to giving Gauthier classified information where it involved slight risk; he took his Secret Police affiliation lightly, and had early come to the conclusion that spying was a game that could, with a little deftness, be played on both sides; he had acquired a new boy friend and wanted an increment to his two other monthly sources of income. Gauthier seemed to know all about his habits, so there was no need for tiresome explanations.

In a car parked on Boulevard Bab Menara one April evening, Ben Larbi handed over three typewritten sheets of paper stamped in purple ink *"Très confidentiel,"* which he had pilfered just ten minutes after the Ministry closed for the day. For this he received two hundred-dinar bank notes folded into a cheap white envelope. In return, he painstakingly wrote out, in his florid, uneducated hand, the sum, the word *"reçu"* and his signature on a sheet of blank paper, which Gauthier slid into his pocket. The pen Ben Larbi used was his own— nothing could incriminate Gauthier, apart from the fact that the IOU was in his possession.

In the following months Ben Larbi signed numerous receipts. Occasionally, to keep his superiors satisfied, he drafted brief reports about Gauthier, but they tended to be dull, for he perceived the danger of arousing the police's interest in the Frenchman, who must now be protected as a major source of remuneration.

Ben Larbi assumed that further profitable transactions lay ahead. He felt no pangs of guilt about the arrangement. If the French learned about the stresses within the government, he reasoned, what harm was there in that? Astute, vigilant and vain, smarting with desire to regain their lost influence and exclude the Americans from the desert, they were, on the whole, well disposed toward their former protectorate.

Who was Ben Larbi, the Qiryat wanted to know. Following intensive questioning and diligent cross-checking, Gauthier drew up and submitted a complete dossier on his protégé.

Ali Ben Larbi grew up on the island of Djerba, off the Saharan coast.

There were thousands like him in Tunisia—slim adolescent Arabs, as svelte-hipped and taut as flamenco dancers, who prowled aggressively around the tourist hotels with a terrible single-mindedness of purpose. His sole possessions in those days were a pair of slacks, Italian plastic sandals, an argotic knowledge of French and desperate cheek that went camouflaged as Mediterranean gracefulness. When he was idle, he walked hand-in-hand with male friends of his age through the windy, littered village square or sat playing cards in wicked cafés—but other ambitions itched at his mind.

By sixteen he had rubbed up against every European, male and female, chance threw him into contact with. One evening, near the old Turkish mosque, Djemaa Turki, he met a Swedish boy in a white frilly mesh playshirt. Within minutes Eric was patting his brown arm. Ben Larbi asked boldly, for the first time, for some money—and, to his gratification, without haggling obtained ten dinars. He was on his way.

When he arrived in Tunis he found employment at the Ministry. He was one of many minor-grade bureaucrats in a recently decolonized country. He was underpaid and overworked. He was a bachelor. At first, he had haunted the little corner stand-up bars where crowds of men munch *kemia*

40

and sip glasses of coffee in the suave prickling hour just before nightfall. Off duty, he dressed in the height of Tunisian street elegance—a pink *ajouré* shirt adorned with black buttons and opened to the navel, hip-hugging sea-green jeans and perforated white shoes. His coarse doll's hair was combed with meticulousness; a black cowlick caressed his olive forehead. His rather thick lips were grayish blue, as though bruised. He cleaned his nails in public with a steel nail cutter he had filched from a hotel lavatory. Soon, he began to pass after-dinner hours with a sly, pustular dark-browed boy, strolling down, then back up the center mall of Avenue Bourguiba where the birds set up a mad tweetering in the ficus trees at nightfall. The pleasures of Tunis are quickly exhausted, especially by those with little money and no introductions. The salary he received left no margin for swinging in discotheques.

Then he crossed Gauthier's path—and a not-so-subtle change came over him. He dressed more conservatively in dark, sleek suits, and wore sunglasses and neatly trimmed sideburns. He took a three-room apartment in a staid building that housed an insurance company on Rue Ibn Khaldoun across from the Maison de Culture and furnished it in severely European style. No Oriental geegaws of hammered brass for him: he brought in a German record player, stocked a brightly painted cupboard with Scotch and aperitif wines, and thumbtacked to the wall an airline poster showing snow. But there were also a divan, a rush mat, a hassock of soft gazelle leather, a framed photograph of two teen-age boys on a beach, a garish yellow wrought-iron table, and vases without flowers.

Finding bachelor quarters is not always easy in an Arab town. Landlords recoil before renting to single young men. In the old days the situation was the following: In the homes of prosperous merchant families, one room adjacent to the street was set aside for a bachelor son's escapades. It was called the *chambre de veillée*. It was furnished in good taste, with rugs and other objects of value. But when the great families started to move out of the medina, the sons followed —so as to continue having their meals cooked and washing done by their mothers' servants. Or if they struck off on their own, they could seldom afford more than a mean one-room flat.

Ben Larbi was lucky: he had gotten his place through a friend. It was only four blocks from where he worked. He would not have wanted to live in the old quarter because of the promiscuity and noise and filth; the new neighborhood was more his style. The nail cutter was gotten rid of. The pimply youth disappeared (after stealing a few dinars from a bedroom commode) and was replaced by smoother-mannered, more mature companions whose interests embraced politics and revolution. At the Ministry, Ben Larbi received a promo-tion—and the increase in salary justified the amelioration in his living arrangements. His biggest problem was to conceal scrupulously any sign of undue luxury. Occasionally he crossed the street and attended lectures at the Maison de Culture given by the Party; he was seen, and this helped at the Ministry.

Gauthier oversaw the metamorphosis. The thought oc-curred to him that he was contributing on a modest scale to Tunisian cultural development. From time to time he sur-prised a flash of craftiness in the haggard eyes set deep in the clay-colored morose face. Could Ben Larbi be trusted?

42

Certainly not; but his need for unvouchered funds in cheap square envelopes was a powerful incentive, and Gauthier, who kept careful track of his agent's movements, saw no immediate danger of being outbidded.

Ben Larbi's was, in control officer's jargon, a typical case of "misdirection." He had been recruited "under a false flag." He was being utilized without awareness of the end cause being served, a risky technique that is sometimes practiced when an individual is willing to furnish information to a foreign power he believes noninvidious but may balk at serving a country he regards as mortally dangerous to his own.

A showdown was to be expected, and it had occurred last summer, on a windless evening, when they met by prearrangement on a road near the La Soukra golf course long after the last players had left the links. As soon as Gauthier saw his agent's livid, agitated face he guessed at the sort of trouble there would be. He knew exactly how to deal with it—since for some time he had been steeling himself for this moment.

"Dirty yid!" Ben Larbi screamed. "No more reports, documents, lists, not for the scum you serve. I despise them." Then he wept, in quivering, shallow fits that bent double his slender, promiscuous body—weeping being a substitute, it seemed, for retching; but a residue of malice glittered through the light tears. "You are not as cunning as you think; you will pay threefold someday for the harm you are doing."

Gauthier felt nothing, certainly not commiseration.

"Dirty liar—"

"No one has lied to you. Where the information was bound didn't interest you."

Even the exact manner in which the other had learned the

43

truth aroused only a mild curiosity; there were numberless ways for the consequences of a leak to become evident—perhaps the Ministry had circulated a pointed warning to guard against Zionist infiltration, or Ben Larbi had overheard gossip after a meeting of departmental heads or simply recognized in a newspaper paragraph a supposedly confidential item he had passed along. Gauthier experienced no undue alarm; Ha Mossad masked the sources of its information with professional nimbleness until the trail was too cold to be pursued. He knew that if Ben Larbi had really meant to break contact he would not have come to this meeting. The turning point was past. Far too much was at stake—his flat, his clothes, his friends, an entire infrastructure of corruption —for him to rebel successfully. Gauthier felt no akinness to a lepidopterist, but he could not help comparing Ben Larbi's wild fluttering in the net to that of a gaudy weak specimen destined from the very start to become a collector's prey.

"And now what?" he asked distastefully.

"I am through with your lies and your spying."

"Betraying secrets to the French, is this right?"

Ben Larbi screamed in rage, "I respect the French. The Israelis . . ." He lifted his arms skyward in triumph. "At the Ministry they will welcome my identification of a dirty Israeli spy."

"The Ministry will hang an informer for Israel surely." And that was the end of that. As he had expected, there was no need to dwell upon the receipts signed, the money received. So had started a different, more brittle phase of their relationship—but, Gauthier thought, a sounder one. For now Ben Larbi feared serious retribution, and it would always deter him from scurrying to the police. There had been no particular hurry about advising him of his employers' identity, but now that he knew, it was, on the whole, a salutary development that left no room for further misunderstanding; just as from a pimp's point of view, a desirable breakthrough occurs when a whore admits that she is a whore.

At the Qiryat, the General heard about the scene and was pleased too.


They left the restaurant and walked across the street together. The winter sunlight bore down cold and hard, without the slightest promise of spring; an unmerciful wind whipped the empty corners of the square. Ben Larbi shivered and Gauthier was not surprised—city Arabs were uncommonly sensitive to cold. Live in North Africa long enough and you became like them. He knew this sleek race as clever, inquisitive, oversensitive, sensual, theatrical, hospitable to a fault and mindlessly cruel; they could be generous and attentive and intelligent, and they could dash a kitten's brains out against a wall in the same breath. Gauthier had no intention of staying on forever in this luminous exile. It was a decision he had just reached.

"I will notify you about the exact time of the telephone call. You understand how it must be made and from where?"

Ben Larbi grimaced.

"He will trust you. You are, so to speak, his colleague—"

"He is not a colleague" was the prompt response. "He is our friend, he is my brother." This glib flight into metaphor and rhetoric, for Al Houaranni was not related in any way to Ben

Larbi, was typical: any Arab from Syria to Morocco would reply in like fashion. How did you organize an Intelligence operation with language that ran away with the speaker?

At the corner, Ben Larbi thrust out his hand perfunctorily and made off down a narrow side street that lay in shadow and led to the beach. Gauthier continued numbly on his way— there were days when he thought he had died years ago and his ghost went through the motions of living. There had been a stiff offshore breeze blowing since before daybreak. Now in the January afternoon the Mediterranean was the color of mud and the flagstones of the villas were greasy with spray. Over the elongated sand bar the golden Mediterranean wind blew. Out there, the waves were like blue dusky hills in the distance. Gauthier always equated lack of sunlight with death. It seemed natural that Ben Larbi had chosen to depart by this inimical shadowy street. He gave the impression of being as venomous as the scorpions on his native island that slept protected all day in hidden chinks and crevices of stone walls, then at night scuttered out across the sand fields in search of prey. Gauthier thought he had never negotiated before with a mind so dark and, what was worse, so artless. At twenty-four, Ben Larbi had exhausted every emotion but treason.

Venders of cashews and pistachios shivered in the harsh draft. Squatting on doorsteps, befuddled by the sun, they manifested the Arab obsession with shoes, staring at Gauthier's alien footwear. Idle poets of life, they basked like serpents in the chill sun. There were two seasons, they said in Tunis—the good one and the hot one. At heart, Gauthier disagreed; he couldn't wait for the summer to return. In winter he had no hobbies but reading sailing manuals and Admiralty charts, house repairs inspired only horror, he padded to and fro inside his home, grouchy and out of touch with his family. But when summer came, his private hibernation ended, life started up, Tunis again became, as a travel writer had capsulized it, "one of those cities of the sun where light is an element, almost a nourishment." Each Saturday he drove his Bel-Air station wagon to the Sidi Bou Said Nautical Club and lugged his sails, slats, rudder, life jackets and cans of beer aboard his four-meter racing boat. Occasionally with Anne-Marie, frequently alone, he sailed across the width of the bay, tacked up the coast and lay to off what were known, when he had first come to Tunisia, as the Archbishop's Rocks. When he balanced barefoot on the planks of his boat, gripped with his toes, poised dripping in the sun, and plunged clean into the lilting indigo depths—then, he achieved a measure of liberation.

He shook his head as he thought of his agent. Ben Larbi belonged to one of those cells of conspirators that multiplied in Tunis' damp vitiating atmosphere like a virus. Gauthier had first heard about Al Houaranni's trip through Ben Larbi's bragging and had immediately alerted the Qiryat. The following month had passed in devising an operational plan that he knew to be tight and practical. This was how the winter weeks had been spent. Ben Larbi's group—rats squeaking in the basement with their machine guns and burlesque vocabulary. Words like "Inner Committee" and "life" enraged Gauthier. If Al Houaranni were snatched between their fingers, it would teach these perpetual plotters a useful lesson, although that was not the purpose of the operation.

The rancid taste that lunch had deposited like a sourish

film on his tongue was gone. The papers for the three unknown men who would carry out Flood were in his pocket;
the rendezvous had gone as well as could be expected.

Near his station wagon, an Arab urchin hawking for a
restaurant accosted him.

"*Monsieur, la bonne soupe de poisson!*"

"The lunch hour is past, and I have eaten."

"*Alors . . . bon appétit!*" replied the boy smartly, and
Gauthier marveled, not for the first time, at Tunisian aplomb
and inconsequentiality.

CHAPTER THREE
# The Reconnaissance

THE plane from Nice landed when it was already dark. The blue, faintly sinister runway lights glowed like coal embers. In Tunisia there is no dusky transition: night obliterates the land swiftly, without warning, like a betrayal. The three men emerged into the damp, surprisingly sweetish air and made their way in stiff silence to the colonnaded terminal building where pale-blue neon lights spelled out in French and Arabic TUNIS-CARTHAGE.

They approached the arrival hall separately.

Max handed his passport to the Arab police officer on duty. He was young and serious-looking, and wore a gray shirt and black tie. The Bundesrepublik passport was made out to Hans Konrad Stoerchler, forty years old, *Immobilien-Makler*, or real-estate broker; it had been issued, a year before, in Saarbrücken. The officer checked the information on the white international landing card against the passport, made little tally marks on the former for future verification, looked up briefly at the squat, balding man, then rapidly stamped both documents. At the next booth, a khaki-uniformed official collected passengers' currency declarations. Max's angular vestigial Gothic script listed assets of one thousand French francs and two hundred and fifty dollars in traveler's checks —sufficient to justify a week's stay in Tunisia, not enough to arouse distrust. The official waved him on. At the final counter, he reclaimed his scuffed suitcase, got it chalk marked by a shirt-sleeved customs employee and went out past a guard into the waiting hall. Unlike the General, he had expected no trouble: it was too early in the operation for that.

The second man, dark and muscular, produced a German passport in the name of Ewald Horstmann, physical education instructor. The third turned over a dark-blue French passport issued to Jean-Charles Ollivier, travel agent domiciled at 44 Rue de Rivoli, Nice.

The police officer's stamp flew efficiently over the empty visa pages. He was hurrying up his rhythm as the last passengers straggled up to his desk.

No one was detained for questioning.

Baggage lockers do not exist as yet at the Tunis airport; they will come, but for the time there are none, and a make-shift checkroom outside the building, at the end of a short passageway, is the only facility available. Max found the *consigne* without difficulty, fished out a numbered slip from his wallet, and obtained a maroon airline overnight bag stored on a shelf. The young attendant exhibited no curiosity about the man who claimed the bag; later, when questioned by police, he was still vaguer about recalling the identity of the person who had deposited it seventy-two hours earlier. Max paid the charge of four hundred milliemes and returned to the main hall, carrying the unopened bag and the suitcase. Together they did not weigh much in his chunky fists.

In summer this same hall would be thronged with noisy cargoes of critical Germans, venturesome Scandinavian girls who would invite near-rape in oases, and platoons of brash South London bank clerks. But now the scene was different. In the center of the lobby, under a bilingual sign that read POINT DE RENCONTRE, Arab families sat in haiks and djellabas. There were black Africans in transit and journalists burdened with typewriters and tape recorders arriving for Al Houaranni's visit. A dignified Arab in a cinnamon-colored burnous, with polished black shoes and furled umbrella, held two small children by the hand with a patience no European would ever show. Barefoot little girls played on the steep staircase ascending to the restaurant. Up there, a record was playing— the Arab music struck out at Max with its repetitive plaintiveness, he was in Islam again.

At a tobacco stand he bought a token, found a telephone booth and dialed a six-digit number. A tiny lock hung from the box to prevent tokens from being stolen. Max loathed the first moment in foreign cities—the sensation of brutal uprooting, of a sleeve turned trickily inside out—but he knew from experience that the feeling was short-lived. He heard the phone ringing faintly somewhere; then a man's voice, surprisingly close, answered in French.

"Everything is all right," Max said. "The plane arrived on schedule."

There was a slight pause. "And your two associates?" the untroubled, grave voice asked.

"They are safely in Tunis, too."

Max recognized Emir's light, indefinable accent from the tapes that had been played at the Qiryat. In the booth he opened the cloth overnight bag. It contained a sealed letter,

51

which he tore open. Inside were a car key and a ring with several more keys, and still another key that he shifted into his pants pocket—this last was for use only in an emergency.

Outdoors he paused for a moment. His first view was of stunted palm trees tossing their headdress of fronds in the tepid breeze. Then Black and Marston came out of the building with their luggage. The bigger man boarded the airport bus into town, while Marston hailed a minicab. Wryly, Max remembered the days before independence when Maltese immigrants had possessed a monopoly of taxi licenses in Tunis, and the drivers had hurtled their vehicles at suicidal speed through the old quarter's cramped streets, victoriously rounded corners and somehow avoided smashing into anything valuable. The drivers now were Arab and, possibly, more reliable.

In the parking lot across from the main entrance he spotted the Fiat 125. The license plate tallied with the number he had memorized. Max stored his bags, adjusted himself into the smallish driver's seat with a grunt, and checked the dashboard. Motor, headlights and windshield wipers worked. The car's papers—registration card, insurance certificate and road-safety inspection form—were all, as they should be, in the side flap. Max read the Tunisian name on the rental contract without curiosity; it meant nothing to him. He had not expected to recognize it, but he could well imagine how the matter had been handled. A few days earlier, a man, one of Emir's cutouts, had approached Avis' airport office, rented a Fiat for a week after presenting his driver's license but not necessarily his passport or identity card, paid a deposit and driven off; later he had returned unobtrusively, parked and locked the car, and slipped the envelope containing the keys into the maroon bag, which he had left at the checkroom. Then he had turned over the claim ticket to another person, equally anonymous in the chain of complicities that surrounded and sustained the Resident in Tunis.

The cutout had made sure to leave the gas tank filled.

At the airport gate, Max turned right and drove in the direction of the city. A putrid smell of excrement floated on the evening air and invaded the car, and suddenly he remembered. Behind thickly planted rows of eucalyptus trees, he could discern the vast stagnant lake. It was El Behira, Tunis' ancient shallow inland sea into which Carthaginians, Romans, Vandals and Arabs had recklessly spewed waste; modern generations have inherited the embarrassing stink. Nowhere else, thought Max, does History have such a stench. Through the rear-view mirror he watched the lights of cars speeding down the road. No one was following him.


This man Max Weissenberg came down the gangway into Haifa in 1954, a gangling fellow of twenty-three, with wolfish-gray eyes, some cash assets and no fixed compass point to his ambitions. He was possessed by a gnawing hunger for minimal security and sanity in day-to-day relationships with human beings. Two continents—Europe and Africa—lay behind him, where these conditions did not prevail. He had a craving for identification with a country rather than a cause.

Three months after his entry into the New State of Israel, he obtained a position as manager of a recently built resort hotel south of Beersheba. But he displayed no talent for bookkeeping or the handling of scorched, irritated guests. At the end of certain torrid frustrating days, it seemed to him that *he* was the tourist in a flinty wasteland—but if this were so, then where was his permanent home?

Upon the outbreak of the Sinai Campaign he was called up and, on the strength of his fluency in Arabic, assigned to a military-government detachment in Khan Yunis, a dusty, mutinous village in the Gaza Strip. One afternoon a captain from Tel Aviv drove up in a jeep and spoke to him alone. Max picked out three boys in the area who seemed ready to collaborate with the occupying authorities. Later he learned that one boy had been smuggled into Port Said, in return for one hundred Israeli pounds, detected and executed. It was Max's first encounter with Ha Mossad.

Following his brief tour of duty in the desert, he joined an uncle who possessed a ten-acre citrus farm near Natanya. He arrived one March day at dusk. Rolling countryside, windbreaks of cypresses, sturdy farmhouses, formed a landscape of fertility and durability. It seemed to him his first glimpse of a sane future.

He changed his name to Kaleb Levanon, which means the Hound of Lebanon; it is an unusual and imaginative name, and he had chosen it after due reflection. Old friends and distant relatives from Germany remembered and used his earlier name; more important, he thought of himself—in the physical sense of a certain bulk displacing a specific amount of air, and in the religious sense of a determinable individual prey to particular joys and griefs—as Max. However, if someone called "Kaleb!" at his back, he turned around—he was Kaleb, too, but he considered this look-alike and act-alike as nothing more than a good, solid adequate fabrication. This was less than fair, for Kaleb could lay claim to a future, while Max was the slippery, lacerated product of the past. On

54

this score, he was unequivocal: "The past is buried. I gave it a decent funeral," he growled.

In Trier, his native town, there was a somber stone house that overflowed with boxlike cluttered steamy rooms. Through the pear trees one glimpsed the greenish sheen of the swift Moselle and the steep russet vineyards that mounted beyond. Max's father, Julius Weissenberg, was a wholesale grocer who volunteered, in 1938, to serve as the treasurer of the Jewish community—a decision that required extreme foolhardiness or courage, or both. Shortly after the Nuremburg racial laws were adopted, he was imprisoned.

He remained in jail a month. Punctually at 2 A.M. each morning, a *Polizeiwachtmeister*, a young man in a brown uniform, arrived at the side of Julius Weissenberg's cot and tapped him on the shoulder. He learned to be careful, so as not to waken the five other inmates, to slip his feet noiselessly onto the concrete floor and tiptoe out of the cell. The policeman followed him down a corridor; it was quiet at night, and each could hear the other's breathing. A steel door admitted them into a sharply lit cube of a room, which had a hard board floor, hard when you hit it. After the first interrogation, Julius Weissenberg knew what to expect. They used *Gummiknüppel*, rubber truncheons; once, however, they wielded a new instrument—a steel tube about a foot long, from one end of which a tensile coil sprang like a striking cobra about his genitals. When he was escorted back to the cell, he knew that for a few hours the young man would not annoy him again, provided that he managed, as final evidence of reasonableness, to lie down on his cot silently—despite a hysterical desire to scream. This condition made no sense at all, but it impressed Julius Weissenberg.

One evening they abruptly released him, drove him in an official Mercedes to his home, and left him standing in front of the door. Before he pushed the bell, he half turned around on the step and looked down the dark street, expecting to be rearrested. It was a cold fall evening; sweat in pear-shaped droplets formed an icy collar around his throat. The straight pavement followed the line of the house wall to the corner, where the lamppost shone, then it suddenly fell off into indecipherable darkness; the pavement resembled a prison corridor, he realized now. At this moment Julius Weissenberg decided that he had had enough. Until then he had resisted family pressure to flee. He was a burly, permanently aggrieved, opinionated man who had lifted weights at the Handelsschule years earlier; unlike so many, he had wanted to stand his ground and fight the enemy.

All the people who quit Germany in those years remember the formality of *Unbedenklichkeit*, a term the police employed which meant "nothing impeding." Lack of certification of *Unbedenklichkeit* could at the last moment prevent one's boarding a train or ship. In Julius Weissenberg's case the Gestapo drew out their cross-checks until they got what they wanted. In return for a donation to the Party chest of two hundred thousand marks, which entailed the liquidation of more than half of the Jewish community's fund, Weissenberg received his exit permit, on condition, however, that he depart with his last-born son only; his wife and two other sons were to remain behind. He accepted the offer and traveled to Paris. He reasoned that, once beyond the frontier, he would make arrangements to smuggle the remainder of his family out to safety. At the German Consulate, on the strength of his ridiculous title, he persuaded an indecisive consular secretary to advance him ten thousand marks against a check drawn on a Trier bank account, which had been frozen two weeks before by the Gestapo. It was his last encounter with his countrymen. His destination was the United States, but he succumbed to a coronary thrombosis in a hotel room a week later. His eight-year-old son Max was taken in charge by a Jewish refugee organization on Rue des Rosiers and was dispatched to relatives in Tunis. Here Max spent the war years, being frequently mistaken by members of the Afrika Korps for a street Arab. His mother and two older brothers were not heard from again. The marks, exchanged into francs and placed in a safe-deposit box under a Frenchman's name, remained in the vaults of the Banque de France throughout the war.

At the farm, much of what he did was the result of the same patient concentration he had applied to choosing a new name and identity. He married a girl from Natanya who knew nothing of the Rhineland. She bore him two sons, who spoke no German. Kaleb grew chunky; he developed a heavy-footed humor, a grumbling thick sense of irony that did not displease neighbors; it insulated his life, propelled him toward middle age and hurt no one. When his uncle died, he took over the property—house, farm buildings, lemon and grapefruit groves. Terrorists from Jordan slipped into the orchards and slashed the fruit trees at their roots, automatic pistols clattered at night, yet it seemed plain to Max that he had emerged into a Promised Land, an area that did not extend more than several hundred yards in whichever direction he measured.

From time to time he changed into a gray business suit, packed a suitcase and reported at the Qiryat. The recondite assignments on which he went abroad put a premium on perseverance, skepticism and fluency in various languages, particularly Arabic. In Rome and Berne he negotiated with small groups of men—never more than two or three at a time—outdrank and outthought them but firmly dissociated himself from their nervous politicking. This detachment made for successful leadership. The Qiryat esteemed his work; he was promoted to captain. As he struck out across the Piazza del Popolo one evening, he realized that his lack of apprehension about his missions flowed from limited involvement: he was firmly convinced that harm would befall him only at Emek Hefer, the only place on earth that mattered to him.

A month before, he had made the now-familiar trip to Tel Aviv, learned something of Ha Mossad's plans, thought of the operation in terms of demands on his time and responsibilities and volunteered. There is a price to be paid for every felicity. To court danger abroad seemed an honorable way of repaying a debt he owed for the great good that encompassed him within his own fields. To remove a scorpion's sac of venom was likewise a meritorious act—and one of Max's sisters-in-law had been shot dead in the machine-gun raid Al Houaranni had staged against the hospital at Natanya.

In Operation Flood, his code name would be Hound. He had chosen it personally.


Max braked the car before the block of new apartment buildings off Avenue Kherredine Pasha. He had found the address he was looking for with little trouble. It was a short side street that had recently been bulldozed through an empty lot; lampposts gleamed in the dark with fresh dull-green paint. Most of the flats in the development were visibly still unoccupied, but lights shone plentifully from unshuttered windows here and there, mostly in upper stories. It was all uncharacteristically spick-and-span for Tunis.

Max let himself into the hall; he had known beforehand, from the operational plan, that there would be no concierge's lodge. Along one wall ran two rows of metal letter boxes; some bore a raised strip with a tenant's name, but a visiting card had been substituted in many instances for the original plate. If a high percentage of the building's occupants were transients, Max thought, it was all to the good. Banks of bright-red artificial blossoms as deep-dyed as poinsettias flourished in an imitation-marble basin. A thick pile rug in an abstract design engulfed his footfalls.

He took the lift to the third floor and at the end of the carpeted corridor came upon the numbered door he had been instructed to seek out. He could hear no sounds anywhere in the building. His stubby, hard body was awash with sudden sweat. He removed the key ring from the envelope in his coat pocket, unlocked the door and stood a moment on the threshold.

The apartment's anonymity leaped at the eye—oyster-white walls, grège wall-to-wall carpeting, a settee upholstered in a plain umber fabric. Not one object in the living room was worn or out of place—he might have been in a Hilton hotel. A neat smell of furniture polish provided the only trace of a fleeting human presence. It was impossible to decide who had preceded him in the flat—airline stewardesses or Japanese salesmen; Max thought it would be equally impossible later, when they discovered the location, for police to make any firm assumptions about the identity, habits and nationality of the three men who had briefly slept here.

Reassured, he removed his topcoat. He unlatched the French windows and the night air swept in buoyantly with a strong, incongruous suggestion of freedom. He stepped out onto the narrow terrace and looked at the nearby lake, the misty lights of Carthage beyond and the dark ambiguous shimmering sweep of sea. The apartment had a further advantage: surveillance of their movements would be difficult for a security service to establish around this placid building without their immediately becoming aware of it. Now he understood for the first time why Emir had insisted on putting them up in an apartment house.

He stepped back indoors and went to the kitchen. The interior of the Formica-topped buffet was what interested him. There, on one shelf, he found what he wanted—another key, this one rusty and heavy. Also on the shelf—unexpectedly—stood two sealed bottles of Cutty Sark whiskey. Max snorted with surprise; this, at least, struck a human note of welcome.

There was still no sound in the building, but he heard the cozy, faint noise of a radio playing in an apartment across the street. The plane trip, the arrival at night, the drive from the airport had failed to tire him; he was too excited inwardly for that. He went back into the living room and settled down to wait for the others.


Early next morning the three men came out of the building and left in the Fiat. Marston drove through unpredictable traffic, and Max sat beside him. He looked at the people in the street and felt no emotion. The past might strike out at him by surprise, but for the moment it lay quiescent.

Everywhere, on walls and fences and kiosks, were posters of the President smiling and clutching a gift spray of jasmine as he descended an Air Tunis passenger ladder, for all the world like a rug merchant returning triumphantly to his hometown. The photograph had been taken a month before upon the President's release from medical treatment in a Parisian hospital. His opponents no longer surreptitiously pricked out his eyes with a needle on posters and crackling Banque de Tunisie bank notes; he had grown good and gray in office over the hard-fought years; he was admired, and those who were fretting to oust him were too sophisticated to waste their time on fetishistic gestures. There were no posters anywhere in sight of Al Houaranni.

"He won't get any money out of these people," Black spoke up from the back of the car.

"Of course he will," Max retorted. "To do so it is not necessary to have your picture slapped up at every street corner."

"Here we are," said Marston, turning into a one-way street.

They were in the port area. The neighborhood was poor, oily, sluggish with sunlight. Auto repair shops and garages lined both sides of Rue Houssine Bouzaiane; the sound of hammering on metal came from within one shed. A stray yellow dog trotted up inquisitively to the car, then after a moment's hesitation turned and raced off.

Max got out first, crossed the street and stopped before a locked wooden gate and waited for the others to come up. He had the heavy rusted key in the palm of his hand. It was going to be interesting to see what happened. He fitted the key into the lock, heard the oiled click of tumblers, and pushed back the gate. A short weedy cement driveway led between brick walls to a one-story garage. As soon as they were inside the gate, they closed it solidly behind them. In this neighborhood everyone was too busy working to take notice of three men.

A gray Peugeot sedan draped in dust stood in the center of the garage. Marston ran his thumb over the hood and the paint beneath the dust gleamed bright and hard. Lightly opening the door, he adjusted the seat, accepted a key Max handed him, and turned the ignition on. The engine caught at once, as though someone had warmed it up recently, and it ran evenly with the formidable power of an indirect fuel-injection engine. He listened attentively, feathered the accelerator, then bore down and the engine responded. He raced it briefly, cut the ignition, then went through the procedure again. Finally he nodded.

"I can bring this car up to over one hundred miles an hour if we're followed," Marston said. It was the first time anyone had spoken in the garage.

"With all this dirt it looks enough like an old wreck not to draw notice. Be sure to keep it dirty-looking. Come here a moment, both of you." Max motioned the two men to a vacant grime-blackened office with last year's girlie calendar pinned to the wall. Shelves and drawers ran around three sides. Barely hesitating, Max chose the last key on his ring and unlocked the middle top drawer. Within, side by side, lay three dull-black 9-mm. Beretta Parabellum semiautomatic pistols, with full magazines of ammunition. He kept one weapon and distributed the other two.

Black turned the gun over in his big hand before slipping it into his coat pocket and whistled softly with respect. "How did he bring these in?"

"Emir has done an excellent job." Max looked about before he relocked the empty drawer. "It would have been asinine to run the risk of smuggling these ourselves through customs."

"It's funny; I trained with these when I went to college—"

"Harvard, wasn't it?"

Black said, "Yes. Harvard has a gun-and-rifle club."

"Graduate?"

"*Magna cum laude* if I had wanted to," Black replied cryptically. "I can't miss with this old friend."

"The gun will almost certainly not be needed."

"I understand that. I'm a stupid trigger-happy playboy, but the General made his point."

Max looked at Marston, who had lifted the hood and was inspecting the fuel pump. "You plan to take it out for a run now, I suppose?"

"That's the next item on the list," said Marston. From his tone it was impossible to tell whether he was pleased, but Max knew his reactions sufficiently by now to realize that he was boiling over with impatience.


That evening, in the apartment, Max turned the radio on and placed a bottle of Cutty Sark next to the set. The announcer, who had only a slight trace of accent when he used French, described Al Houaranni's arrival on the Beirut flight.

"—At the start of his official two-day visit, the Palestinian

63

liberation leader was greeted by government officials and ambassadors of Maghreb countries," an Arab girl's chirpy voice took up the story.

"Thousands of Tunisians drove and rode to Carthage airport this afternoon . . ." Taped sounds of a crowd's formless wild roar, punctuated by apparently friendly shouts, followed.

Max fixed a drink and listened to the end attentively. The description of scheduled interviews and festivities and a university professor's analysis of Al Houaranni's obscure beginnings as director of an Arab youth welfare center in Nazareth ran on and on. Ten minutes, Max thought as the man and girl announcers finally switched to the next story. Apparently somebody in the government was making up for neglect in the matter of posters by laying it on thick and heavy on the air. Still, they were running no risk of over-popularizing Al Houaranni. The spoken word would not survive tomorrow, or it could be amended to mean something else, but the posters remained in view for weeks, and they showed only the President.

Eyes shut, an expression of disgust on his thin, sharp, practical face, half turned away from the radio set, Marston was listening to the newscast, too. Black sat forward on the settee, raptly reading a French magazine that specialized in the tribulations of royal princesses and Jackie Onassis. Max drained off the whiskey in his glass, rose and poured out another shot. He lifted his glass and found Black studying him.

"Levanon, you drink a lot." Black's tone was half censorious, half amiable.

"I hold a lot," Max grunted, and sipped the contents. He

did not want to explain to Black that at this hour, after the sun had reddened the last lemon trees, he was usually seated in the farm office, with a glass of "Scotch wine" within reach, while he placed a record on the turntable on the desk and listened to wind instruments—oboe, horn and trumpet, especially the clear, sustained speech of trumpets—shaping out of precise themes an indomitable, triumphant universe.

He stepped out onto the terrace and surveyed the plain of low white rooftops reaching to the lake. If all went well, within five days, allowing time for complete operational debriefing, he would be back at Emek Hefer. In fairness he could not ask for a more auspicious beginning. Emir, though unseen, could be counted on; he had amply proved that. His presence, somewhere in the jumbled unsuspecting city, foresaw, arranged, provided and comforted. The two men sharing the apartment were visibly tough and competent; from the start, he had felt no doubt about Marston, but Black was something else again. Amateurs all over the world talked and gestured too much, and Black was no exception—the conceitedness still grated—but the man took orders at least without back talk, and there was not a nerve loose in that big, flexible puritanical frame.

Max glanced up at the sky over this unwarlike corner of the Mediterranean and noted dull gray clouds moving in ghostly procession toward the moon. Tunis was enjoying a gaudy crimson sunset broken up by erratic plum clouds that foretokened an unfavorable change of weather. The sun sank in a memorable blaze into the empty amber western sea. Beyond the shore, out toward Sicily, the sky was bluer than it should have been at this hour; its darkness matched the somber sable mass that was churning wildly landward. A subtle change that he was at a loss to put a name on quickened the salt breeze that licked at his lips. The wind had shifted quarter, it was blowing from the northeast now.

## CHAPTER FOUR

# The Sick Boy

IT was just past noon when the General received the radio message. Decoded, it read: REQUEST AUTHORIZATION POSTPONE FLOOD TWENTY-FOUR HOURS DUE PREDICTED STORM SEBRING. It came from *Keriche* (Shark), a diesel-powered ex-British "S"-class submarine cruising at that moment at one-hundred-foot depth forty miles off the Tunisian coast.

The General spread out the message, studied the time-group, looked at the signature and picked up the phone. He knew Sebring personally and trusted his judgment.

"What sort of weather are they getting?" he asked the section chief who appeared in the door.

"Low-pressure area in the western Mediterranean, a cold front, winds of fifty miles an hour that may attain gale-force ten. In short, Isaac"—the section chief had known the General since boyhood in Pretoria—"they're in for a rough ride. Whether a small boat can put out to sea at all is problematical."

The section chief consulted another chart, which he placed

with the first on the desk. "The indicators we have show no hope of a change for another twelve hours at least."

"Sebring doesn't like postponements any more than I do. He must have waited to be damn sure before he sent this." The General briefly watched the play of sunlight warming his old, splotched hands, and tried unsuccessfully to overcome his feelings. The exasperation he felt was directed not at the submarine skipper, but toward alien forces over which he had no control—winds, waves and tides. He was not a sea lover by nature, and had no taste for operations any part of which escaped from firm ground. "I know they'll break their asses following orders, and they might just pull it off. Maybe Sebring is losing his nerve."

He rose and shuffled down the corridor in his gray sweater and baggy khaki pants to confer with the hard-working men who had spent more than a month drafting, revising and testing Flood's schedule.

A half hour later, he returned to his desk and scrawled out two messages—a reply to Sebring and a five-word order to the Resident—on his note pad. "Get these encoded now," he said to a corporal who answered the buzzer. "Let's not waste time."

Then he rang up the section chief. "On my budget I can't afford heroes," he said with just a shade of nostalgia.


Gauthier heard the boy being sick upstairs and rose from his desk, listening. He went into the hall and called out. After a guarded silence, his son's voice replied, "It's all right, Daddy; it's nothing at all."

Gauthier was alone in the house with his son, who had begun to complain before lunch of stomach cramps; the maid had given him milk of magnesia and bouillon, put him to bed and eventually waddled off to her own home. Anne-Marie, who had left the house in midmorning, had promised to return by three-thirty, and she was late.

Gauthier went upstairs and made sure that the scalding hot-water bottle was placed properly on his son's stomach.

"Did you vomit?"

"Yes, Daddy."

Gauthier went into the bathroom, inspected the mess of yellow undigested liquid and flushed it. He was not sure how serious the cramps were. His six-year-old son had a record of minor ailments, sometimes exaggerated, that boiled up from a subsurface need to groan and be fussed over, but Gauthier had trouble standing up to a child's rage when pain—even shallow or imaginary pain—flickered close; it thrust him back perilously toward the terrors of his own boyhood.

"Does it still hurt?"

"Not all the time—it goes away and comes back."

"If it continues to hurt, I'll call the doctor."

Gauthier returned to his study but continued to listen. On the desk lay the story he had just dictated to Paris. It ran to more than twelve hundred words and would keep the news staff satisfied; they would have a far more exciting story in several hours, but they could not possibly know that. He wondered when Anne-Marie would be back.

Without waiting further he called the nearest doctor. The voice that replied was young, which reassured Gauthier; he had no faith in stiff numb old men to whom the suffering of others no longer represented a challenge but seemed inevitable and normal, even a nuisance.

"He has a fever of 38.6—it was 38 after lunch," Gauthier said. "Can you examine him here?"

There was a pause during which the doctor's furry breathing occupied the line; he was a general practitioner they had never resorted to before who lived ten minutes away. "This afternoon I am afraid not. I have patients who have been waiting for hours and have come from as far as Salammbo."

"I dislike taking a child who is running a high fever out in this weather."

After listening, the doctor said, "Has he diarrhea?"

"No sign of it, but he's vomited."

"It could be appendicitis. Bring him in your car, keep the windows shut and I'll see him immediately." He added—it must have been a useful lesson he had picked up at medical school for handling parents—"We'll both save time this way."

"I could come later this evening."

"As you wish, but it is never advisable to let these cases wait if the stomach pains are acute."

Hanging up, Gauthier thought: The hell with it, I am not going, he will simply have to wait no matter how it hurts until his mother returns.

Annoyed at himself, he stepped into the garden. There are splendid views of the sea from Carthage. Almost all the homes face the Gulf, but Gauthier's house, uncomfortable, askew, spacious, turned its back to it. He preferred the less infinite panorama from Rue Didon—of hills the drab color of camels on which temples and baths and basilicas had once thrived, and the sand bar bearing the populous suburbs of Kherredine,

Le Kram and Salammbo curving and narrowing away like a serpent toward the dreamy lake. Here was the Tunisian triptych of time, ambition and collapse.

For an hour thunder had been rumbling intermittently on the horizon; now the storm sounded closer, and the growling reached him from a middle distance, as through layers of cotton wadding. Suddenly warm swollen drops splattered on Gauthier's neck; then the screen of rain materialized, opaque and broad, moving in upon the land swiftly without a sound. A needle of lightning stabbed the lavender sky with the enormous clarity of a giant neon sign.

He returned indoors. It was now four o'clock. At five-twenty, he was scheduled to take in the Qiryat on a shortwave single side-band transmission. Weekly or twice weekly, depending on circumstance and need, Gauthier did this; the frequency and hour varied according to the season, because of sunspots, and the site varied according to opportunity. The illegal broadcast seldom lasted more than six minutes, but into this brief space of time was compressed the reason for his being in Tunisia, and indeed—the General would have said —for his whole life. On these afternoons friends were never invited before seven; unexpected callers were shooed away on a number of pretexts. The Arab maid-cook left the house early and Anne-Marie looked after her son when he returned from his classes.

By five, in winter in Tunisia it is dark and the beaches are deserted. When Gauthier drove off in his station wagon, he had within a radius of five miles a choice of unobtrusive sites from which to enter into contact with Ha Mossad. There was a stretch of broken road near Hamilcar; closer by, a stagnant pond that archaeologists claimed was the emplace-ment of a Punic port; and the entire gray foreshore, littered and forlorn, that reaches south to La Goulette. This was the reason why he lived in Carthage. When the moon rose over the blowy bay, even the most indigent Arab drew his burnous close and crept indoors, and Gauthier had the lonely coastline to himself. In summer the problem was not the same, for static interfered with reception, so he broadcast less and later at night and entrusted much material to a courier who flew to Rome.

The transceiver was a solid-state miniaturized suitcase model that weighed more than sixty pounds but occupied little space. It fitted into a specially designed recess behind the footwell, directly above the station wagon's left rear wheel. Gauthier could get to it by lowering the tail gate, unbolting the muddy spare tire and folding back a section of floorboard. Converting the station wagon into a mobile instal-lation had been his idea. He used the car's twelve-volt storage battery to power the transceiver, even on the rare occasions when he broadcast from his garage; this did away with the necessity of drawing on house current and precluded the tell-tale dimming of lights that might ensue. There were other refinements: the luggage rack on the roof concealed the aerial, and Gauthier made sure that there were always smudges of oil on the floorboards over the transceiver's hid-ing place to deflect suspicion from that part of the vehicle.

Single side-band transmission requires concentrated effort and expertise. "Second best won't work," they had repeated during training; "the problems to be overcome are mental, not just manual." Over the years, although he was not talented with his hands, Gauthier had developed proficient rhythm and speed. To communicate with Tel Aviv, he rode as close as possible to the Cairo frequency of the *Voice of the Arabs*, which the Tunisians jammed, because shortwave hams generally move away from troublesome areas for fear of wasting their time. If some persistent amateur got in, the high-speed messages were in themselves meaningless, reduced to digit-groups which, on the air, sounded like Donald Duck quack-quack. The real danger lay in someone becoming interested in the mere fact that the transmission occurred. To lessen the danger, the Qiryat constantly varied its time schedules and Gauthier avoided interference with regular programs by broadcasting sufficiently far from Radio Tunis, in town, and the television tower on the crown of Bou Kornine across the bay.

Nonetheless, he had had one close call. One evening he had lowered the tail gate and was about to warm up the crystals of the transceiver when a Tunisian police car drew up out of the night mist and stopped, its blue dome light flashing.

Gauthier sat frozen where he was.

"What do you want here?" asked a booted policeman who walked across the sand. The other remained at the wheel of the car.

"The tire is losing air, but I cannot change it here. In my opinion, the jack will slip."

The patrolman walked around the station wagon, inspecting it from all sides. "This is your car? You have the papers?" His tone was neither friendly nor unfriendly.

Gauthier searched in his wallet, found the registration card and handed it over. He realized the explanation about the tire was perilously hollow, but there was no other plausible explanation for his presence on the beach, except one which he held in reserve. He watched the policeman check the plate number in the pencil beam of a minuscule flashlight.

"Where do you go from here? Home?"

Gauthier stirred restlessly.

"A young woman is meeting me—"

"Everybody says that. Is this your home?" He pointed to the address on the registration card.

"I live in Carthage, yes." Then Gauthier had an inspiration and added, "Perhaps she is not coming at all."

The policeman said with a trace of derision, "If you keep it up she will catch pneumonia. There is a garage three hundred yards down the road for your tire."

Gauthier caught a glimpse of two dark official faces shiny with mirth as the police car reversed on the sand and headed back toward the city. Naturally they found it barbaric and outlandish, typically the behavior of a *roumi*, to court a girl on a cold winter beach. His palms were sweating in the silken damp night breeze. Suppose they had delved deeper into the rear of the station wagon? He must never let it happen again—running into the same two policemen must be avoided absolutely, because the same set of circumstances repeated would stir awake even the most sluggish police mind. He would do better to drop the leaking-tire story.

From that evening on, he sought places on the shore where he could back his car far out of sight of cruising patrol cars along the beach road. There was still risk, but risk that had to be run. By changing the transmission site each time, he ran far less risk than in communicating from a fixed site. Cohen had been ruined in Damascus because he transmitted from his flat. A direction finder always sooner or later homed on to a fixed site. He had learned that in the early days at the Qiryat.

74

This time his son called him.

"It hurts here," he said, indicating his abdomen.

"Did you vomit again?"

"A little."

Gauthier glanced at his watch: he could be at the doctor's and back, allowing for a consultation, by five-ten. He did not want to leave the house, but he did not see how he could avoid it. By hurrying, he would be back in time to take in the call; the margin of time was slim but adequate.

Bundling together his son's raincoat and scarf, he hurried back upstairs. There was really no choice: How can you remain numb to a child's pain? He heard the doctor's voice again, and then his own, working out a practical compromise. Damn and redamn her! he thought with anger that actually blunted his vision. It's not me, it's not what is at stake in two hours, but her own son—can't she at least worry about him?

When they arose it was already dark, or so it seemed from the expiring light in the sky. Then Preston realized it was rain, sweeping in from the bay in silver pencil stripes that made no sound as they struck the beach and splotched the low garden wall. Far out to sea, an artillery battle of thunderclap and lightning flash was raging inconclusively.

The air in the room was close; he had been so impatient this time that he hadn't thought to unlatch the window. On bare feet he went across the tiled floor and pushed the window ajar. The sea breeze billowed in.

"Come back," she said.

When he lay beside her again she moved comfortably against his thigh. After a moment she asked, "What are you thinking about?"

He started to say, "You," then more truthfully amended this to: "About us."

She looked at him sideways. "Suppose this time I had not come—what would you have thought?"

"I would have been disappointed."

"So would I. I almost didn't come. I promised Alex to be home early." She rose and began to dress. "I'm going to meet Al Houaranna tonight."

"Who isn't?"

"I like the Moroccan ambassador," she said. "He makes indecent proposals to me right in front of Alex. Alex loathes him. But he says sometimes it's useful to go, because people at these parties are convinced you are holding back what you know—and they say things themselves to provoke you."

Preston let his silence convey his skepticism.

"I never learn anything," she continued. "All diplomats are liars and their wives think only about who is sleeping with whom. But I enjoy myself once I get there as I don't expect to find out anything and I like champagne when it is *brut*."

"Champagne, Pucci shoes, chitchat with terrorists . . . you're the last of the glamour girls, Anne-Marie."

"I know my expensive tastes terrify you. The ambassador should marry me—we both like to spend. Alex should have married Lucia; they're both very practical, and she loves to be pawed in public, which would have pleased Alex for a while. I don't, you know."

"Don't what?"

"Like to be pawed."

"I've observed that."

"You're so American," she said. She combed her hair before the mirror; when she became aware of his examination she smiled briefly. "I'll put some makeup on. Why is Al Houaranni coming here?"

"To put a little excitement into our futile sybaritic lives."

"You know everything, or at least you always have an answer ready. I think you're a spy. That's what they say about you at the Chateauduns. I've heard terrible things about you."

"Do you believe everything Lucia Chateaudun says?"

"Sometimes—especially if it's about you."

"Anne-Marie, *je t'aime. Vraiment,*" he said in his counter-feit-sounding French.

"*Vraiment?*" She mocked his accent; she never spoke any-thing but English to him. "In six months you won't even remember my name. That nice little package in Carthage—what was her name? I must write her a postcard—"

"I've already had five months with you."

"Five months and ten days." Anne-Marie's accuracy was dazzling when the subject interested her.

"How many boy friends do you have?"

"I have only one," she said, taking her coat from the closet. "My husband."

"Most of the time I believe that."

"Of course. I don't care for you at all, that's why I come here." She drew his face down to her mouth, and he caught her shallow complacent peppermint breath. As soon as she rose from bed she assumed a role, he thought—until the next time she tumbled into bed.

The first time she had come to his place she had said, "The

thing I like best about you is your need of a woman. So obvious when we met. How could I resist?"

"No. Not any woman. I wanted *you*."

She shook her head. "You needed someone: it's different. *I* wanted you."

Now he said, "When are you going to make up your mind to leave him?"

"Never. Don't look that way."

"Well, I suppose what we say doesn't matter much."

"What we do is nice."

He went out onto the small flagstone terrace. "It won't go away," he said of the storm. He heard the rain as it dropped down through the pine branches pattering on the hard sand and simultaneously spilling loudly out of the gutter on the side of the cottage. High above, in the upper reaches of the sky, the thunder made a clumsy noise like furniture being moved about.

"Stay a little longer?"

"No. It would be unfair to Alex."

"To hell with Alex."

Anne-Marie held Preston's wrist and read the minute hand of his watch. "I'm already late, and we'll see each other this evening. I want to be home—really, the most important thing in my whole life," she said, in explanation rather than justification, "is my son."


After his wife's death in Paris, Preston went down to Tunisia. He had heard little of the country, a small dry dagger of Franco-Arab design that stabbed southward into the shriven rocky emptiness of the Sahara. About what happened

78

under Tunisian skies, he had no clue and, until now, no curiosity. Then it occurred to him that the country's reputation for soft compliance might serve as a warning: beware of a people who carry jasmine bouquets and let the days run volitionlessly through their fingers like prayer beads. These early months were a dull interlude, without pain but empty of joy, seasons without odor or taste; he saw time pass as from a hospital window. But Tunisia's greatest triumph lay in reawakening the physical senses. The lash of a shower after a morning on the beach, the sheer pleasure of ice-cold Ain Garcia mineral water, the freedom of the green sea, the pursuit race between moon and sun . . . he had not reckoned with the summer.

All too soon the terrible North African torpor of midsummer came over them all. The movies were too sticky for comfort, and most restaurants in town were shut through September. Shoeshines buzzed around the café terraces like wasps. The decomposing feces smell of El Behira became revolting on breezeless summer afternoons. "Parties and picnics," Mills, his chief, told him, "take your pick." But now in August even the parties gave out, as diplomats flew north to spas and Brittany beaches. The brown-backed European girls in their strapless summer print dresses swayed and glistened in the heat. In the windless evening his head drooped, he couldn't think lucidly, his nerves fretted him into rows.

One night, out of boredom, irritated with the obtrusive presence of the Secret Police in the Tunisia Palace bar, he went to a brothel in the reserved quarter. The girls were Mediterranean—Sicilians, Neapolitans, overblown Jewesses and raucous Arab teen-agers. There was a rumor that one of

79

the stylish houses contained an American whore, a redhead from Texas, but he never saw her and the rumor was no different and no more verifiable than one he had heard in Casablanca and Marrakesh.

Near the entrance to the *souks*, he passed a tiny *maison de passe* known archly as L'Hotel du Grand Bonheur, and a pimp said to him, "I can get you a general's wife—clean, not too old. She is upstairs in the room, waiting."

"No."

The man asked suspiciously, "What do you like—virgins?"

"Do you know any?"

"*Little* virgins," he prompted despairingly.

Preston waved him off, and ended up with a fat-cheeked, bonny girl who was amateurishly dabbling in prostitution, whom he picked up at closing time in a bar-discotheque. At twenty-two, she was worried when the telephone didn't ring; worried about her hips; worried that her landlady was checking on her. Whenever an opportunity arose, she ran off with a man to Hammamet, danced all night at the Yasmina and came back to Tunis feeling reassured. "I have lots of men friends," she boasted; "they don't like it when I play hard to get."

The next morning Preston drove to the Cercle Nautique at Sidi Bou Said. He had to deliver a message from Mills to one of the members. Beside the cheery white clubhouse stood, gleaming in the morning light, a restaurant called La Caravelle; it had a patio with three red-brick barbecues, a straw-thatched bar, geraniums and blue chairs. The man he was looking for sat among a small group of members, including a French girl with eyes as green as a pool.

Anne-Marie wore navy-blue jeans and a striped jumper, and

her blond silky hair shimmered whenever she turned her head in the shade and sunlight of the patio. Soon the other members wandered away, and Preston found out that she was waiting for her husband to come back from a race. He asked her why she wasn't out there where the heat haze glistened on the water.

"You're curious," she complained.

"Have dinner with me and I'll explain the reason why."

"No."

But when he rose to leave, her glance, light and warm, fell directly on him for the first time. "Don't go away, I enjoy talking to you," she said in her clear voice.

And that was how it began.

Gammarth's villas, eighteen miles from the city, belong these days to wealthy Tunisians who have replaced French colons. Hidden from view behind white stucco walls as thick as ramparts, the houses' true dimensions cannot be made out from the road. The style is native (a surfeit of Moorish arches, a frieze of green tiles), with aberrations—a nouveau riche emphasis on domes and cupolas, secretive patios which a Spaniard might appreciate, nurtured plots of lawn only the rich can afford in this dry, devouring land.

Preston's cottage was modest. Whitewashed and compact, it stood unobtrusively behind a row of young sweet-smelling eucalyptus trees near the Hotel de la Tour Blanche, just before the last sharp bend the asphalt beach road describes before climbing up to the mottled green-and-chestnut cape. A short clay path that could be used as a drive led to the edge of the cliff overlooking the brown churning sea.

Preston had had a hard time finding this cottage. He appreciated it—this was home, even if in winter the electric radiators behaved unreliably. It cost him little; the living room was comfortable and filled with hi-fi equipment and an assortment of raw spirits from the countries he visited. It was with relief on most evenings that Preston turned his back on Tunis' malodorous affairs and made his way homeward through the erratic traffic to Gammarth. His nearest neighbors were a British banker and a Tunisian doctor.

Preston had a vigorous shock of premature ash-gray hair, curious eyes of frosty blue-gray and a tall, trained frame like a knotty-pine board that was just beginning to spoil. He also had a chin as refractory as sandpaper. Men liked his air; women certainly were willing to listen to whatever he chose to tell them, even if they disbelieved him. When, later, both men and women detected an impatient face, a mouth a bit too tight and an actor's ingrained restlessness, their doubt about his trustworthiness was balanced by his serious busy manner.

At the American Embassy he held the rank of second secretary, but it was far from clear just which section he belonged to. In these sophisticated days, everyone, even in Tunis, knew what this imprecision meant. Besides, he just didn't ring true as a bona fide Foreign Service officer; his neck hairs curled too abundantly on his nape, he wasn't servile with Tunisian functionaries, he didn't eat economically each midday at the Embassy cafeteria. He volunteered no information, but occasionally someone asked; then Preston said, "Yes, I'm with the CIA." The admission generally left the asking party feeling vaguely let down—and it had the advantage that it gave away no details. In fact, he carried on liaison with the

Tunisian Sûreté, an overt function. The work he did was not operational. "You won't be thrusting and parrying much here," said Mills.

In winter Preston appeared turned out in a blazer, a somber tie and darkish-gray trousers. Anne-Marie was amused by his dress and distrait air of elegant impoverishment. "I think you must have the largest collection of mohair and flannel blazers in this city," she said. All his accessories were perfectly distinguished, overdistinguished—the wristband of fine soft crocodile, the thin gleaming cigarette case, and the lighter from Van Cleef & Arpels given him by his wife. Anne-Marie, of course, sniffed the recklessness in Preston as soon as she met him: this was catnip for her. She was not a girl to waste time on Embassy second secretaries; her taste ran more to painters and sculptors, who treated her with indifference. Why—it was a thought she dared not utter aloud, even to Lucia Chateaudun—are all the men I become interested in mixed up with Intelligence?

For his part, Preston had a thief's sense of time, of the necessity of making every moment work to advantage before someone—the police or God?—broke in and discovered what game he was playing. He had lost a nice wife who understood him—through his own carelessness, in an auto accident—and this could not be made up. For a while he had no woman, he was solitary, and he started developing the self-sufficient but slippery personality of a man too much on his own. He was suffering from an inability to believe wholly or for a long spell of time. Then came the encounter with Anne-Marie, and he began to see in Tunisia an opportunity. So many intruders had overrun the country that it could be said to

83

belong to everybody, even himself. Perhaps here he had found one of the rare places in the world where a man could literally start afresh and make new mistakes.

Almost six weeks before, at about the same hour, Gauthier had been driving down the grade from Raouad Beach toward Gammarth when, out of the corner of his eye, he had caught the flash of a red sports car, like the shiver of a cardinal's plumage against somber foliage, in the courtyard of the seaside Hotel de la Tour Blanche. By that time he had already covered a hundred yards; he hesitated, then drove back. Gauthier parked his station wagon outside the hotel, and entered the courtyard. He read the plate number—it was Anne-Marie's Triumph parked between a palm tree and a hotel delivery van.

The Tour Blanche did little business in winter, and most of the windows around the square faience tower from which it derived its name were shuttered. Below, on the beach, the dressing rooms were locked and the postcard stand was boarded up. At the desk, the Arab on duty knew no Madame Gauthier; only one elderly Belgian couple were staying at the hotel, and they were not in their room.

"What is the car doing here then?" The clerk could not see the courtyard from the desk. He craned forward, saw the Triumph, then shrugged stupidly, and Gauthier understood that either he knew nothing about the owner, or that if he did, nothing further would induce him to tell the truth.

Gauthier returned to his station wagon but did not drive away at once. At breakfast, Anne-Marie had volunteered the information that she would spend the afternoon in Tunis, first at her hairdresser's on Rue de Serbie, then with Lucia Chateaudun, the wife of the French Embassy's Political Section chief, at a sculptor's *vernissage* in the old quarter. Nothing in the program had suggested a circuitous side trip to Gammarth. The Chateauduns lived much closer to town, Anne-Marie had no winter friends in Gammarth, and the summer friends were all gone.

Gauthier juxtaposed his discovery with certain things he had noticed about his wife in the past month. That she had had several temporary lovers during eight years of marriage he thought highly probable, but on the basis of the evidence, these affairs had been brief and inconsequential; now, on the contrary, what was going on could scarcely be casual—given the state their marriage had reached.

Feeling angry and frustrated, a combination of emotions that he seldom experienced, he closed his lids over his eyes; when he opened them, everything round about—the shore fringe of eucalyptus trees, the oiled road—was unchanged, except for a young Arab who stood only ten feet off and stared at him curiously. Gauthier closed his eyes again; this time when he reopened them, the Arab was gone. He put the station wagon into gear and, without glancing back, drove to Carthage. That evening Anne-Marie described in detail her visit to the sculptor.


He felt a woeful understanding of her. Oddly—not so oddly, once you stopped for a moment and reflected—he felt that it was he who had betrayed, if betrayal involves the deliberate mishandling of hope. He had had a succession of love affairs, too, as brittle as bones, which snapped quickly and mended with little trace. Tiring of inaction, she had acted in her own way.

During these weeks, Gauthier looked at his wife from a different distance. His eyes followed her like those of a big animal too lazy to spring, or too indifferent, and one day when she offered her cold mouth to him he realized that it was too late. Between them, exchanges grew rare. They were isolated from the past by a gray anonymous reach of time; as for the future, there was not the slightest signpost to furnish a clue where they were heading. He settled into this stiff relationship, realizing that he was being as dishonest as she.

In spite of his promise, the doctor had kept them waiting; then he had examined the boy's throat, checked his temperature (which showed no change), tapped his belly and drawn a wince of pain, instructed him to go and urinate, heard out the recital of what he'd eaten, and stood back in somber judgment.

"Vomiting dehydrates—give him a lot to drink, keep him warm; and he must take these as soon as he's back in bed." He consulted a big medical dictionary on his desk, then wrote out a prescription for sulfanilamide tablets.

"It's nothing serious, you're sure?"

"I shall drop in tomorrow morning to see how he feels." Then the juvenile mien of professionalism went slack with disappointment. "He'll come around in two days. A minor attack of intestinal flu—it's nothing."

His manner nettled Gauthier: here was a doctor fascinated by the mystery of multiform disease but bored by day-to-day therapy. What the hell was he doing outside a laboratory?

Rain sluiced down the steep streets and formed yellowish gullies in empty lots as Gauthier drove hastily home. He stared at the dashboard clock. It was already five-ten. He cursed the doctor, who had caused him to lose twenty precious, critical minutes. No matter how fast he drove, he could not reach his house in time to take in the call. With its inhuman punctuality the Qiryat would try to raise him, and for the first time in his career he would be absent. This would astonish them, and they would try again, a bit more insistently. But there would be no panic; prudently, the Qiryat would go off the air, then with the same grave insistence try again to contact him. Exactly twenty-six minutes later. Gauthier smiled thinly as he recalled how, years before, with pedantic emphasis, they had outlined the emergency procedure that had never proved necessary. After all these years, it was the General who was proved right.

He flicked on the car radio and heard a voice describing the storm's westward progression. Although the rain had let up, the sky showed no break anywhere on the horizon; the persistent grumble of thunder sounded directly overhead. On this sullen afternoon nothing was going exactly as it should. Roads would be slippery, rendering the escape more difficult —on the other hand, he thought, the police might find pursuit of the men who had kidnapped Al Houaranni more difficult too.

His son sat next to him peering in composed silence at the drenched hills. His thin unadventurous hands rested on his knees. At six, he gauged his father's anger sufficiently well to know when to sit still.

Glancing sideways, Gauthier saw that his son's cheeks were still dry and flushed. There had really been no choice. . . . He worried a great deal about his son—fair and polite without, but dark and distant within, a pallid, quiet child who tired easily and didn't play as much as he should with other youngsters. Periodically, Gauthier suspected that his own carefully disguised tensions had seeped at birth into the boy's blood.

As he approached his house, Gauthier saw a red Triumph turn sharply into the driveway, churning mud against the stone wall. He braked hard and leaped out. Before his wife could utter a word, he hustled the boy out of the cold toward the door.

"Go to the pharmacy and get this filled." He handed her the prescription. "I am terribly late. We'll talk later."

Anne-Marie stared at him, her oval face overwhite against the dirty day.

"It feels better now, *maman*," the boy said.

"What does?" she asked angrily, really becoming aware of him only then.

She bundled him up protectively—more against his father than the weather, it seemed—and hurried him indoors.

The rain pelted down once more and the palms on the street rattled unappeased. Gauthier slammed the station wagon down the incline into the garage and left the doors open. Raising the Qiryat was no problem, but in this wind he wasn't sure of reception. He had not meant to take in the message here, but now he had no choice. He studied the two adjoining houses. It was difficult for his neighbors to peer into the garage over the wall, and unlikely that they would be tempted to do so in this weather. The garage's angle concealed him, and anyone who saw him would suppose that he was tinkering with the station wagon out of the rain.

By the time he was ready to take in Tel Aviv, it was five-forty-four. He closed the garage doors partially and got into the rear of the car. As soon as he adjusted his earphones, flicked on the send-receive switch and tuned to peak reception, he heard the incoming signal. Then the message was transmitted. It was not very long; confirmations of previous orders never were; then several digit-groups followed. He guessed what they were about.

He tapped out an encoded standard acknowledgment. It would keep them off his back; he would furnish an explanation about his tardiness later. They would not be satisfied with this way of doing business, but what concerned them immediately was that he was back at his post and nothing was seriously wrong.

The signal ended. Gauthier leaned back and turned the switch off, dizzy with momentary letup from tension. The confirmation was in and he could advise the three men waiting in their apartment . . . if they were waiting. They had expected his call almost a half hour ago. If they had already started out, it would make no difference: he had received the go-ahead. He heard Anne-Marie's car drive off to the pharmacy. It was pouring again outdoors. He re-entered the house through the basement door, sat down in his study and decoded the digit-groups. It took a few minutes. He read the words on the pad—at first, their real significance did not sink in. The message read: OPERATION CANCELED. ADVISE HOUND IMMEDIATELY. REQUEST EXPLANATION YOUR ABSENCE.

## CHAPTER FIVE

# The Black Beach

"WE'LL give him five more minutes," Max said.
"Has he ever been late before?"
"No."

It was as though a successful business relationship had revealed its first flaw. Max kept from glancing at the telephone on the gate-leg mahogany table next to the couch. Irritated, he went to the window and surveyed the gray street below. The sky presented an impenetrable front of clouds along the rolling semicircular horizon, which lightning flashes illumined without warmth. The blackness of the sky, Max thought, was like the dark of Shabbath at dusk, spreading over the entire land, shops and homes, towns and hills. Back high beyond the city, thunder growled and suddenly it showed a flash of white teeth across the whole lake. The storm was circling—filmy dirty rags profiled against a darker expanse that hovered over the hills around Carthage and Gammarth.

Max contemplated his two subordinates. They were waiting without complaint, each exhibiting the style he had developed to cope with inertia and nervous worry. Marston sat stiffly upright in an armchair, deep-set eyes fixed obstinately on the wall opposite; dressed in a navy-blue suit and spotless open-necked white shirt, he looked like a chauffeur on his day off. His ungainly long nose twitched. In repose his dignified features resembled a Sicilian's, but in fact, Max knew, he was a sabra, who had reached adolescence on the littered, scorching pavements of Manshieh, the decrepit no man's land between Jaffa and Tel Aviv. Black was smoking with application one of his awful rum-flavored Swiss cigarillos to the stub. His restless eyes roamed about the room, settled on Max and hastily moved away. What was he eternally seeking, Max thought with impatience—a gold mine?

As if in reply, Black began in his nasal, snobbish voice, "This redheaded girl in Rome said she wanted one hundred dollars to go with me, to help pay for her trousseau. Can you imagine?"

"Where did you meet her, Noah?" Max asked softly.

Black said shortly, "In a nightclub."

"Did you pay for it?" Marston asked.

"I used an expired credit card and she fell for it." He smiled to himself in his spoiled, lazy way, then crossed the room, picked up the receiver and listened for a moment. "It's working all right, so that's not the problem."

When he estimated that five minutes had passed, Max checked his watch and discovered that Emir's call was more than fifteen minutes overdue. "We are staying here," he said, "until this call comes through. I cannot understand what is delaying him."

"If you want to be at the hotel in time, we'd better leave now; the storm will cause traffic jams," Marston said.

"We can afford five more minutes."

They waited in bland silence. After twenty-four hours' cohabitation, Max had a reasonably accurate idea of what each man felt. "The orders were clear on this point: it takes a new message to cancel or postpone at this stage. Lack of confirmation does not equal cancellation."

"It would be better, nevertheless, if he called," Marston said.

Max began to button up his coat. "We have no choice— Al Houaranni's timetable is not flexible, nor is ours," he explained.

Marston watched him and said, "You're taking the responsibility?"

"Isn't this obvious? Could I forgive myself—would anyone at headquarters understand—if we sit on our behinds, letting this opportunity pass, and Emir calls to confirm when it is too late?"

As they rode down the lift, Black said without conviction, "Maybe Emir's phone is out of order."

"If you're not satisfied, Black, you can stay behind."

Rue Houssine Bouzaiane was astir with a stolid mass of men, women and youngsters hastening on foot through the glistening rain toward the lights of Avenue Bourguiba. The three men entered the garage, leaving the Fiat parked down the street; later in the evening, it would be removed and returned to Avis by the cutout who had rented it for Max. There was no reason why the police should associate the car with this street or with three men who had used it for inconspicuous transportation during a twenty-four-hour period. "Avis did not earn much with us," Max observed, once inside the garage.

"We drove a total of thirty-eight miles at a weekly rate of twenty-five dinars—we'll do more tonight without paying for it," said Marston, making a final inspection of the Peugeot.

"You will probably need these later," Max said to Black, bringing out a pair of handcuffs from the side flap, then replacing them.

Outdoors, under Marston's restrained handling, the dusty Peugeot edged forward through the swelling number of pedestrians. People in the street ungrudgingly made way for the vehicle; as it drew abreast, they glanced inside at the occupants and shouted, "*Anti Tunsi aua ella la?*" which in Arabic means "Are you Tunisian or not?" "*Nam Tunsi!*" Max called out in gleeful response.

In the dark gusty streets there was a recognizable sense of excitement. Ramadan had officially ended. Simultaneous cannon peal from Franceville and a muezzin's televised call to *moghreb*, the evening prayer, from the Zitouna mosque, had put a close to a month's strenuous fasting and praying; and if not all had fasted with equal piety, all were certainly about to celebrate. From a nearby hall they heard the whining discordance of flutes and cymbals and drums and an Arab woman's shrill chant: "*Yaa Tunis! . . . Yaa Tunis!*"

Marston drove slowly up the avenue. Before the Hotel Africa, a crowd waited, good-natured and shy, for a glimpse of Al Houaranni. Limousines were aligned at the entrance, and a profusion of Tunisian and Palestinian flags fluttered, drenched, above the door. Close by, a detachment of motorcycle troopers with helmets and scarves stood beside their machines out of the rain. Marston came to a dim, unpaved alley behind the hotel and parked the Peugeot in front of the employees' entrance. The hotel was new; a wheelbarrow

93

rested in a spreading puddle beside a pile of sand. Here the sounds of celebration from Avenue Bourguiba reached them as muted and unreal. As Max and Black scrambled out of the car, a flashlight beam shone full on them and a policeman suddenly stepped out from behind a pillar.

Max said promptly in Arabic, "Here are the passes."

"Wait where you are," ordered the policeman. He reached out with his left hand and then turned the beam down on the stamped and countersigned Interior Ministry passes. "There are three of you for two passes," he observed.

"The third man is the driver. He will not come up with us," Max said. The policeman was young; from his manner, Max judged that he was respectful of authority, vexed probably at being assigned to guard the hotel's spooky rear entrance while in front, noise and light and the crowd's respect made a policeman's lot worthwhile. "No one is to know Al Houaranni has left. You have been given a certain responsibility—this has been made clear to you, I think?"

"Yes, Sidi." The policeman's teeth shone as he returned the passes. "You are a little ahead of time," he noted.

"The Blade of Allah would rather be early than late at an appointment. Should we be different?"

Exactly as Emir had detailed it in his floor plan of the hotel, the freight elevator was located just beyond the delivery entrance. Max and Black rode in silence to the seventh floor, then walked down the uncarpeted corridor in the service area to a swing door that led to the guests' quarters. They were looking for Suite 700. They rounded a corner and came abruptly upon two squat Tunisian plain-clothes men who stood before a double door. One of them dropped his hand warningly as he saw the two unknown Arabs.

94

"Stop right there," he said. "Who the hell are you? This floor is off limits to everybody."

Max rumbled, "Salah Al Houaranni is awaiting us." Just behind him Black stood loose and ready, but it was not much reassurance.

"Move away, stand clear so that I can see you," the plain-clothes man ordered Black.

He was swart and suspicious. First he examined Max from head to toe, then Black. The second detective had moved backward and stood in front of the numbered door beside a table, arms slightly flexed, like a karate fighter. He had Tartar eyes set in a broad doughy moon face broken up by the aftereffects of smallpox into ridges and ravines. Each communicated his taut distrust to the other, Max thought, like a pair of Dobermans.

"How did you get up here?" the first one demanded.

"You will ask inside; you will find that all is in order," Max said sternly. Using the freight elevator had one glaring drawback: coming upon the two detectives from this unexpected direction had contributed to their nervousness.

The second one, who had been observing Max fixedly, said, "Come here." His pudgy hands ran under Max's armpits and around his waist and down his trouser seams. He grunted and removed the Beretta from inside the jacket. "Where is yours?" he asked Black, and took it too.

"We are authorized to carry these guns," Max told him.

"They are confiscated temporarily on my authority." He placed them carefully on the table. "Go down below or I'll arrest you."

"Do you want to see our passes?"

"I don't give a shit about your passes."

95

"We have orders."

"I don't give a shit about your orders."

"As you wish. You will discover that Al Houaranni is waiting impatiently." Max laid light stress on the final word. "How do you think we got this far without being stopped?"

Back talk was a mistake, for the second one, looking mean, stepped forward and said, "You are under arrest. Do not move." The first one appeared annoyed and snapped, "I will decide this. If you are not on the down elevator in ten seconds you will be arrested. Only Interior Ministry passes are valid to enter the suite."

"This is what we have."

Under the swart man's scrutiny, while the second plain-clothes man covered him, Max carefully brought out the two plastic-sheathed cards for verification.

Without consulting the other, the older detective nodded, rapped twice on the door, which immediately opened, and disappeared inside. They could hear his rasping voice behind the varnished panel. Then he reappeared and motioned to them to enter. Reluctantly, his colleague moved aside to let them pass without taking his eyes off them.

The weakly lit suite smelled of stale air and cold coffee and medicine. In the center stood Al Houaranni. It was a shock for Max to come upon him in flesh and bone—upon this Palestinian Arab whose appearance, habits and behavior he had studied for weeks on end with relentless microscopic concentration. He seemed frailer and grayer than in the wire-service photos. His eyes were very dark and brilliant under ghostly white eyebrows. He wore mustard battle dress and scuffed dull para boots. The Blade of Allah, as his extensive publicity referred to him, dressed like a field officer who had recently returned from fighting in the desert; but the military effect was offset by a television set and a plate of half-eaten tangerines placed on a hassock. Al Houaranni had just been watching a rerun of his day's activities, which had included a visit to the École Supérieure d'Agriculture, a dam and a rug factory, on the news.

Max flicked his hand to his heart in salutation. "*El Hayeb!* We have come from the Inner Committee as you requested."

Al Houaranni was eying him quizzically. "What is your rank in the Army?" he asked in a dry, surprisingly youthful voice.

Max got the drift of the question. With a polite military salute, he introduced himself and Black. "Captain Ben Said . . . and this is Lieutenant Cherif." Only then did he become aware, in the suite's gloom, of another person—a man tall and gaunt like Black—who remained motionless and observant in one corner, with no word of identification. One bodyguard inside, two detectives outside, and a hotel packed with police on every floor—probably it had been deceptively easy getting into this armed camp.

Al Houaranni chewed a tangerine, section by section, eying them doubtfully, then sipped a glass of mineral water and belched. "How is it you came early?" he asked. His chin was arresting—it was as firm as the forehead was skimpy, which created a disturbing impression of overriding willfulness that fueled a narrow mind. As for his voice, it was well pitched, steady, cultivated; the unshakeable confidence it contained came as a shock.

"Sidi, the government knows your reason for being in

Tunis. Not every minister in the Cabinet approves of your visit." Max saw by the somber eyes that, from Al Houaranni's point of view, this remark constituted a perverse sort of flattery. He controlled himself with an effort. It seemed utterly unbelievable that in less than a half hour they had managed to get from the garage into this lunatic's room. He was not altogether sure the words he meant to pronounce would come out as intended. "The government suspects something is wrong. In the past four hours the police detachment has been reinforced around the hotel; although the Sûreté will deny it, this is meant not to protect you but to spy on you."

"I know this." Al Houaranni looked suddenly impatient, but it did not matter, the trick was to keep talking and distract his attention until the telephone rang.

"This is why we suggested that you become indisposed—"

"I can appreciate your concern." From the way Al Houaranni opened his mouth to say something further, Max knew that he was still dissatisfied. "I expected you a half hour later."

"We came early to confuse any traitor who may have penetrated the movement."

Al Houaranni made no effort to conceal his skepticism, but he indicated two armchairs near the television set. Reluctantly Max sat down—once seated, they were, so to speak, no longer free; he wanted to be out of the suite immediately after the telephone call came. Facing them, the bodyguard remained on his feet. His attention was focused entirely on their movements; he still had not uttered a word.

"A suspected traitor should be liquidated—" Al Houaranni began, and then the phone rang.

The bodyguard moved in the corner, and Max observed

that he cradled the handset against his left shoulder while both hands remained free.

"Is it—?" Al Houaranni rose, took the telephone, listened to the voice carefully, then replied, "It is also my wish."

Max heard the rain thudding wildly against the window. He remembered that when he had read the operational plan, it had seemed to him that the entire mission would hinge on this voice intruding into the room with its authoritative, counterfeit reassurances. And the call had come when needed. It was perfect timing.

"The Inner Committee confirms everything you said. To be honest, I did not until now believe a word of your story."

Max rose gravely and repressed a smile. Al Houaranni couldn't very well distrust a fellow conspirator inside the Interior Ministry who was informed of the extremely prudent measures that had been taken to stage a secret meeting far from the Hotel Africa.

"We shall tell the two spies in the corridor that I have recovered and am going to the Defense Ministry after all." Al Houaranni turned to his bodyguard and Max's heart skipped a beat. "Remain here and give whoever comes to the door the same answer . . . I have gone to my scheduled appointment. When they find out it's untrue"—his thin zealous lips hinted for the first time at humor—"it will reinforce my reputation as a cunning adventurer and troublemaker. Your reputation as my bodyguard may be tarnished, but this is of relative unimportance."

The man, who might have been taken for Al Houaranni's younger brother (but Max knew that he had none, only a covey of sisters in various Arab capitals), made a strange, frustrated down-glancing gesture with his left hand.

"It is more important for you to remain here," Al Houaranni said with surprising courtesy, and Max finally understood that the bodyguard was dumb.

"I shall be gone exactly one hour," Al Houaranni continued. "During this time, your group will be responsible for my safety. I suppose that this is not asking too much?"

"Everything has been arranged as you wished," Max replied.

The bodyguard still looked uneasy.

"Do not worry about me; I have an escort of two, and I succeed only when I take risks. Remember the answer you are to write out for those who are curious about my whereabouts." He glanced at his watch. "Are we ready?"

They left the bodyguard suddenly unemployed in the bleak suite, with the television set and the tangerines. In the hall, Max informed the older detective: "Al Houaranni will return within one hour."

"Where is he going?"

"To the Defense Minister."

The swart plain-clothes man began to precede them down the corridor.

"And our weapons?"

At the swart man's signal, the second detective opened the table drawer and silently handed back the two Berettas.

"Not that way, and you do not need to come," Al Houaranni told the older policeman. "I am guarded enough as it is."

"The motorcycle detachment is waiting in front—"

"This is why we are leaving by the rear entrance."

In the ripe-smelling freight elevator, Max restrained himself from crowding his quarry too close. How was it that Al

Houaranni, who had spent five years directing terrorist commandos, sensed no danger? What was wrong with his sense of
smell? Couldn't he catch the cheesy odor of a trap? It seemed
fantastic. Max cast a doubtful, covert glance at the man and
caught a glimpse of vague gray feminine hair, dark fanatical
brooding eyes and unyielding olive chin. Apparently his ad-
dictive need to conspire benumbed even his sense of survival.
With this thought it struck Max that *now*, without warning
or prayers, was the true moment to strangle the monkish,
skinny, stubborn neck until no life beat against the fingers
and the problem of the Blade of Allah's influence on the
young would collapse once and for all. Max counted down,
letting his anger subside; he was trembling with rebellion at
his own murderousness. Beside him, Al Houaranni stirred
and Max found himself being inspected by those lively glittering eyes. There must surely have been a form of thought
transference, yet Al Houaranni showed no uneasiness.

"Can we return from Mutuelleville in ten minutes in this
storm?" he asked.

"The driver is excellent."

Black stood like a giant statue at his side, and added need-
lessly, "The Inner Committee is anxious to talk with you about
the situation that will come into being after the coup. There
are unresolved problems. One is relations with brother Arab
movements."

"Let the coup succeed first, and"—Al Houaranni stared
him curiously in the eye—"let it be consolidated." The man's
straightforwardness impressed Max.

They emerged from the hotel into the sticky wetness. The
policeman was nowhere in sight; Marston was responsible for

that. He sat in shadow at the Peugeot's wheel, a little nervy anonymous fellow whom no policeman would fear until it was too late.

Al Houaranni paused with his thin hand already on the car door. "There is no policeman on duty—"

"He was here and cleared our passes," Black said, again volunteering information uselessly and dangerously.

"It is strange—" The delayed, overdue trickle of suspicion that was running through Al Houaranni's mind clotted his voice. With desperate agility he pivoted, drove an elbow low and hard at Max's jaw and broke loose toward the hotel, his shoes making a scuttering sound like slippers on the gummy pavement. As he tried to cry for help, Max grabbed at his neck and sank two fingers deep into the open mouth and yanked at the wet membranous lining. In one elastic stride Black caught up with them and smashed his fist down over Al Houaranni's unprotected ear, then received the limp body as it began to slump sideways. The shout for help expired into an inarticulate gasp.

"Open the door, " Max whispered.

Getting a purchase on the frail figure by the armpits, Black dragged it to the car and deposited it half on the rear seat, half on the floor and climbed in alongside. Max fumbled in the side flap and handed Black the handcuffs. They snapped shut with a steel click. "What are you waiting for, man, for God's sake!"

Marston shot him a swift, incredulous glance and slammed the gearshift forward. In the next instant the Peugeot skidded away on the worn stones from the dimly lit rear entrance. The scuffle had lasted only a few seconds; as far as they could tell, no one had witnessed Al Houaranni's attempted escape.

"The policeman?"

"I put him in the tool shed and taped his mouth. He won't be able to call out for help—they'll have to look for him."

"Did he give any trouble?"

"No."

"What do you mean—no."

"I took him from the back."

From the rear, Black grunted. "Can't you go any faster?"

They had left the port district and were approaching the city limits. "Now I can," said Marston, and the car slid forward on the slick highway surface.

Very quickly they put Tunis behind. After a short time the divided highway became a broad, bumpy road that ran past a cement works. In the headlights' beam they made out factories on either side.

Max's jaw hurt, and his bruised hand was shaking; he placed it in his lap. Turning half around, in the dimness he made out the inert body in battle dress coiled up fetuslike on the floorboards, the delicate head resting against the seat cushion. Black sat above his trophy with a hunter's grim, conclusive air. He held the Beretta pointed at Al Houaranni's head.

"How bad did you hurt him?"

"His ear will give him trouble when he comes to."

"Why is his mouth bleeding?"

"I had to clout him in the teeth. It isn't bleeding anymore."

"He almost ran out on us," Marston said. "What do you think of this Arabchik?"

"Thanks to your big mouth, Black. Who told you to start a conversation?"

"I didn't tell him anything he couldn't see for himself."

"He grew suspicious."

Black snorted. "He could smell your sweat, Levanon. In the elevator, I was afraid you'd collapse before he did."

Max was silent for a minute. "Captain—from now on, that's how you refer to me, Black. Nothing else. Don't call me anything else. When we get back to Tel Aviv, I'll make out my report." In his anger Max found that his hand was throbbing; he restrained it and with an effort turned away. He spoke to Marston. "Any trouble with the car?"

Marston shook his head.

"No one is following us?"

"If someone does," said the Manhattan-accented voice from the rear, "I'm going to dump the evidence."

"Black, one more word out of you, and I'll write you up unfit for further operational assignment."

They were speeding southward down a four-lane road. Rain, borne in from the sea they could not make out but whose presence they sensed, streamed against windshield and windows. An abrupt violent exclamation of lightning low on the horizon electrified the countryside. To the right, vines marched in ghostly ranks into the misty night, and above the vineyards loomed the shoulder of Bou Kornine. Thunder echoed and bounded off its uninhabited slopes. The storm seemed to be roaming back and forth indecisively in the night.

"They'll have trouble putting a boat ashore," Marston said.

Max studied the smoky horizon but saw no sign of a break. Now that he no longer had the kidnapping itself to worry about, he thought of the rest of the operational plan. The region of Qelibia had been chosen because few people lived there in winter and its beaches were deserted and they could hope to reach it in two hours, and because the road to Cap Bon started not far from the Hotel Africa, which meant they could be out of Tunis, where the alert would first be raised, in a matter of minutes. He would not allow himself to worry too much; it sufficed that they held Al Houaranni alive in the rear of the car.

"There's a town ahead," said Marston.

Max saw a few bleary lights rushing up toward them through the rain.

"Slow down," he murmured. He recognized the place: Hammam-Lif. It consisted of rows of unfashionable villas and a broad tree-lined main street on which fronted a couple of cafés, a gas pump, a grocery and a police station. He had spent a weekend here as a teen-ager; he remembered a dance hall where the tough gangs congregated. As they approached the main street, his hand tightened on his pistol. Without turning his head he said to Black, "Is he conscious?"

"Don't worry, he isn't about to sit up and shake hands."

Max saw an official in a gray uniform moving about in a lit room of the police station, but there was no sign of excitement. The Sûreté in Tunis might be alerted by now, but it was unlikely that they had already radioed Garde National posts throughout the country. His watch showed six-forty. They had been on the road twenty minutes; they were making good time and could afford to slow down to avoid attracting attention.

Shortly they abandoned the main southbound road for a secondary road that bisected the cape. At infrequent intervals cars came toward them from the dark interior. The continuing swish of rain drowned all other noise, but the fragrance of orange blossoms crept out insidiously toward them in the sopping dark.

During the next hour and a half they passed fallow muddy fields, crossed wadies in spate, rattled over unsure iron bridges, caught glimpses of distant uninviting hills, almost drowned the generator at an inundated crossroads, slithered on a stretch of mud between rows of cork oaks and swept past an ancient filigreed mosque that rose stately and mysterious, like a haunted ruin, out of a cluster of verminous shacks.

Around him Max felt a difference in mood, a perceptible letup in tension. Marston was driving with utter concentration and enjoying the wet night road.

"How is this fuel-injection engine working? Is it living up to your expectations?"

"This car drives as good as my taxi," Marston said.

Black leaned forward, murmuring into Max's ear, and Max lit a cigarillo for him. The rum-perfumed smoke drifted forward toward Max. He listened to the savage wind and settled his bulk against the seat back.


"He's showing signs of life," Black said.

"Get him ready. We're almost there."

La Plage Noire, as it is still known, lies almost at the extremity of Cap Bon, north of Qelibia. The shale coastline is indented with coves difficult to reach from the road and unknown to most travelers. Tamarisk groves rooted precariously in crumbling rock ledges form screens around the inlets and filter the sun's rays so that the water seems dark and fathomless, hence the name one little-frequented mouth has received —the Black Beach.

At the turnoff from the main road, a stone track led down to the water. Jouncing between giant cactus hedges, they came to a shelf of black porous stone on which the rain danced heavily. Here the open sea was nearby and they heard the storm flailing the shore. On this particular night, the sky was so somber that the coast was absolutely featureless. Ahead lay a clump of tamarisks wildly shaking and straining in the wind. Marston braked the Peugeot with a jolt.

Al Houaranni sat up on the floorboards, looking about carefully and trying to memorize details.

Black said to him in Arabic, "I'll get out first, then you come slowly. The gun is pointed at your forehead."

Al Houaranni muttered but clambered out as he was ordered and stood shackled beside the car, watching the three men. "What have you done to my ear?"

"You can hear me; this is all that matters."

Marston picked a way through the spiky underbrush with his flashlight and reached a rock ledge, followed by Black and Al Houaranni. Max brought up the rear. Below and to the left was a sand beach. Past the foreshore were outcroppings of black boulders. The sea smacked the rocks with a roar, tossing up geysers of spray, and poured impetuously into the sheltered deep cove.

"I don't see them," Max shouted against the uproar of wind.

Jerking his head at the sound of Hebrew, Al Houaranni cursed mechanically. *"Yhouds!"* he said. Then he asked tersely, pointing out at the darkness, "Israel?"

"Turn this way and shut up," Black told him.

Marston probed the sea with his flashlight. Out there the rollers were like snowy hills; then they came sprinting in, erupting and flowing onto the short incline of beach like a foaming avalanche. "They can't put a boat through that surf; they'll swamp. Of all the nights to pick for this operation . . ." Rivulets sluiced down Marston's face. He began to hop up and down in a futile effort to shed the rain from his wind-tugged clothes. Small and neat, he didn't like to be rained upon, it washed out his urban nattiness.

"Where the hell is their boat?" Black said.

"They are out there somewhere; we shall see their signal in a minute," Max said, but thought that his voice sounded as hollow as the booming of the surf.

"What time is it?" cried Marston into the wind.

"We are exactly on time, this is not the problem."

A lighthouse beam flitted across the hills. "Even in this weather someone is going to see us," Black spoke up. His voice sounded as cold and steady as the water surging and ebbing at their feet.

"We have to wait," Max said. "Don't talk; just watch him."

"Cowards," said Al Houaranni, "caught by the storm." In the midst of darkness and wind, bareheaded, wrists shackled, in drenched battle dress, he seemed in his natural element—an unforgiving, ascetic, woebegone prophet of disaster. No one answered him.

"By this time," Marston said, "the Army, the police, every unoccupied Arab in this country is hunting for us . . . and the boat is late."

Then Black said, "There it is—I heard them."

They studied the front of black frantic water but saw no form emerging out of the rain; the sea slapped with sudden sharpness against the boulders, making the sound Black had mistaken for a boat's noise. "There is nothing out there but fog," Black said.

"It is incredible," Max said in a momentary lull of wind, "the obstacles we overcame to get this far, and now we are stalled by the weather."

"Listen, Levanon, no one is going to try to bring a boat in through that; I've sailed enough to know what I'm talking about."

"I can see this for myself."

"Then what are we waiting for like idiots?"

"The operation has not been canceled; we have no choice but to wait." Max was shaken by a dizzying temptation to kick out at the black crashing surf. It had been planned for the sub to surface close to shore and north of where the *lamparo* fleet spread out its nets. There had existed a danger that the fishermen would see the signal flare, but so what? The police would find the abandoned Peugeot the next morning and trace it back to its owner, who was out of the country. The prancing sea would wash out the commando's existence. That had been the operational plan.

Max could understand that no submarine skipper wanted to surface close to the rocky shore in this storm if he could avoid it—but why hadn't they been advised? He had expected this mission to be tight, rapid, intricate and precise "like the work of Swiss watchmakers," as they liked to say at the Qiryat. This was how he had represented it to himself—although from the outset, in the General's drafty office, he had felt a pang of doubt. The operational plan did not call for a drawn-out wait on the beach with the object of the exercise. Now, however, they had him—a gray, skinny, argumentative albatross—around their necks . . . for how long? Max cursed politics, he cursed the Mediterranean in winter, above all he cursed Emir.

"We can fall back on the house," he said. "I have the key. But I don't want to do this unless absolutely necessary."

"The plan provided for use of the safe-house in an emergency."

"What do you call this—an emergency, simply because a storm has put them off schedule?"

"If it's the storm," Marston interjected. "You wouldn't wait at the apartment."

"He was trying to do for the best," said Black unexpectedly.

The storm was deployed on a vast front, and each successive sheet of lightning illumined a broader range of sky. A thunderclap exploded earsplittingly overhead in a supreme expression of anger. Its echo reverberated around the cove and jarred the hills. They could no longer hear the plash of waves for the falling rain.

"To wait here longer is dangerous," Black said stubbornly.

"Who is going to see us? The *lamparos?* They are not out tonight."

"If the boat were coming, it would be here by now."

"Israeli thugs," Al Houaranni said, and spat on the gray sand. "When you walked into my room, I almost ordered you killed on sight."

Max took no notice and asked, "How far is it to the house?"

Marston said, "Ten minutes' drive."

"Are we going?" Black asked.

"Yes. We have him, this is what counts."

"What do we do with him?"

"Bring him along. What else?" Max replied and turned

away impatiently. "Marston, you'll drive without lights until I tell you otherwise."

In the lightning's successive flashes he could make out the thunderheads moving back out to sea, like a victorious flotilla. The downpour was subsiding, but the lightning flashed obstinately and the sky continued to catch blue fire. In the storm's wake the sea was running high, deluging the rocky foreshore.

Black prodded Al Houaranni forward. In silence they picked their way back to the end of the track; the steady soughing of the wind off the sea followed them. They got into the Peugeot and it turned and bumped off between the high cactus hedges toward the interior's enigmatic dark.

## CHAPTER SIX

# The Ambiguous Man

LIKE several other mission chiefs in Tunis, the Moroccan ambassador devoted a measure of time to the pursuit of pleasure. He collected Persian miniatures and owned a pure Arab race horse which he ran at the Ksar Saad track. In winter the cream-and-green salon of his residence saw use twice a week as the scene of elegant receptions that turned quite jolly after initial start-up stiffness.

Preston arrived at seven-thirty, and the first thing he overheard was a woman saying, "Al Houaranni's late."

Then another voice nearby said, "Gauthier is here without his wife."

"That nice little French girl? She's attractive."

The Irish minister's daughter eyed Preston and asked, "Is it true that he works at something terribly secret for the Americans?"

"Dear Signorina Kelly, everybody belongs to the CIA," said the Italian admiral who was holding her glass. "I do. I can get you in if you like."

Among these shards of conversation, Preston picked his

way lightly, impenetrably; his enigmatic chill face and uncommunicative deportment alike smacked of you-will-have-your-little-joke-but-when-the-revolution-comes-who-will-be holding-an-IOU? This was the reason why he was invited to many dinner parties at this small post where everyone assumed that he was in league with the devil, though most refrained from asking outright for fear of spoiling the fun. The suspected ability to make mischief and create scandal lent Preston an extra, useful dimension, like a suburban housewife who is known to moonlight as a stripteaser.

In one corner Preston perceived Gauthier, thick shoulders thrown back, drinking with impressive aloofness while a Slav at his side embarked upon what seemed a very long-winded tale. Preston felt a light stab of privation and admitted to himself that he missed the conspiratorial sense of standing within fingertip-grazing distance of Anne-Marie's slender thighs among a roomful of oblivious or not-so-oblivious people. Love throve on equivocal situations.

With formidable emphasis, the ambassador, an overbred young man in a lustrous suit, pressed arriving guests' hands; it was impossible to decipher whether he was vexed by Al Houaranni's tardiness.

A butler came up and said, "I have a call for you, sir." Preston followed him down the hall. The fluent English-speaking voice that came over the line was foreign.

"This is Kheli. Do you think you can come to my office now?"

"I'll be there in twenty minutes."

Preston returned to the salon for a moment. The Slavic-looking man had moved on and Gauthier had disappeared. At the door, the ambassador said, "It's a pity. Al Houaranni has been delayed; we are all so disappointed. I know how much he would have enjoyed talking with you."

The Interior Ministry never shut down completely, but on this evening many of its employees had ceased work early to celebrate Ain Seguir. Two policemen had taken shelter from the rain in sentry boxes. Preston showed his identification at the desk and waited while the night duty officer telephoned upstairs; then he took the lift to the fourth floor, where a sign said POLICE DES ÉTRANGERS, and followed an unshaven *chaouch*, who was waiting for him, down a corridor to the only bureau where a light burned.

An Army officer sat alone behind a big wooden desk. He wore the tabs of a colonel, and his tea-colored skin through use and age was honed smooth as a razor blade. His stiff gray hair was cut in a brush on top, but some tufts sprouted unmanageably from his ears. This, and his flat truculent snout, made him resemble both Colonel Naguib and a wild boar.

"*Asslama.*" He gripped Preston's hand without the Moroccan ambassador's fervor but with far more force, and said briefly, "We have problems. Al Houaranni has vanished."

"I was beginning to think something like that. He didn't show at the Moroccans'."

"There is little doubt he's been kidnapped, but whether murdered is something we'll know later. As you can imagine, I am up to here in manure."

The colonel had risen to *commissaire de police*, then had obtained assignment to the Consulate in Marseilles, where he checked on politically unreliable Tunisians, then had been involved in oil negotiations. For the past year, he had furnished Preston with classified files on suspect agents in whom one Service or the other was interested. Tunisian Counter-intelligence maintained similar "support" arrangements with the French and the British; but Kheli did not personally like the *chef de poste* Paris had recently assigned to Tunis, and the D.I. 6 representative never had stimulating news to impart. The relationship with the Americans was more taxing but more satisfactory. The colonel thought Preston told the truth three times out of five; he judged him to be serious and appreciated the fact that he was a man to whom one could recount a few confidential sandalous tales late in the evening without next morning regretting it. Preston liked the way M'hamed Kheli grappled with a problem like a Turkish wrestler until, slowly but unfailingly, he secured a stranglehold on it.

"Here are the facts. . . . Does this make sense in a nasty way? Al Houaranni was supposed to meet the Defense Minister at five-thirty, but at literally the last moment—five-fifteen —he was stricken, or so he claimed, by a case of acute indigestion, and remained in his hotel suite. From Al Houaranni's point of view, the Defense appointment was important—I can now tell you that he hoped to obtain a considerable amount of armaments—therefore he wasn't likely to cancel the meeting without good cause. This sudden indisposition was a typical trick. No one in our escort party recalls his feeling previously unwell, and there is no record of his summoning a doctor to the hotel. Given the man's methods, it was precisely to prevent his springing any last-minute surprises of the sort that I posted two men outside his suite, frankly to keep an eye on his movements.

"At any rate, a patrolman assigned to the Africa's rear entrance stopped three men who arrived in a car at six-five. When they showed Interior Ministry passes he allowed them to enter. I stress this because without these special passes they could never have gotten near the hotel. Obviously, someone in this Ministry supplied the passes. We are investigating this aspect. Two men rode up to the seventh floor and one stayed with the car. Later, the patrolman was found gagged and bound in a nearby tool shed.

"At six-ten, the same two men arrived at Al Houaranni's suite. He expected them and received them at once. About a quarter hour later they all left together, without the body-guard—a sign of confidence if ever there was one. Al Houaranni never returned.

"The bodyguard and my two men became worried at approximately the same time—seven o'clock—and gave the alert.

"Their description tallies with that of the patrolman. The two men who led Al Houaranni away are Arabs, probably Tunisians, although that's not definite. One of them had an accent of sorts; the one in charge is short and stout and in his forties, the other tall and younger. The chauffeur is small and neat, but we don't have much of a description for him. The car is a gray Peugeot 504 sedan; it carries Tunisian plates, but unfortunately we do not have the complete license number.

"Now, this interesting detail: *Another* car drove up to the rear entrance at about six-thirty and deposited two men who went straight to Al Houaranni's suite. They were not stopped downstairs because, as I said, the policeman on duty had meanwhile been overpowered; but a hotel employee saw them.

When they learned that Al Houaranni had just left, they turned on their heels and went away immediately without asking further questions. If my men had been smarter, they would have detained these two and started promptly worrying about Al Houaranni's whereabouts. You will not believe this, but this second group of men *also* had Interior Ministry passes to gain access to Al Houaranni's suite."

"And no one knows who they are?"

"We have a summary description of them too, for what it is worth. There is no doubt, according to my men, that they were Tunisians."

Preston nodded. "So, in short, two groups of men arrived at the hotel between six and six-thirty. Al Houaranni expected to go somewhere with one group, that's why he pleaded sick, but another group turned up and somehow persuaded him to leave voluntarily with them, is that it?"

"Yes, that's my conclusion. But who? So many answers fit. Al Houaranni was not, after all, popular everywhere, neither in Egypt nor Syria."

"Not to mention Israel."

Kheli's voice assumed an aloofness that prepared Preston for what was coming; he had heard it before when the colonel floundered, as he put it, in manure. "My main purpose in interrupting your evening was to ask what *you* know about this *salade*."

The question irritated Preston. If he had possessed prior information, which he had not, how could he admit it? It was silly on Kheli's part to put such a question. "No matter what you imagine, we are not in contact with every opposition group in this country—of which, you must admit, you have a growing number. And other intelligence services certainly do not tip us off about their operations, if you are assuming they are involved."

Kheli considered him in silence, then apparently decided to attack the problem in a different way.

"If it's ransom, we'll hear soon enough; if it's vengeance, the body will be found."

"Why are you so sure it's a Palestinian group?"

"What is your theory? Arabs working in the pay of Ha Mossad? It's possible."

"His terrorism was directed against the Israelis. On the other hand, would they want to alienate the only Arab country that practices a moderate policy toward them?"

The colonel had remained standing; for a Tunisian he was unusually tall. "Is this what you believe—that the Israelis mounted an operation?"

"I don't believe anything. I'm not even sure Al Houaranni has been kidnapped. When I walked in, you said, '*We* have problems,' and I wonder why."

"It would be better if your people had a finger in this," said Kheli with a toothy charming smile he used when he played with his grandchildren, "because then we could strike a deal."

"And the notion occurred to you that we did—"

"Naturally. It will also occur to others."

From the back office emerged a captain Preston knew as the colonel's deputy. His name was Hacine Fawzi. He was a stocky, short, dark-browed man in his mid-thirties with frizzy hair and stiff cadet-school manners. Preston had never seen him smile or shake hands or let his face muscles relax. He carried a sheaf of telex messages.

"Colonel, Carthage airport, frontier posts, Coast Guard bases and harbor masters are on alert. An intercept with the car's description has gone to the Garde National."

Kheli said to Preston, "It could not have happened on a worse night—thousands of cars are in Tunis for the end of Ramadan." He consulted his watch. "Eight-fifty—"

"Can they be out of the country by now?"

"Surely, if they left by plane; there are several flights to Paris, Marseilles and Rome. By car, more difficult—it is a two-and-a-half-hour drive to the Algerian frontier. In either case they would face the problem of getting Al Houaranni past police and customs, but I suppose he has been drugged. What else is there?" he asked the captain.

"I have just received a query from Reuters," Fawzi said.

"Tell them Al Houaranni is still indisposed, but emphasize that it's nothing serious or they'll think we have poisoned him. They won't believe a word anyway. We can expect an outcry tomorrow through the whole of the Middle Eastern press. But for the moment we are not saying a thing."

After Fawzi had gone, Kheli folded his arms on the desk and surveyed the framed portrait of the President on the wall opposite. His silence lasted a moment. "This affair puts my job in jeopardy. The President's staff is demanding to know why I failed to anticipate a hostile operation against a sensitive target. You know the sort of comment—'Why must we spend all these dinars on an Intelligence Service to be always taken by surprise?' They choose to forget that I recommended against Al Houaranni's trip. They overruled my objections, and now they are in a panic. When the opposition learns about this *chackchoucha*, this mess, we can expect some nasty recriminations. Al Houaranni is one of these homeless heroes

119

an Arab street crowd immediately identifies with for mysterious reasons that simply defy common sense. It just isn't done, to allow him to be snatched out of his hotel under the noses of the police!"

Kheli considered Preston again, eyes smoky and melancholy. "Can we count on your cooperation? I think your people are anxious to see my government stay in power. After all," he added, with fine, acid humility, "we are moderates."

"What sort of cooperation do you have in mind, M'hamed?"

Kheli snorted with contempt. "Do you think we can find this gang on our own? Fawzi's Western-style efficiency doesn't bluff *me*. Radioing alert bulletins around the country is about the extent of his capability. Do you know what we call *'travail d'Arabes'*? Oaths will be sworn to capture the bandits, Al Houaranni's qualities will be extolled, but nothing constructive will occur except by sheer chance. As for the Garde National, orders will be misplaced, time lost. The people who organized this were well informed and are professionals. Naturally they chose the end of Ramadan, when half the population is tipsy and the other half busy exchanging gifts. Nine o'clock—they have more than two hours' head start. I have no illusions; we will not catch this gang easily— if at all."

Preston uncrossed his legs and rose. He was embarrassed by the colonel's outburst. He knew that the Tunisian police were simply not that inefficient, and knew that Kheli did not believe it either. However, he appreciated the amount of pressure that was driving the colonel to pocket his pride; he also felt a swift, selfish astonishment at the idea that in this self-indulgent, languid capital something important and unpredictable had occurred. "After breaking the news at the Embassy, I'll contact you about active cooperation," he said.

"It's a pity the rest of the world will raise such a howl about this affair," Kheli said. His worn snout wrinkled with malice. "A Palestinian career terrorist who conspires against us, is fascinated by Hebrew literature and goes out without his bodyguard . . . who really cares what happens to the bloody old fool?"

"Cooperation . . ." repeated Mills noncommittally.

His button-down cotton shirt shone a ghostly pale blue in the semigloom of the Embassy office illumined by one parsimonious desk lamp. He had been working late this night. Mills worked, smoked, drank and plotted in shirt sleeves; occasionally and reluctantly, he struggled into a jacket to attend a reception or to brief the ambassador. Both trousers and jacket were cut a shade too tight and tugged against his stout formidable ex-paratrooper's body.

"How long have you liaised with Kheli—less than one year?"

Preston answered the unuttered question: "He levels with me—I think he abhors outright lying. He omits when his interest lies that way, but he doesn't look you in the eye and romance you."

"However, this time his interest—or someone's—may lie in mounting a major provocation. We've had our fingers burned before in these inter-Arab squabbles. Why not pay ourselves the luxury of watching this one from the sidelines?"

"We could do that."

Mills removed a half-typed sheet of paper from his electric

typewriter. "Here's my estimate of the consequences Al Houaranni's trip was going to have on the local situation. I can now tear it up and start all over again. And they call this a rest-and-relaxation post."

Mills came from a large, politicking Pennsylvania family of stockbrokers and corporation lawyers. In his mid-fifties he was slightly past his prime, but he benefited from the momentum of the '40's and '50's when his career had given rise to a legend the public had never heard about but which Intelligence professionals in Washington and London recounted with satisfaction. They—and the passage of time—had embellished and refined the legend. On a bleak night in March 1948, when Soviet tanks and weapons carriers were ready to ram past Checkpoint Charlie in Berlin. Mills had sent an urgent message to Washington from one of his high-placed sources in Pankow that had averted the Communist invasion of western Germany by minutes—so went one story. A few years later, in Prague, over the ambassador's heated objections he had smuggled two Socialist Party leaders across the border in a car that reached Vienna riddled by seventeen machine-gun bullet holes but with all occupants alive—this was another, more recent tale. Mills had not carried out all the feats with which he was credited. The incident at Checkpoint Charlie was pure fabrication by his friends; but the story about Vienna was true.

The post in Tunis was meant for a man edging toward retirement. Mills was a realist and accepted the fact. He went boar hunting up on the Algerian frontier, bought a burro for his son, drank the full velvety red wines of the Haut Mornag valley, and met many rascals. Except for the ambassador, who was a transient, everybody at the Embassy liked Mills.

The light shone indirectly on his round intelligent head. "It's quite a switch. Normally, Kheli would do his damnedest to prevent us from moving in, then politely inform us of the result—*that's* liaison. This time he's asking for help. In a situation like this we're supposed to be the kiss of death, so he's taking a big chance. Why?"

"For one thing, he has a suspicion tucked away in his mind that we know more than we're letting on; for another, he's worried about his job."

"What did you tell him when he asked for cooperation?"

"I didn't hold out much hope."

Mills grunted. "If an opposition group had planned this nonsense, it's a fact that we would have heard about it, and even felt duty bound to tip Kheli off. But there wasn't a hint of trouble from any of our sources; in fact they were jubilating over Al Houaranni's arrival. One group set up a secret meeting with him—"

"That's probably the second car that arrived at the Africa."

"At any rate, *they* had no reason to remove him from circulation."

"His enemies do. The Israelis do."

Mills brushed his face with his freckled paw. "Could be. What the hell are they doing coming into my area without my permission?" He grunted again. "In this type of situation, I tend to play like the police and let the hoods kill each other off. Of course, we're not above aiding our friends—if we have any."

"Kheli has done us favors in the past."

"I can see that you're straining at the leash. I was mistaken about you, Preston; either you're pro-Palestinian or you're a glutton for work."

"Francis, what shall I tell Kheli when I call him back?"

Mills opened the window to admit a draft of damp stinging mist. "Since Kheli took the initiative, the ambassador won't be able to complain again that I'm 'exceeding my responsibilities'—how the little man loves that expression! There's no reason why we shouldn't cooperate with a friendly Service. That's what you're here for. And if we don't extend cooperation, the competition may. Keep in touch with Kheli, tell him what we know, which for the moment is nothing. When we learn a little more, perhaps we can utilize some sources he doesn't have."

"It won't be a bad thing to have the colonel indebted to us," Preston observed.

Mills smiled faintly. "He'll probably ask for another favor."

## CHAPTER SEVEN

# A Clash of Bone and Blood

W HEN Gauthier heard the phone ring in a void of silence at the other end of the line, he slammed the receiver down in an uncontrollable movement of anger that nearly knocked the instrument onto the rug, then he hurried back to the garage. That the three men had left without confirmation struck him as incredibly stupid.

Glancing with sudden, undisguised hostility at the upstairs bedroom, he drove off in the station wagon.

He drove fast. Once he had to swerve sharply to avoid side-swiping an Arab who was pedaling into town on an unlit bicycle. If only the damned destructive miserable rain would stop, thought Gauthier. He was not a man given to believing much in second chances; Intelligence work provided few examples of blunders successfully retrieved—of course, it was different for newspaper correspondents, who spent a portion of their lives dancing nimbly over past misjudgments. As a child I was a foreign correspondent once, he thought.

Like a bad conscience, the rain drummed regularly; it was

a nasty night full of wild black ideas scuttering like sodden leaves in the dark.

At La Goulette, he was held up by a stop light. The celebration of Ain Seguir was under way: lights softened the squalor of rows of cluttered flats; within, people moved like fish in a tank. Dinginess? They were dry and happy and together. Among these people, Gauthier had the impression of passing as a disease carrier.

A darkened shop window cast back the image of a thickset man, fair hair disarrayed, staring from the car in tight-lipped exasperation. He remembered absurdly the display card in Paris buses: "No one to talk to? Call VAL 50-70." It occurred to him that in the same predicament his instinct was to signal Tel Aviv.

Rue Houssine Bouzaiane brought no relief. Down the street, he saw the parked Fiat 125, but knew it was pointless to approach it. The garage doors swung open when he pushed lightly, but revealed no car within. Gauthier left as disconsolate as he had arrived.

Ten minutes later, he stood, feeling a fool, outside the Africa, where a semicircle of bedraggled shivering onlookers waited stubbornly for a glimpse of their hero. The police had moved under a marquee, out of the rain, also waiting. Weren't they aware of something wrong? Gauthier dug his nails viciously into his fists inside his raincoat. He wished that somehow he could have alerted them to stop the operation harmlessly before it was too late. After a moment, he turned away and slipped down a side street. No one followed him, and he came alone to the rear of the hotel.

The employees' entrance stood dark and unguarded.

Opaque puddles were spreading before a sand pile at the freight receiving door. In the alleyway there was no sign of the Peugeot.

Gauthier walked rapidly back to his station wagon, not bothering to wipe away the rain streaming down his skull onto his shirt front. It had taken him fourteen years of painstaking effort to build up his cover, establish his network of agents and acquire the Qiryat's confidence; it was an important mission aimed not only at spying on the government but infiltrating the international Arab community, for which Tunis acted as a sounding board for what was planned in Algiers and Tripoli and even Cairo. Arabs tended to talk freely when in Tunis, and he had taken constant advantage of that weakness. All this jeopardized because he had been unwilling to run a risk of letting his son wait another hour for medical attention! Gauthier thought that he had been idiotic; all the more so since it had not been appendicitis after all.

Arriving traffic was dense in front of the Moroccan Embassy. He parked his station wagon, slipped a comb through his hair, wiped his shoes with a rag, then, combed and cleaned, stepped into the vestibule. An attaché he knew greeted him, inquired about his wife and moved away without waiting for the answer. In this fluid, distrait press of people, Gauthier did not expect Anne-Marie's absence to matter.

He asked for a shot of Scotch neat, downed it and, although he disliked the whiskey's mellow, almost insipid taste, felt thankful for the warmth that spread like a balm through his chest. He had to make sure that Al Houaranni was not, by some incredible reversal, present. Also, in view of the hysterical suspiciousness that would sweep Tunis as soon as the kidnapping became known, it would do no harm to establish his own presence here. He calculated that he could disappear after a quarter hour; he wanted to be home before they started putting up roadblocks.

"Where is Al Houaranni?" he asked abruptly of the man standing nearest him at the bar.

"He is unforgivably late. The ambassador is upset but is trying to conceal his annoyance—it is a good test of his diplomatic skill." The guest's wide cheekbones seemed to push his sly dark eyes up against his lids. "Do you know the definition of diplomacy?"

Gauthier drained off the remainder of his glass and did not respond. Across the room he spied, standing unsociable and observant, Preston, the tall, spare American who was rumored to be with the CIA. Anne-Marie had recently said something funny about him, but Gauthier could not recall her exact wording. Gauthier watched this rather conceited-looking acquaintance of Anne-Marie's and wondered if he were her lover. His wife had no special liking for Americans or diplomats. What about spies? Gauthier checked a temptation to become better acquainted with Preston. If he were CIA, it demanded a far more careful approach. Gauthier had neither time nor patience for that game tonight.

A woman's high laugh of scandalized delight pierced his consciousness like a needle. It seemed to Gauthier that, as the brittle minutes passed and Al Houaranni failed to appear, an undercurrent of gossipy maliciousness expanded recklessly through the elegant room. He murmured thanks to the ambassador's wife. He made for one of the leather-paneled doors. He saw Preston following a butler down the picture-hung hall. Gauthier hastily put on his raincoat and stepped out into the street. The sky was electrified by livid flashes. In his mind's eye he saw three men and a fourth waiting on a black beach for a rubber boat that failed to emerge out of the bitter dark.

The night-wide bedlam of static and music and multilingual chatter burst into his earphones. His hands were steady enough as he sought the frequency. Finally he found it and transmitted the call signal, wondering whether they would notice a change in rhythm due to his tenseness. At the Qiryat they were obsessed by the pitfalls of *Funkspiel*. They had lived through the agonizing days when under the control of Syrian Intelligence Cohen was tapping out his last tortured messages from Damascus and they suspected the worst and were helpless to come to his assistance. Gauthier considered his pale, tough fists with hostility; refractory gray objects, they could defeat him through their nervousness. He repeated the call signal.

The Qiryat came up fast, and he began to transmit the digit-groups.

MESSAGE RELAYED TOO LATE TO OBTAIN ACKNOWLEDG-MENT. FLOOD PROCEEDING ORIGINAL PLAN. CONTACT TEM-PORARILY LOST WITH HOUND. BELIEVE WAVE TAKEN AND ASSUME CONTINGENCY ONE BEING FOLLOWED. PLAN CONTACT HOUND EARLIEST POSSIBLE CONSISTENT WITH COVER. ADVISE WHEN NEW ATTEMPT WAVE REMOVAL PLANNED. URGE SOON-EST POSSIBLE.

Then coldly he continued. DELAYED RELAY DUE URGENCY SONS HEALTH. WILL FURNISH DETAILED REPORT SOONEST PRACTICABLE. RECOGNIZE THIS INSERTED NEGATIVE FACTOR

INTO OPERATION FOR WHICH ASSUME TOTAL RESPONSIBILITY. DOING MAXIMUM REDRESS SITUATION.

He had known exactly what he wanted to say; he had known it since he stepped out of the house several hours ago. He had phrased and rephrased the next-to-last sentence during the drive to Tunis until, factual and purged of special pleading, the wording and meaning corresponded precisely to his intention.

The reply came immediately, and it did not take him long to decipher it.

REESTABLISH CONTACT WITH HOUND AND INFORM HIM WAVE REMOVAL IS RESCHEDULED PER CONTINGENCY ONE. GIVE RELAY THIS MESSAGE HIGHEST PRIORITY WITHOUT EN-DANGERING COVER. ESSENTIAL MAINTAIN HOUNDS SECURITY.

FYI. LAUNCHING BLACK CAMPAIGN WAVES PRESENCE AS PER OPERATIONAL PLAN.

CONTENTS PARA TWO NOTED. PENDING INVESTIGATION YOU ARE HELD PERSONALLY RESPONSIBLE FAILURE RELAY MESSAGE AND CONSEQUENCES. AWAITING DETAILED REPORT AFTER FLOOD TERMINATED. UNDER NO REPEAT NO CIRCUMSTANCES IS CONTINGENCY ONE TO BE MODIFIED OR REVISED. ACKNOWL-EDGE AND INFORM HOUND OF THIS.

The reply meant, *en clair*, three things: First, the Qiryat had decided to order *Keriche* to embark the three men and Al Houaranni one hour earlier on the following day. Second, it was instructing its agents abroad to spread unfounded ru-mors about Al Houaranni's presence in various European and Middle Eastern capitals, to mislead the Tunisian Sûreté and gain time. (In a matter of hours, the Greek police would receive a tip that Al Houaranni had taken a taxi from Athens' airport into the city; simultaneously, a Beirut journalist would report that Al Houaranni was staying incognito at a luxury apartment building in the Corniche district.) The Qiryat had originally planned to disseminate this misinformation once Al Houaranni was safely aboard *Keriche*, to confuse the enemy as to how he had actually been spirited out of the country; now, in an emergency, it was simply moving up the hour for this diversion. Finally—and this produced a grimace on Gauthier's part—the Qiryat harbored no illusions about its field agents' violent reactions. UNDER NO . . . CIRCUMSTANCES IS CONTINGENCY ONE TO BE MODIFIED OR REVISED meant that, though he had become an embarrassment, Al Houaranni was not to be killed. As for recriminations, they would wait; an operation's outcome took precedence over the sanctioning of an agent's bungling.

Gauthier slid the transceiver back out of sight. His duty was to convey these new instructions as quickly as possible to the three men on Cap Bon. There was no doubt in his mind where they were. A month ago, without ever believing that it would be needed, he had arranged to rent a vacant house in the hills behind Qelibia as a fallback position; he was sure that they had retreated there where they would be relatively safe. He calculated that if he left immediately he could reach the house by midnight. However, the terse little phrase WITHOUT ENDANGERING COVER lodged awkwardly in his mind. He could reckon with being stopped by the police —they had surely set roadblocks in place by this time—and they might question what a foreign reporter was doing on a country road on this particular night when he should be in Tunis covering Al Houaranni's visit. As soon as news of the kidnapping broke, furthermore, his paper would begin calling, urgently demanding a detailed story. He wondered what would happen if he waited until morning—the roadblocks would still be in place, but there would be more traffic and his own presence less obtrusive. It would give him more time to remove and conceal the transceiver, for there was no question of driving along heavily patrolled roads with that incriminating rectangle of evidence stored under the floorboards. Objectively, waiting a few hours made no difference, since the second planned embarkation would not take place until evening; subjectively, he thought, with a fresh grimace that broadened the scimitar lines around his nose, the price was high—a night of wrenching uncertainty for the men in the safe-house.

But maintenance of cover had priority.

He set his lighter to the paper bearing the deciphered digit-groups and waited until it was consumed, then he ground the charred scraps into the soaked earth. It was no longer raining. He closed the garage door carefully, then he walked up the drive and entered the house.

In the living room the radio was playing and Anne-Marie was waiting.

"He's asleep now. I gave him two pills and left the door open in case he cries." She sat down near the stereo console and considered him bleakly. "Did you go to the reception looking like that?" He was wearing a gray suit and muddy shoes, and he looked damp and moody. "If the *khedima* had been here to baby-sit, I would have gone on my own—"

"We have kidnapped Al Houaranni," he interrupted her.

She stared at him. "Why, in Heaven's name?"

"Because we had a chance to," he said sharply. "But the operation has gone wrong, and three agents are perhaps lost because of an idiotic mistake."

"Are the police coming here?" she asked.

132

"Why should they . . . unless our people are taken."

"Is there a chance of that?"

"Not for the time being, I imagine."

From the alcove she brought out bourbon, a jug of water and a bucket of ice and prepared one glass for herself, then one for him. "Is Al Houaranni dead?" she asked him.

"No—although he deserves a bullet in the skull. That is not the important thing," Gauthier said shortly.

"What is the important thing?"

"To get the men who kidnapped him out of the country as rapidly as possible."

He looked at his hands—they were now completely steady, anger had a disciplinary effect on his nerves—and said, "I am accepting complete responsibility for what misfired tonight. It can possibly end with the blowing of my entire operation in Tunisia." His mind began to pick up momentum, like the whirring blades of a fan. "Didn't I repeat that this was going to be a difficult day for me? That it was absolutely vital for you to return home on time?"

"I wasn't *very* late."

"It's not even worthwhile asking where you were. I don't want to hear a lie."

"I won't lie to you, Alex," Anne-Marie said carefully in her clear, incorruptible voice.

"And this neglect of your son—"

"That's unfair," she said immediately. "When I left he was all right. For once it was simply your turn to look after him when he fell ill."

"Do you realize the situation you have put us in? You are imperiling men who are risking their lives to carry out a mission they believe in."

"Kidnapping somebody? God, Alex, are you proud of that!"

"There have been other days in my life I was less proud of."

"You're wrong."

"Wrong!" A shiver of triumph ran along his spine. "Removing a terrorist who orders hospitals machine-gunned—it's not a bad day's work at all. It could have been a superb operation."

She looked at his bony Flemish head, his sunburned neck and his eyes, which under better circumstances were the color of a fjord that sparkled in the sun. In his slate-gray suit from Paris' Avenue George V, with that cutting chin and athletic body, he presented an austere and refractory figure. There was always a certain well-clothed brutality about Gauthier, and looking at her husband Anne-Marie thought the past was his *mauvais ange*.

Her green eyes studied him from curious depths, accusingly. "Was it necessary to kidnap him?"

"Is it necessary to do anything dangerous and violent? It is perhaps preferable to be an ambassador and race ponies."

"Don't think that because you are always at war, Alex, you have a monopoly on courage."

"I asked you to be on time, that was all—but it was essential."

"And none of this would have happened if I had returned at three-thirty?"

"Certainly not. They went ahead because they did not receive a message canceling the operation. Now, by daybreak the entire country will be at their heels."

Anne-Marie set down her unfinished glass on the coffee table. "I know it is very unfeeling and cruel of me not to worry about men who are desperate and alone, and for whose safety you are responsible—"

"This is a cause I have given a major part of my life to, and you are wrecking it."

"Then what are you doing here?" she asked angrily. "Why aren't you with them?"

He scowled and flushed with the effort of controlling himself. "Because it can do more harm than good," he snapped.

"It's such a disease," she cried, "all this spying. You can't do without it—being the opposite of what you seem, living in a different time zone than everybody else. It wouldn't be worse if you stuck a needle into your arm."

"Your reasoning is absurd. I am not doing this, after all, for my pleasure."

At times, she was as set and unruffled as a lake without a gust of wind. "You can't go on living the way you do," she said dolefully. "It must be a nightmare."

"If I can get my operational work done, everything will be all right."

"Why is it you are so generous with your concern for others, Alex?"

"Instead of giving priority to our future, you mean?" Gauthier finished his whiskey. "Tell me, do you seriously believe this is the time to begin a discussion between us?"

"Yes, it is the time," Anne-Marie said.

"I don't agree."

She rose and brushed out the folds from her skirt. "I am very sorry about having caused you so much trouble and worry, Alex. But I don't think we should remain together; there's no point any longer."

"I should have encouraged you to leave last summer. You wanted to."

Although there was whiskey left in her glass, she began to prepare another drink for herself, then pushed the decanter aside.

"It's not much of a life, is it?"

"It's no life at all," she said and left the room, but then she changed her mind and re-entered for a second. "You're wrong about the date."

"That's when everything went wrong."

"Whatever you want to call it went wrong before, but you weren't unhappy enough to notice it."

Eight years, he thought after she had gone. Eight years of shared bed and food—and worry over a boy with an apprehensive mind. He remembered the girl he had brusquely courted—no virgin, but unsure of herself in bed, as impatient between sheets as when she maneuvered a sports car through traffic. When had he fallen out of love with her? He thought it was the day he had spotted the red Triumph parked before the Tour Blanche; but for the decline that had, inevitably, led to that discovery, he was to blame. He knew that people liked his wife. (One day he had walked into the bar of the Tunisia Palace and found Wilcox of the BBC holding forth. "He has a nice French wife who looks after him. Hullo, Gauthier. I'm talking about Anne-Marie. Most attractive girl, I thought, when I first met her. The gal grows on you. I think you have taste, Gauthier. And God knows, first time I met you I didn't think that." In his own way, he had returned the compliment. "And so I hear," he had riposted in his accented, dancing English, "you have a new flat, and a big bed to entertain in . . ." Someone—Lindt, of the Swiss Consulate—had laughed and said enviously, "Gauthier is always happy. But does he need a big station wagon as well?" "It's to show off, you oaf.") She had so much to offer, above all, that absolute unquenchable instinct for life that might not always be attractive or aesthetic but which at least was real and had purged her of all fear.

Eight years of cohabitation with a willful French girl, what an unsparing clash of bone and blood that had been! Gauthier ran his thumb along the tall glass but felt no stimulating chill —the ice had long since melted.

. . . They had been beating up to Spartivento all afternoon and saw the mountains for the first time at dusk.

Then, at night, the volcano's cone glowed like a giant match tip high above the black plain.

They put Stromboli behind them and caught the lights of Messina and the snowy halo of Etna far beyond the somber shore along which a car ran, its headlights' beam flitting through the trees.

"Happiness . . ." began Gauthier uncertainly. "It may be possible."

"If only this could last!" She wanted to sail over the black water endlessly, with nothing to recall her home.

Before the night was over, there was a quick stir of excitement aboard ship and presently they learned that they were going to the rescue of a Spanish tanker that was in distress a mile off to starboard. At dawn they raised the first batch of survivors—a sullen group huddled in a lifeboat who did not wave when they steamed up. Several crew members were floating in an oily patch, their inflated life jackets masking their chins, alive but as rubbery as dolls. Gauthier remembered one sailor clinging until his knuckles were gray to the ship's side without enough energy to hoist himself aboard the ladder. "*Muy cansado*," he had murmured in a hoarse voice when he was eventually fished out. Very tired, he was very tired. . . .

He must have dozed off and confused what he remembered with the present, for a dream recurred that he himself was drowning, drowning—submerged among incurious faces that saw straight through him.

About a half hour later he was still seated stiffly in one of the armchairs, reflecting, the decanter untouched, when Paris rang.

Darcy, the night editor, said, "I expect you are finishing up a new lead for us?"

Gauthier said nothing and knew that his silence would be interpreted as hostility.

Darcy's breathing was quite audible. "The American agencies began topping the story a half hour ago with a lead that raises more questions than it answers. When you get into the second paragraph, you understand that no one in the government has actually confirmed Al Houaranni's disappearance. It is all supposition, especially the part about a politically motivated kidnapping. Shall I read it to you?"

"No."

"I am sure that you have a firmer story—we need one."
Then Darcy's sham Quai d'Orsay manner broke down.
"What the devil is going on there?"

"Call me back in twenty minutes and have the secretary
ready to take dictation."

"It is really a fantastic development."

"You'll be all right with what I have."

"If you dictate the story now, we can make changes later."

"No, I don't want to do that."

Gauthier went into his study and turned the light on, then
remembered that he had left his empty glass in the living room.
He poured more whiskey than usual out of the heavy decanter
and returned to his desk. Slipping a sheet of paper into the
typewriter carriage, he settled down to work.

Anne-Marie lay in bed wide awake. The thunderstorm was
subsiding in defeat; the night stirred wet and earthy around
the solid stone house. Shortly after their marriage, the Qiryat
had authorized Gauthier to disclose to her his activities as the
Resident. He had made the disclosure in his own manner:
"A man in Switzerland told me, 'You always have to let your
wife know what you're up to—otherwise she thinks you're
fooling around. But never reveal or discuss operational
details.' "

She had accepted this pact. Occasionally she was tempted
to break it, but his taciturnity had discouraged her—as had
the suspicion that most of what he touched was slime.

Still later that night, Anne-Marie heard her husband climb the stairs, pause before their son's door, then approach the bedroom they still shared. He said nothing to her as he undressed. But later, in that room as gray and lightless as a womb, while she stiffened with revolt, he moved and took her.

## CHAPTER EIGHT

# The Dialectics of Terrorism

THE house stood back from the coast road, and the sea appeared far below, half a mile away, through trees, but they could not hear the sound it made from this distance. A sunken bleached path twisted up the barren slope past a vacant cabin, climbed a rise, dipped, then climbed again between cactus hedges and came to a dead end before the house. Beyond began a desolation of stone and scrub tenanted by lizards. The path did not venture up there. There was nothing of interest up there. Before reaching the house most drivers became discouraged by potholes, and where the path widened before the empty cabin they backed around and returned downhill. The two-story house had blue shutters (to ward off the evil eye), a roof of orange tiles and a terrace enclosed by a stone balustrade. Cypresses sheltered it from view, and last year's mosquito screens were still nailed to the windows. It was a summer place for someone who enjoyed seclusion and a view of the distant sea. It was, thought Max, an ideal safe-house.

He came out into the pure North African winter morning.

The damp puddly earth underfoot and the vivid sharp green of the cypresses outlined against the hills were the only reminders of the night's storm. The sea had resumed its rhythmical lazy advance upon the shore, but from here he could only suspect the two distinct sounds it made—its glassy fracturing slap and lurch as it collided against the rock-strewn beaches and its sonorous drum roll where it heaved far out. The sun warmed his body, and he stood immobile, allowing the heat to sink in. The house possessed neither central heating nor space heaters—as far as he was concerned, this was its only shortcoming. The night before, while Marston had stood watch, he and Black had crawled into bed wet and cursing under heaps of Berber blankets, not daring to set a fire in the stone fireplace; it was unlikely that smoke would be spotted in these desolate humpbacked hills, but they could not afford the risk. Max looked around the large cement-and-dirt forecourt and frowned. He prayed that no one had seen the parking lights that Marston had been obliged to turn on to find the path in the dark. The Peugeot was backed out of sight into the garage, but for all he knew its presence might already be known among a few farmers. In the emptiest landscapes of Tunisia, whether you tried to make love or relieve yourself in solitude, there was apt to be an Arab behind a bush silently observing each movement.

He re-entered the house and searched through the kitchen unhopefully for tea bags, found none and opened a tin box that contained a package of rusks. He crunched one with restrained hunger. Then he made coffee on the gas range with thrifty unhurried gestures and filled one cup for himself; he would have preferred a glass of hot acrid tea with lemon as his wife prepared it in a samovar. On the shelves were neatly stacked cans of sardines and ravioli, but he decided against eating right away.

He prepared cups for the two men in the downstairs bedroom but decided not to awaken Marston. He placed his cup in the sink and went across the hall.

Al Houaranni sat handcuffed to the sturdy post of a double bed; he was guarded by Black, who had come gun in hand to the door at the sound of Max's step. Black's heavy beard had sprouted overnight, giving him more than ever the misleading hard-featured appearance of a Bedouin.

"This turd hasn't stopped complaining. You can listen to him for a while," he said, taking one of the cups in Max's hand.

"What is he specifically complaining about?"

"The cold. It will be pretty ridiculous if he dies on us now of bronchitis."

"This won't happen," Max said. "I'll get him to Tel Aviv if I have to lend him my coat."

"Why didn't Emir think about installing a couple of space heaters?"

"All right, last night you froze your balls off—it won't kill you. As it is, Emir thought of a great many things on our behalf."

Black did not reply, but shrugged bitterly and left the room.

Max set the other cup down in silence on the night table, within Al Houaranni's reach, then sat on the uncomfortable divan that ran around the wall and, Beretta in his lap, eyed their prize.

Al Houaranni did not touch the cup of coffee on the table. He looked wiry and resistant to Max. A muddy feverish glint in Al Houaranni's eye and a raw dark bruise on his cheek-bone were the sole visible ill effects of an unsettled night. "I'll make fools of you in Tel Aviv," he rasped in his composed throaty voice. "My trial will be shown up before dozens of foreign observers as a sham. You are not stupid enough to think it can be held in secret?"

Max checked a movement of crossness with Black for having talked out of turn again and watched Al Houaranni with extreme interest. He had spoken in English and Max replied likewise in English. "You are, frankly, a disappointment. I had expected—well, a man who is bigger physically and mentally."

"Dayan would shrink too in captivity, let me assure you." Being shackled and kept at gunpoint appeared paradoxically to increase his self-confidence, for he snapped, "Three Zionist terrorists hunted by four and a half million Arabs! You are going to discover how moderate Tunisians are. Do you think they are going to forgive being made to look stupid and inefficient? I know the government doesn't give a damn whether I am found alive or dead, but the people do. You have created a situation where they *must* treat you like criminal sons of dogs—*ibn el Kalb!*" There was no worse insult he could have uttered in Arabic. "And now here you are locked up with a raging Palestinian terrorist. I wonder who is in real danger."

"Even if this house is discovered, we hold you as hostage. Why don't you think about this?"

"I put my faith in my supporters and my religion."

"That has never stopped a man from dying," Max observed.

Al Houaranni's smoky eyes gleamed, his swart chin shot

out. "Why don't you have the courage to kill me outright—now—without a trial? This would become you."

"Believe me," Max said, "I would prefer to have orders to execute you. In my opinion, a trial is superfluous for someone who does not believe in trials."

"I suppose you are referring to Eichmann. Do not compare me to that unhealthy opportunist. He believed in Eichmann; I believe in a war." From the bed, Al Houaranni observed him steadfastly. "I wonder whether you fully comprehend that I would be ready to die if it did some good? But the result must be worthwhile and important. If my death guaranteed eliminating the three of you, for example, it would be insufficient, since you are minor assassins."

"We in this house are all ready to die," replied Max cheerfully, knowing that he was enunciating a truth and not really caring how this conversation ended. "However, not exactly for the same purpose. No one healthy really wants to die," he added.

Al Houaranni continued to watch him with rapt interest. "Whom do you do this for? Ha Mossad Lealiyah Beth?" Max noted that he pronounced The Institution's full name—it meant The Organization for the Second Emigration—with bookish precision, the accent falling correctly on the fourth syllable. "This makes you a terrorist too. Who mailed the bombs to the scientists in Cairo?"

When Max did not reply, he pursued his idea. "You are trying to neutralize me through terrorism although you call it a trial."

"We could set you free—and the ridicule would ruin you."

"I think it is too late for that; you badly need a hostage."

Max rose. He regretted that he had begun this conversation.

What exasperated him was Al Houaranni's candor; when it came to terrorism, he was a stream of eloquence in which any reticence about justifying atrocities was impetuously swept away. This, and his turgid thousand-and-one-nights manner, provided an essential clue as to how, in just three years, he had thrust upward from editorship of an obscure Lebanese political monthly to chieftainship of the Palestinians' most aggressive guerrilla groups.

A toilet flushed down the hall, and then Black's heavy footfalls ascended the staircase and receded in the back of the house. Black was going to wake Marston; he could not let him alone, thought Max angrily. Here, in the sunny bedroom, the morning was peaceful and becalmed. Max could entertain the hazardous illusion that, while they were not yet safely in Tel Aviv, one thousand miles away, they had escaped from Tunis' slithering politics and stood in a neutral halfway house.

In speaking of the readiness to die, Max felt that he had not yielded to bombast; but it was likewise true that every man's motivation differed. Black, for instance, had visibly volunteered—Max was sure of it—out of a desire to prove himself; what drove Marston was not so simple to analyze, but just possibly a grudging inarticulate inhibited notion of duty lay sightless in the thicket of his mind. Max diverted his thoughts elsewhere with embarrassment. He did not like to ponder over his own actions; his perception of his innermost motives was no clearer than when he had sat, numb and vulnerable, in the General's office. He thought of his sister-in-law—the one who had been killed in the Palestinian raid on Natanya Hospital—a stern woman with a mouth as grim as a sword cut. They had never been close—certainly he was not in

146

Tunisia, shivering under the same roof with the Blade of Allah, "the conscience of the Arab world," because of *her*. It was completely out of the question.

"If you had not killed, you would not be here," he said.

"If I had not ordered killings, my refugees would be written off, like the Armenians in Turkey and the Jews in Germany."

"They are not *your* refugees. Who gave you this right?" Max grunted. "They have become an excuse for bloody-minded vengeance."

Al Houaranni studied him again with witty forbearance, as though this were the only feasible method to deal with imbeciles. "In a deadlocked political situation terrorism tips the balance. This is its sole utility, surely you grasp this? Listen to me, I have become expert at recognizing a man who has murdered, not in anger, but deliberately, out of rational conviction. You are a terrorist, perhaps almost as much as I." He added tartly, "I am less sure about the underbred American bully who guards me; he wants dearly to kill—an Arab, if possible; me, in particular—but I suspect he has always backed away from killing."

"In your position, I would be very careful to avoid antagonizing him," Max said. What Al Houaranni had just asserted was both true and false, at any rate it jarred a nerve; Max had murdered twice—once on the Channel boat crossing to Southampton in a fog, another time on a narrow mountain road near Berne—but both actions dated back to his early association with Ha Mossad, a time in his life when he had been less gingery about violence.

"We have forced you to adopt our method."

"No, this operation simply demonstrates that some men are ready to run a risk to remove an intolerable danger. Our way puts an end to your terrorism."

"Reverse this and it is also true. *My* terrorism puts an end to *your* way."

Max felt no respect for Al Houaranni's argumentative obstinacy, no more than he would have felt for a dog who refused to let go a bone. But Al Houaranni's mind was agile, he admitted to himself: it was a refined bit of copper compared to most blunt Jewish minds, a dagger threatening a howitzer. Perhaps this in the long run was the danger? Certainly no understanding or compromise was possible with this sophisticated, intolerant mind. This conclusion did not come in any way as a surprise, but although it reinforced a long-held belief it left Max gloomy.

"You are a racist nurtured by the American College of Beirut," he objected.

"I admit to being *partly* a racist. Your rabbis turn my stomach; and no matter what you do, you will always be a heavy-footed desert tribe, gross, grasping and conceited about your religion. But this is beside the point, since my policy on land is not the outcome of my personal feelings; moreover, in fairness, there are your qualities: the literature, for one thing —I like Malamud's stories," he interjected bizarrely.

"Malamud does not write in Hebrew," Max growled.

"One of his stories—about a poor man with an idiot son—would not leave my mind."

"On the ruins of the Jewish State you would generously contribute to a multimillion-dollar center of Jewish culture," Max sneered.

"On land that is once more ours."

Max shook his head irritably. He could not abide this special sort of sentimental deference urban dwellers displayed for earth they trod without contact. "What did you learn about land in the magazine offices of Beirut?"

To his surprise, Al Houaranni replied, "It is all that counts —far more than political institutions."

"You know nothing about it."

"Do you? Here in the middle of the countryside you stick out like three city Jews. If I take off my uniform, I am at home immediately."

Black and Marston stood in the door, looking inquiringly at Max. In spite of the night's drenching, Marston's navy-blue suit had retained its extravagantly dapper lines, but semicircles of fatigue underlined his dark eyes.

"You are supposed to be resting so that you can relieve me at noon."

"I'll rest in my own bed." He held a transistor set in his hand. "This was upstairs, so we can catch the news. There's no problem with the tread marks in the courtyard; the rain washed them out."

"Did you check the road?"

"Too rocky for tread marks."

"I thought we could see Sicily from here," Black interrupted. He was standing at the bedroom window, glaring at the hills that dropped down to the sea.

"Well?" said Max impatiently. "Are you a strong swimmer?"

"I can't see it."

"Only forty-three nautical miles—there must be something wrong with your eyesight," Marston jeered.

"Can I talk to you in private?" Black said to Max all of a

sudden, with nervous urgency in his voice.

"Watch over him a minute," Max instructed Marston, then—puzzled—preceded the other into the kitchen.

"What are we going to do?" Black asked as soon as the door was shut.

"How do you mean?" Max said shortly. He still had not forgiven Black from the night before, and was persuaded that henceforth their relationship would always contain the germ of an armed truce.

"You stayed awake all night waiting for Emir to turn up. Why didn't he?"

"I don't know—but we carry out the plan and put Al Houaranni aboard *Keriche*. The mission has not changed."

Black said too quietly, "And how long are we expected to wait for *Keriche*?"

"Until it comes."

"Or until the house is surrounded. Emir has broken contact, but you won't admit it."

"I didn't expect you to be this nervous," said Max, and there was no sarcasm, only worried annoyance in his voice.

"Then where the hell is Emir?"

"Don't become a defeatist on me at this stage. We will get new instructions—you recall the contingency plan? Meanwhile, as long as we hold this admirer of Jewish short stories we are in a reasonably strong position. Never leave him unguarded, never unhandcuff him, never let him out of the bedroom. The only reason to move him is to take him to the toilet, and then he still goes handcuffed. Until dark, I want you and Marston to stay out of sight; there's absolutely no reason to go outdoors. This house is a godsend as a hideout; during the day it is not cold, there is food and a radio—"

"Whose house? You don't know; maybe it's a trap."

"On the contrary, I do know. It belongs to a man who is indebted to Emir. Why are you suddenly going to pieces on me like this? It's not in your character."

A minuscule but visible alteration occurred on Black's hirsute face. "Arabs maim Americans who serve in the Israeli Army. On Dizengoff Street, I heard stories about what they did to a Californian—"

Max avoided looking at him. "Then why didn't you give up your citizenship?"

"Why in hell should I?"

"Because you are dissatisfied with the way things are."

"Why are you so nosy about my affairs? 'Who were your parents?' 'Where did you go to school?' It's worse than being at camp."

"Camp?"

"*Summer* camp; not concentration camp, damn it. Lay off —I'm not in your league, I know it."

Max shrugged blankly and left the kitchen in haste. To know Black better was to discover his failings enlarged; after forty-eight hours, it was like looking at a stereoscopic photo where every fold and crevice of terrain stands out in unmistakable relief. Max thought that he preferred Marston because he was a sabra. Black behaved as part of a minority; as it happened, a moneyed, politically powerful minority, but still a minority. No, this was unfair; he was assimilated in America, but this was exactly why he was out of step in Israel. You couldn't belong to two places in one lifetime. His own experience proved that, Max reflected; he'd had to disown one entirely to come to terms with the other.

Marston switched off the transistor. "They're looking for

us," he said, "the whole damn country. The police don't think we escaped over the frontier."

"If you are not going to sleep, why don't you stand watch and prepare some food?"

Marston nodded and left with the transistor; he had glanced only briefly, without interest, at the prisoner.

A minute later, Black re-entered the room, his mouth twitching in fury. "I caught the ten o'clock news. Last night a Palestinian commando blew up a hotel outside Beersheba . . . they estimate six dead."

"Is that all?" Max asked. He was astonished by Black's reaction. Beersheba seemed so far away—impassively, he wondered whether it was the same hotel he had mismanaged so long ago.

"Did you give the order?"

Al Houaranni replied with an ambiguous shrug, and Black lunged at the bed, forcing Al Houaranni's head backward toward the coverlet while beating down his free upraised arm.

"Stop at once, you stupid New Yorker!" As Max yanked furiously at Black's shoulder, he heard a flat wrathful voice.

"Let him alone and keep him quiet." It was Marston. He stood in the door, dry, nervy and unamused. "There's a car coming up the road. I can't tell how many men are in it."

## CHAPTER NINE
# The Hill of Days

THE Information Ministry spokesman scanned the position paper on his desk and repeated with unconvincing finality into the forest of microphones: "The government will capture the kidnapper-terrorists within twenty-four hours."

Slight and studious, clad in a wine Mao jacket, the spokesman cut a brave figure at the far end of the arched room. Twice a week he briefed a half-dozen pliable local journalists; he wasn't used to addressing a clubby group of expensively tailored foreign correspondents who esteemed one another and distrusted him. He would have said, had he dared, "I have nothing to say to reporters."

"The bandits cannot escape dire retribution," he went on courageously—his prose was as sugary as date pastry—but a plain note of doubt tinctured each syllable.

Finally, one journalist lifted a thick paw and launched the attack. "Does the government have any idea what to do next?"

"What do you think of the report that—"

"It's madness."

"And the report that—"

"The story has been around Tunis for weeks."

"Is the President going to—"

"I cannot confirm that."

Preston glanced restlessly about the thronged room, at the mute *chaouchs* in each embrasure, the ogival universitylike windows through which the sun streamed, the pair of dour translators who looked as though they might whisk the spokesman away if his sleek voice uttered the wrong set of truths. The heart of the matter, whatever it happened to be, Preston concluded, would not find tongue here, at least not through this inhibited source.

He had risen early and come to the Information Ministry with a specific objective in mind. He wanted to draw upon whatever rumors the reporters of Tunis were exchanging; for the Agency, this was not necessarily an unproductive approach—rumors were clues, and journalists in private were at times more astute than in print. Before the start of the briefing, he had chatted with two wire-service correspondents, but the results were meager. Without surprise he counted, seated discreetly in the back of the room, several attachés from other Western embassies, who were visibly present for the same purpose. He looked about for Gauthier. Gauthier, if he wanted to, could be a better guide to last night's events than the spokesman, but Gauthier was nowhere visible.

Finally, tiring of the seesaw of portentous question and bland answer, Preston exited into the hall under the *chaouchs'* impassive stare.

When he stepped into his office the direct outside line was ringing.

"When can I see you? I have something to tell you."

He hesitated. "Today is going to be awfully difficult—"

"It's important."

"I'm swamped. Let's make it tomorrow?"

"It concerns us; otherwise, you know that I wouldn't disturb you at work."

This time, Preston thought, Anne-Marie's voice sounded strained. "The Dar Es Zarrouk, at one o'clock?" he proposed. "If I'm late, you'll know that I'm still here." Suddenly he wanted very much to see her.

"Even earlier if you like."

Preston worked on the third floor of the Embassy, in a specially locked office marked CONSULAR ARCHIVES. He went downstairs to Mills's office on the second floor but failed to find him. Instead, he ran into Carlson of the Political Section, a rotund young man with a golden cowlick who exuded enthusiasm for his assignment to Arab affairs. "It's shocking. I know Al Houaranni personally. Disregard the slanderous junk the press puts out and he's really quite an interesting, farsighted man. In Washington, of course, they couldn't care less, even," he added with uncharacteristic peevishness, "if we lose a friend and the kidnapping triggers a coup d'etat into the bargain."

Preston's eyes grew frostier than ever; he was short of free time. "My motto is, don't wait for the coups d'etat to come to us—go out and strike a blow in support of our friends."

Carlson flushed. "Oh, come now, someone may overhear you."

Back upstairs, Preston dialed Kheli's number and got through at once.

"Did you attend the press conference? There is honestly

little to add. No trace of the Peugeot or the men; I am afraid ransom is not what they are after."

"What about the second car at the Africa?"

There was a barely noticeable pause. "We have developed no leads there either. The Sûreté is going over all plane and ship manifests of the past month—as you know, it's a long process. However, I am not about to despair. This is a professionally coordinated operation in which numerous people took part; sooner or later there is bound to be an informer who comes to the police with a story to tell. It's always the same. Have you people any news?"

"No, Colonel; no news at all," Preston replied. He set the phone down, reflecting that it would not be all that difficult for the Sûreté, if it wanted to, to trace ownership of the second car.


"Is it real?"

Anne-Marie had detested Sidi Bou Said in midsummer— detested equally the vulturous shopkeepers and the unresisting tourists. Shortly after their first encounter, Preston had invited her to lunch at the Hotel Dar Es Zarrouk perched on the huge red cliff. From the terrace they had steeped themselves in the celebrated view and watched the sun pour down indiscriminately upon the cypress-framed sea, the eroded hills and the far-off blur of Tunis' white rooftops. The prospect here was as limpid and harmonious as from a Tuscan villa but she was unimpressed. "It's too soft and dreamy," she had complained then. In truth, she was surfeited by this sensuous tepid country that clung to your body like warm sand to we toes; in the long run, this unfailing clarity of light, the inhuman white purity of mosque and marabout, the humility of the starving soil, simultaneously chilled and unnerved her. Without quite admitting it, she needed the shadow of evergreen defiles, needed the challenge of cold and fog as a dog needs a bone to bite on. ("Alex isn't like me, he always wants heat, he's like a lizard," she had said about her husband on another occasion, with no discernible note of sympathy.)

Preston did not quite share her opinion. Sidi Bou Said was a resort of writers and artists; wouldn't it also suit people who in a more modest way were attempting to reshape their world?

"Do you mean you never came here before?"

"Once. We can see our house from here." What they could actually see was the Cathedral of Saint Louis standing up like an extravagant confection of nougat on the tumulus. "Alex likes the view—he calls Carthage the hill of days. I know what he's getting at."

The American she was seeing for the second time wore a sand-hued linen suit and his eyes were a Celtic blue, and she remembered everything of what he had told her that day about his wife and his arrival in Tunisia and his cottage in Gammarth.

Now he slid into the chair facing hers in the winter restaurant, and she watched his movements, made an attempt at a smile and indicated the illustrated magazine from Paris on the table. "I've been reading my horoscope. For Gemini it says, '*Amour: soyez prudente si vous jouez avec le feu. Jours néfastes: 13, 18, 22.*' What day is today?"

Preston smiled at her fondly. "The twenty-third. I can tell fortunes that way too."

"I thought we'd do the questionnaire . . . the one that tells whether we're meant for each other. Of course," she remarked, "it will be terribly depressing."

She didn't realize it, he thought, but this eternal bruised hopefulness of hers constituted, in his eyes, a major part of her attractiveness.

The high-ceilinged airy restaurant was decorated with sham-Oriental chandeliers. Between the bulbous domes of villas glistening in the midday quiet, the green of a pool flashed.

"Do you remember when we came here?"

"Yes, I remember; you exulted about the view. You always describe things better than they really are—because you attach your feelings to them. *Tu es tellement romantique!*" It did not sound like much of a compliment.

After they had ordered, her good humor returned temporarily and she said, "So here you are, a more or less presentable American, with diplomatic rank, a beach house, a Porsche and an adoring girl friend. What are you going to do with them?"

"Enjoy them all—in order of priority, naturally."

She did not smile. "Right after I called you, I felt annoyed with myself. I don't like mistresses who make nuisances of themselves, but I needed to be with you, and here I am. Last night I had a bad scene with Alex."

"Another?"

She drank her wine and patted her lips. "It was over you, at least indirectly. I returned home late and he was furious. In some ways he is right, but I really think this time something has cracked between us."

"Does he know that you're having an affair?"

"He's no fool. He's had enough girls of his own to detect the atmosphere. Moreover, I did not deny everything."

"That your marriage has lasted this long is the real surprise."

"There's much more to it than you," she said rapidly. "I am as fed up with him as he is with me. Do you think I would be unfaithful if I were happy? I am not promiscuous."

"Why are you not happy, Anne-Marie?"

"Are you serious? Do you really want to know? Last summer he started in over Marc, and he's been sullen ever since. I have a son who needs help; Alex loves him but has no idea what to do for him. I wanted to leave but he talked me out of it. What I have in common with Alex is the past, and it irritates me. Because I so badly need to believe it, I keep telling myself that there must be more to life, somewhere, with somebody. He's changed," she commented, and Preston took note that when Anne-Marie—or people in general—remarked of a person that he has changed, invariably it implied for the worse. "He was different before."

"Before Tunisia?"

"You mean in Vienna and Beirut? I didn't know him then."

"I think he's forfeited his claim on you."

She shook her head. "He'll always have a claim on me. It isn't at all the way you imagine between Alex and me."

"Does he know that you're here with me now?"

"Suppose he does? Are you uneasy? I think you are a man who can handle himself in any situation. It's myself I'm not sure about." She shook her head comfortlessly a second time. "No, he doesn't know that I'm having lunch with *mon amant*. He left the house early this morning—"

159

"He didn't come to the Information Ministry briefing."

"No? I suppose he's chasing the Al Houaranni story elsewhere."

"Does he know where Al Houaranni is?"

Anne-Marie's green eyes measured him prudently. "No, why should he? Alex has good sources—they tell him more than most, he's so identified with this country and then, Tunisians like him—but in the end, despite what you may hear, it amounts to the same as other correspondents get."

"I would like to see Alex."

"Who knows when he'll be back?" she countered vaguely. "Why do you suddenly want to see him? Apart from me, you two have nothing whatever in common."

"Perhaps he can help me find Al Houaranni. The Embassy is interested."

"That creepy religious terrorist! In the end, I am happy not to have met him last night. We're for the Jews," she declared firmly. "At least I am. I never really know where Alex stands on an issue; he won't discuss politics with me."

"When Alex returns, will you let me know?"

"It will hardly be an appropriate moment. When he does return, I plan to talk to him about a divorce." She meditated for a moment. "Perhaps he'll welcome the news. I want to be with you," she said.

"When did you decide that?"

"This morning." She entwined his fingers possessively. "When we're at your house, I want to stay with you for good and not be anywhere else. I want to be with you even if it doesn't work out later."

"What makes you think it won't?"

"Tell me, do you know what you're letting yourself in for with me?"

"I have a fair idea."

"*Au fond*, you're as unreliable as Alex is."

"Anne-Marie, come off it. You don't like reliable men."

She smiled as wanly as a plaster Madonna. "Let's be happy," she ordered him. "Just this once—for a change? To be happy, you have to be involved. Why aren't you?"

"I thought I was doing my damnedest to become involved with you." He watched her fair silken hair untamed in the mild breeze and felt happy.

"My father always seemed to be standing off from whatever happened; you had to cross a moat to reach him. You're not like that, not yet anyway, thank God."

They had moved from the restaurant's interior, and they sat before the hotel, on the high graveled terrace, basking in the winter sun, like cats. The bougainvillea loomed behind them forming a dense mauve screen. It was out of season. There were no boats below on the placid winter sea. No one came down the village's white contemplative streets. The winter heat and death-still whiteness were said to heal distress. "You enter Sidi Bou Said as you enter a convent," a Tunisian had said, inspired.

Anne-Marie's smiles today were fleeting, like clearings touched by sunlight on a cloudy day. Preston decided that the enduring impression of bed and pleasure she created was instinctive, a natural phenomenon for which she could claim no honest credit; but he also thought that she was generous—

in a chaotic, undirected way, in the way a flood is generous. For example, when her father had retired to an Alpine hamlet in his late sixties, on an impulse she had spent a month with him, and it had turned out to be the last summer before his death. She had always been devoted to her father, and Preston had observed that the yardstick by which she measured men tended to be that blanched, taciturn figure out of another, less querulous age.

*Pendant que je t'aimais*
*Pendant que je t'avais*
*L'amour s'en est allé*
*. . . Il est déjà demain.*

A record was playing by an open window, and Anne-Marie listened to the acidulous refrains—with their good dollop of hard, uneasy truth—Georges Moustaki plucked from his guitar, and then she resumed: "When Alex was my fiancé, he wanted to be with me all the time. I think he loved me too much."

"You probably didn't think so then. Believe it or not, I was like that too."

She looked up swiftly. "And your wife—was she as unfaithful as I?"

"In the end, it might have been the other way around—I would have been the unfaithful one."

"And she was killed while you were driving a car drunk in Paris?"

"Let's not rake that over."

"How much do you miss her?" Anne-Marie was in an aggressive mood, whetted by the unhelpful sun and the formalized white starkness of Sidi Bou Said.

Preston answered coldly, "Too much," and looked at this girl he now loved. "It's awful—like a disease."

"What is?" she asked immediately.

"Not sharing, which is what you're really talking about when you bring up involvement." After a moment he changed the subject and said, "When did Alex work in Vienna?"

"He didn't. He was born there, but his mother was French. Gauthier is his mother's name; she took it back after her divorce."

"What nationality was his father?"

"Czech. He put Alex in the French *lycée*."

For a moment his preoccupation with Anne-Marie and worry about Al Houaranni had merged; the effect was the same as when one superposes two slides and a composite image appears. Why did she hold back the truth? She's like Kheli, Preston thought angrily; she tells me only that part of the truth that suits her. Who tells the whole truth in this crooked town?

The reference to his wife had briefly and unwillingly transported Preston back to Paris—Paris, which he visited no more but which nagged at him with its sordid ambitions and slatternly streets; Paris in the late fall with its roasting chestnuts, trench-coated pimps in doorways, the colorless smog-swept sky, shivering queues in front of movie houses, furred, perfumed whores, beggars in church doorways in the lee of the wind . . . Vigorously, Preston shook himself free of this particular obsession.

"Tomorrow morning I'll drive to Raouad and wait for you," he said. "If you've had enough at your house, I'll book you a room in town."

163

"No, *tu es gentil*. You know, I do love you, only I don't think it will work out." Anne-Marie stared at him. "*Your* past justifies *my* skepticism about *your* future."

The sun lay chill on his temples, yet his feeling of happiness survived somehow, obstinate and irrational, as he walked her back to the parking lot where she had left the small red Triumph. Then a predictable thing happened. Beside the car she abruptly fumbled at his chest and swung full into him; her hand rose defensively, her cheeks vanished in a waterfall of hair as spicy-smelling as hay; from within this body as capricious as a wave, he heard a murmur, an exclamation . . . whether of impatience or rage, it was inarticulate and buried alive.

When the secretary brought the folders with the traces on Gauthier, Preston did not open them at once. He sat at his desk and assembled his thoughts as if he were about to play chess. Two facts intrigued him: Gauthier had attended the Moroccan Embassy's reception the night before while most correspondents were at the Defense Ministry or the Hotel Africa; conversely, Gauthier had been absent this morning from the press conference that most newsmen had attended. Neither fact meant much. Perhaps Gauthier chose not to run with the herd. Anne-Marie said that her husband had left at daybreak to cover the story. It was entirely possible. Perhaps Gauthier had uncovered a source no other journalist had. The Paris morning papers had arrived; Preston read Gauthier's two-column by-lined story, but no—it contained nothing different from what the other papers were saying.

Preston recapitulated what he knew about Anne-Marie's husband. He could afford a large high-rental house, two cars, a maid, a sailboat and Anne-Marie's trendy clothes. He had lived in Tunisia fourteen years, knew the elite, such as it was, and was introduced into the small, nepotic, intelligent circle around the President that set policy. Preston knew that Gauthier was liked by the Tunisian Information Minister. Gauthier was a type of Frenchman—rational, competent, solid—who, unlike the colons, seldom said anything nasty about the President. He moved almost wholly in a French-speaking milieu; a previous American ambassador had tried to cultivate him but encountered a cool response.

Preston made a grimace of distaste. Virtually everything he knew about this man derived from Anne-Marie. Not that Anne-Marie disclosed information heedlessly, but everyone blindly gave something of himself away in anger and pain—or love. Where did you draw the line? When you made love to a man's wife but refrained from listening to what she said about him?

Preston thought that the facts about Gauthier formed a credible pattern that raised no unanswerable questions. Gauthier earned a correspondent's salary and drew an expense account; the house was located in a slightly fallen-off residential quarter; a maid's wages did not run high in Tunisia; and as for his wife's clothes, Preston understood that Anne-Marie paid some of her own bills with income from stocks her father had placed in her name. Gauthier's style of living corresponded to what he was—a bureau chief who took advantage of assignment to an underdeveloped country to organize a pleasant life for himself and his family. But a man working for an intelligence service, Preston thought, would be armed with just such a set of verifiable explanations, and Gauthier was a likely recruit for the French.

He opened the folder.

It contained clippings of several of Gauthier's articles written a year earlier, a transcript of a tape recording made by the Police des Étrangers (which Kheli had provided in slightly censored form), a carbon of two dispatches signed by the American ambassador citing Gauthier as a source, a report on a conversation between Gauthier and a visiting French author at the Tunisia Palace bar, a photograph of Gauthier aboard his boat, another—barely recognizable—of Anne-Marie taken six years ago, a membership list of the Tunisian Foreign Press Association on which Gauthier's name appeared among the board of officers, a biographical fact sheet and a draft of a negative recruitment evaluation signed by Preston's predecessor two years ago, a photostat of two checks Gauthier had drawn on a Paris bank to pay for the purchase of a German stereo head set, and two round-trip air tickets between Tunis and Paris.

Slim pickings. The tape recording, as described in Kheli's accompanying note, covered a twenty-four-hour electronic surveillance of Gauthier's office in the Colisée building; it was part of a spot check on foreign newsmen. Kheli's services had furnished the transcript as part of their standard monthly exchange of classified material with the Agency. The only comment on the attached memo was a bleak *Pour vos archives* that bore Kheli's initials. Gauthier's conversations, live and telephonic, with a number of people, which had been picked up by wiretap and a miniaturized microphone of French make, were unrewarding.

166

Preston turned to the smudged, almost illegible second carbon of a resident-permit application Gauthier had filled out in 1957, just after his arrival in Tunis. This record, too, had been provided by the Sûreté. Reading it gave Preston a certain sense of nostalgia. In that same year he was married and living in New York; a group he belonged to had staged *Androcles and the Lion* on East Ninth Street—without success. Was Gauthier older? Just slightly. More than a decade's wear and tear had left him with a girl he was still married to, at least for the moment, a son, and residence in Tunisia. Considering the man's personality and his fierce-beaked competitive instinct, the rewards seemed disproportionately meager. There was more—there had to be—to Gauthier than his family, his boat and his placid, well-upholstered semiexile. What, for instance, had drawn him to Tunisia in the first place? It was not a choice assignment. And kept him so long? There was a faint tinge of corruption on the air, but to listen to Anne-Marie, Gauthier was the least voluptuous of men.

Preston glanced over the entries in Gauthier's thick flowing script. He had put down October 2, 1927, as his birth date, which seemed right, and Amiens, France, as his birthplace, which did not. Hadn't Anne-Marie said he was born in Vienna? Preston referred back to the fact sheet. The brief biography was based on information Gauthier had supplied when he applied for a French passport shortly after the Liberation. This information had also found its way into the Agency's name traces. Under Place of Birth the typewritten notation said: "Believed to be Amiens, France." Then was Anne-Marie wrong? But how could she be, about something like that? Preston read down the entire biography but found nothing else that contradicted what he knew. He referred back to the notation and read more carefully. Gauthier had apparently failed to provide an *extrait de naissance* with his passport application, but had furnished an attestation that he was born on October 2, 1927, at the Clinique Saint Martin in Amiens. The attestation bore the clinic's stamp and was signed by the *chef de clinique*, whose name was virtually undecipherable, although below the typed subscription read Dr. Jacques Strauss. There was appended a note from a *commissariat de police* in Amiens stating that Gauthier, Alex, born on October 2, 1927, of Eric Vacek and Madeleine Gauthier, had reported the destruction of his birth records in the burning of the *mairie* on May 20, 1940. The police statement itself was dated November 9, 1945, that was to say, Gauthier, when applying for his passport after the war, had requested and obtained the statement to explain why he could not furnish a standard birth certificate. The passport had been issued, and it no doubt carried Amiens, France, as Gauthier's birthplace. So by the time he had landed in Tunis twelve years later several successive passports had been issued, each repeating the same information. On the strength of this he had obtained his Tunisian residence permit. In the disorderly post-Liberation period in France it was not unheard-of to obtain a passport based on shaky credentials. Many had done so. And it was a rule of thumb in intelligence services that it was easier to check out a person's recent activities than his far-off past; it took hard digging to go far back. Obviously the vagueness about Gauthier's birthplace had been examined when headquarters traced his life for Soviet connections; but once the findings were negative, the file, like dozens of others, lay dormant. If the findings had been positive, the Agency would have dug farther and harder. As it was, a not wholly satisfied researcher had inserted a small note of doubt: *Believed to be.*

Preston wondered who Dr. Jacques Strauss was, and what his exact relationship with Gauthier had been. He wondered why Amiens police years ago had shown remarkably little skepticism about the destruction of Gauthier's records. And why, in the first place, had Gauthier gone to such trouble to cover up his real birthplace? He had a French mother who had brought him up in France, and so presumably he was entitled to a French passport anyway. What was wrong with being born in Vienna? Preston shook his head slightly. Gauthier would have a shock if he realized that someone was poring over this ancient history now. Of course it might not mean much, and there was no reason to connect this long-ago hocus-pocus with Al Houaranni's disappearance.

The folder contained virtually no information about Anne-Marie apart from the photograph and a foxed photocopy of a French police report that covered the month she had spent with her son at Annecy, in the French Alps, visiting her father. Naturally the DST would be routinely interested in a French citizen who resided permanently in North Africa and returned home on holiday. Preston glanced at the date: July 1969. In addition to dates, the report bore only two type-written lines: *Fille très chic. Soumise à des passions aussi superficielles que passagères.* Preston set the photocopy aside with repugnance. What prying cop had dictated that patronizing assessment, and on what sources was it based? A hotel hall porter? A barman? The only fair method, he thought in passing, would be to allow Anne-Marie to peruse *his* file. Well, who knew? Perhaps she had access to it.

169

Preston sat thinking of Gauthier and Anne-Marie when the senior secretary, an Irish girl from Montana, entered and asked whether she could remove the folders.

"There's a demonstration over Al Houaranni's disappearance down the street," she informed him. "It's turning into a riot." When it came to bad news, she was the best-informed member of the station.

He heard the scattered unruly noise still far off. "Are you worried, Pat?" He liked to tease her. "If they break in here, you can handle yourself. I've seen you at parties."

"Oh, I'm not worried." She smiled grimly. "I can teach students about street fighting."

After she was gone, he continued to sit there. He had no desire to speak to Mills about Gauthier, which would mean bringing up Anne-Marie. He had never told Mills about his relationship with Anne-Marie, and he was not sure whether Mills was aware of it. In his dry way, Mills had simply remarked about her one day: "That girl has no more idea how to use her beauty than some people how to manage an inheritance." The comparison was pure Mills. What did the biographical data in the folder amount to? A hint—the barest and most circumstantial of hints. There seemed little doubt that Gauthier had at one point long ago lied to obtain a passport; what his motives had been remained as elusive as his actions in the past twenty-four hours, but it could be connected with espionage on behalf of the French or, for that matter, the Israelis. Physically, Preston couldn't think of a more appropriate candidate for Israeli Intelligence than Gauthier, with his Northern complexion and eyes, his fair wife and Viking son.

Preston felt no special hostility toward Israel and no particular admiration for Al Houaranni. This sort of obsequious deference toward the first gun-brandishing Arab chieftain who might become a power in the Middle East was best left professionally to Carlson. However, he had been encouraged by Mills to obtain information. This, after all, was what he was trained for and paid to do, and so who could hold it against him if he broke a foreign agent's cover? Cut out the double-talk, he told himself. You're interested because Anne-Marie's husband may be the foreign agent.

One thing was clear, Preston thought; he wanted to aid Kheli, and in the situation that had developed there might be little time left to do so. The quicker the assistance was provided, the better. Should prejudicial information about Gauthier turn up, Preston further thought, it need not be shared with Kheli . . . indeed, it need not leave this office. Mills had hinted at that.

He buzzed the secretary on the intercom.

"Where is he, Pat?"

"He never tells me. Perhaps he's leading the riot."

Preston chose the direct outside line, reached for the scrambler and began to dial Mills's home number.

## CHAPTER TEN

# On the Road to Cap Bon

G AUTHIER rose before daybreak. He cast an expression-
less glance at Anne-Marie's recumbent figure, then he
moved on bare feet out of the bedroom. In the hall he put on a
fresh suit, laced his shoes, and entered the room of his son,
who was awake and sitting up. The fever had dropped during
the night; the lackluster skin was clear; and his son asked
where he was going.

"To work," Gauthier replied ambiguously, looking at the
jumble of game boards on the carpet. "When I return, we'll
puzzle out that one."

Gauthier sniffed the predawn air; he thought it smelled
lazy and friendly, without purpose, like a puppy. Had they had
similar weather last night, Al Houaranni would now be miles
out at sea . . .

Removing the transceiver from the recess under the station-wagon floorboards was harder work than he had anticipated. The suitcase was heavy and he grunted with the effort
of lifting and carrying it carefully across the garage. Looking

around for a temporary hiding place, he saw what he wanted —a dim corner stored high with gear he had recently brought back from the yacht club. He stored the set under a tarpaulin, then dissatisfied with the canvas's bulky appearance he placed oilskins, rubber boots, a scoop and a hurricane lamp around it in careful disorder. Neither Anne-Marie nor the maid was likely to rummage in that mess. Then he got to work unscrewing the aerial from the station-wagon top; after that was done, he walked down to the end of the garden and stowed the aerial in the kennel he had built from loose pine boards and which Anne-Marie's setter never used. Before he opened the garage doors, he had another thought. He took three soiled rags, pliers and a monkey wrench and deposited them where the transceiver had been. The recess could, after all, seem suspicious by its very emptiness.

It was seven-thirty by the time he was ready to leave. No one was about yet in the house.

As he drove down the steep street, he switched the car radio on. An announcer was playing a selective roundup of taped reactions to the kidnapping from other Arab capitals— Cairo, Tripoli, Rabat, Algiers. Indignation seemed to be the prevailing mood; the foreign reports omitted all criticism of Tunisian security practices. Gauthier thought he had only to twist the knob a half-turn to *Voice of the Arabs* to hear a different story, but he did not bother. The announcer began reading off a list of labor, student and rural organizations in Tunisia that were patriotically volunteering their services to run down the Zionist criminals. The special broadcast yielded no surprises. The only interesting development was the government's decision to pin the blame for Al Houaranni's disappearance on Israel; on the radio the accusation came out sounding like certitude. But do they really know for sure? Gauthier wondered. Or are they bluffing?

In the rear-view mirror, he saw no car behind his own; at this early hour, virtually all traffic was inbound to the city. He had decided against taking the ferry at La Goulette. In terms of distance it was a shortcut to the Cap Bon road; but in terms of time it could take longer if he had to wait for the boat, which ran every quarter hour. He drove down the lake road. Then he turned left and picked up the four-lane highway that leads to Hammam-Lif and Hammamet. He would need two hours to reach the house. All told, he planned to be absent from Tunis a total of five hours. His absence would be noticed, particularly on this day of crisis, but later he could legitimately claim that he had been chasing down material. Al Houaranni's kidnapping was the sort of fluid story that lent itself to rushing energetically back and forth from one source to another.

He thought of what remained to be done. There were bound to be prickly and overlapping political developments in Tunis. He would have to file a story on that—and inform the Qiryat of what he found at the safe-house. No matter what he found, Flood no longer enjoyed the vast advantages of surprise and a head start. His original operational plan had called for action that was determined and swift. An operation that dragged out in time quickly became an embarrassment to those who mounted it; nonetheless it had to succeed, he was more determined about this than any operation he had planned in the past fourteen years. This evening, almost twenty-four hours behind schedule, Al Houaranni would be taken aboard the submarine. Afterward, for as long as necessary, Gauthier would carry out no further operational activity. The abandoned Peugeot would, of course, be discovered at La Plage Noire; the police would trace the vehicle back to an Italian businessman who had flown out of the country two days ago. Under another name, the same man had rented the apartment off Avenue Kherredine Pasha. At each stage Gauthier had employed a cutout; in each case, the police would eventually piece together what had happened, but the trail would not lead backward to the Resident.

Ahead, the highway curved left. Police were waving traffic down and directing it into a single lane. A rectangular rubber strip with steel spikes had been rolled out obliquely across the concrete highway surface behind a row of two-by-fours. As Gauthier drove up, a helmeted trooper signaled to him to stop. He saw another trooper standing off beside a ditch, a machine pistol resting in the crook of his arm, the barrel pointing down at his car's tires in case he failed to brake.

The first trooper came up and saluted. He was chesty and thick-calved, clad in blue jodhpurs and black jackboots. Gauthier handed him the car's registration and his resident permit; he did not plan to bring out his press card unless they attempted to prevent him from going on, for he was not sure how they were treating the press in this affair.

The trooper peered into the interior. "Where are you going?" he asked.

"To Qelibia."

"Open up the hood."

The second trooper came up and walked nonchalantly around the station wagon. He looked at the tires, the tail gate and the engine, but he took no part in the inspection. Gauthier had the impression that he would have asked the vehicle's purchase price in dinars but was held back by the seriousness of the occasion. The first Garde National was taking plenty of time checking the license and engine numbers, but across the road they were being just as meticulous examining the line of waiting inbound cars and carts and small trucks. The conscientiousness would last through midday; then, if past experience was a guide, it would flag as the Gardes Nationals became itchy and thirsty. By evening, spot checks would replace systematic examination. Practical compromise was the outcome of every Tunisian undertaking.

"Are you taking this route back?"

"Later today," said Gauthier.

The trooper's face was unfriendly. "What do you do in Tunisia?" he asked with stolid suspiciousness.

The question was futile and unwarranted. Gauthier appraised him and decided that lying would be risky. "Here," he said, displaying his Tunisian press card.

The trooper reacted as Gauthier had expected—he studied the press card stupidly, making a show of the unimportance it had for him. His line of reasoning was obvious: he had found a European who could not be charged with spiriting away a kidnap victim, but to balance matters a little harrassment could be inflicted for form's sake.

"Where are you going?" he asked the question again.

Gauthier said wintrily, "To Qelibia." I can keep my temper, you overfed bastard, he thought, as long as you can play this time-wasting game.

"Open the back of the vehicle," the trooper ordered, and made a comment whose meaning Gauthier did not catch. Both men stared at him intently. They were like highway patrolmen everywhere.

He unlocked the tail gate and stood back to let them see the cluttered rear section. The first trooper eyed the haphazard accumulation of beach toys, blankets and discarded oil cans and said, "Is there something under that?" pointing to the bolted spare tire.

Gauthier stared at him in turn, incredulous. "Tools and rags," he replied.

"I do not believe you," the trooper said. He issued instructions in a rush of Arabic, and the second man clambered into the back and poked about the tire until his fingers discovered the split in the rubberized floor matting.

"Wait," said Gauthier crossly. "I can do it faster than you."

When he had the floorboard panel prized up and folded back, he eased himself backward out of the car and stood aside for their inspection.

The heavy-set trooper cast a cursory glance at the recess's contents, but he had already lost interest in this aspect of the questioning. Stubbornly he held on to the registration papers. "This is made out for Carthage," he observed. "Do you have a reason to drive to Cap Bon?"

Gauthier swore lightly but audibly. The incident with the recess had left him feeling hollow and ill in the groin, and he found this sort of amateurish interrogation ludicrous. "I will furnish explanations to a responsible—" he began, when a Garde National officer with braid on his uniform standing up the road blew his whistle and beckoned impatiently for the station wagon to drive on. By now, other cars from Tunis had formed a lengthening line and were beginning to sound their horns. The first trooper handed back Gauthier's papers and said stiffly, "We shall be here tonight when you come back."

His colleague grinned, showing healthy yellow teeth. *"Au revoir, monsieur le journaliste!"*

Gauthier waved to the second trooper in farewell.

I can always take another road home, he thought.

Soon he reached the fork and bore off down the cape road. Twelve hours before, during the worst of the storm, Al Houaranni had been abducted along this road . . . but the police had absolutely no way of knowing that.

The air was growing warm now, and the sky ahead was bland. Gauthier was glad that he had left early; he had a habit of looking upon the morning as an ally that reinforced his capabilities. The land rolled away monotonously on either side, vast undeveloped dun fields that demanded a backbreaking sum of labor and sacrifice. Arabs got up in crash helmets and long trailing woolen robes motorbiked in dignified fashion across the impoverished landscape. Over the entire cape brooded a quality of played-out struggle, as though History had moved away from this place once and for all, abandoning it in limbo; it was the same atmosphere that permeated Carthage. Everything, even Time, was eventually smothered here in sunlight and silence.

In a way, he had come to love this land; he remembered it as it had been when he had arrived fourteen years before, just as colonialism was coming to an end. Tunisia was, in essence, a modest juxtaposition of sloth and amiable cupidity, with a nice dose of tolerant worldliness. The fourteen years had become an open-ended commitment unforeseen at the start; a watershed too: life as Alex Gauthier the correspondent demanded his time and wits. At first, it had resembled an assassination of his real personality, but after the first two years he had grown at home in this new skin, exactly as they had forecast at the Qiryat; and now it was his former self that seemed not altogether true; at times, it required an effort to remind himself who he had been.

Some time after entering Ha Mossad, he had been given a form and asked by a psychiatrist to describe what he liked in life. He reckoned up the things that he had truly enjoyed and wrote them down—snow falling when he awoke, two boxer dogs, the great seaports he had visited, like Hamburg, a girl in Liège whose slow-melting capitulation was like butterscotch in his mouth, farms, autumn, the sea, winning continuously one night at the Montreux casino, the trip with Anne-Marie to Piraeus. There was also the warmth following victories that later turned meaningless and sour, but he omitted this. The examiner read the sheet of paper and grunted. "This is a good list but you left one thing out," he said.

Gauthier thought the man a fool. "I left many things out. It's not meant to be a bloody gift catalogue."

"The important thing that would have helped me isn't here," the other said nastily, "—your childhood."


Gauthier came to Qorba, a grubby market town. His throat was chafed with fine dust from the road, but he decided against stopping. A few miles farther on, he caught his first glimpse of the sea, and he felt buoyed up. The sea always did that for him. He drove through Qelibia. Fleetingly he saw chickens, school children and old brittle men. Shortly afterward, the countryside in all directions turned green; there were many wells, long-horned cows grazed tethered to spiky trees, shawled women in bright skirts waited their turn around a stone fountain. This was no longer poor country. Two little girls on the road waved to him. Mounds of red peppers dried on the ground beside a farmhouse, and the sun shimmered on a roan horse's flank.

He knew that Anne-Marie was going to leave him, and despite his anger he regretted it, but he worried more about his son than his wife. He hoped that the doctor's diagnosis was right and nothing more than intestinal flu was involved. The boy ought to be brought up elsewhere, not because there was anything wrong with Tunisia, but because everything was wrong with his father's existence. Of his present life here nothing would remain, Gauthier thought; his son would live elsewhere and become committed to a totally different way of life.

Anne-Marie could fend for herself in any place. He looked at the date palms that leaned toward the blond beach. The trees throve on little nourishment and grew slender and tall and were hardy. Women were like that—they created the impression of having appeared upon earth long before men, of having become molded early to its ambiguities. If there was one lesson he had learned from living with Anne-Marie, it was the value of pursuing a goal unrelentingly day after day. Anne-Marie wanted to package as much into life as possible, and he knew no one more likely to succeed at that. Anne-Marie's weakness, Gauthier thought, was that she wasn't intelligent enough to want to change the shape of the box.

Gauthier wondered who her lover was, but did not settle upon a plausible candidate. He also wondered what in moments of carelessness and high pleasure she told her lover that in the end would destroy them all.

He recognized the side road ahead and turned up it. He was almost at the safe-house and his heart beat a little faster. For two hours, he had thought about himself, Anne-Marie, his son, Tunisia and the sea. The time had passed quickly.

Spying was such a small part of a spy's life!

A neat, slim man in a dapper suit stepped out from behind a cactus hedge and stood directly in the middle of the bleached twisting path.

"*Shalom*," Gauthier said, then continued in his uncertain, self-conscious Hebrew: "I want to speak to Levanon. Tell him that it is Emir."

The man made no move to turn aside.

Although Gauthier saw no gun, he was reasonably sure that the man must have one tucked in the pocket of his navy-blue jacket—and that other guns were trained on him from the screened windows of the nearby house.

"You'd better follow me," the man said at last, in French.

"Do you want the person you are holding to see me?"

From the house came a second man, thickset and balding, older than the first, in a rumpled black business suit and open-necked checked shirt. He crossed the garden where last year's zinnia stalks lay black and limp.

Frowning in the midday glare, he said, "We have been waiting for you. You are Emir; I have your description. Marston, get inside and keep those two separated."

"Am I an umpire who doesn't take sides?" the dark, wiry man said, this time in Hebrew, and went back into the house.

Gauthier studied the second man. A *Yekke*, a German Jew, he thought.

"There are new orders," Gauthier said and described what they were. "*Keriche* will put a boat ashore one hour earlier tonight, at eight-fifteen, and you will be taken aboard. You have less than ten hours to wait in this house. I am not saying it is without danger, but it is feasible."

Max shrugged. "This is a subjective appreciation."

"It is obvious that *Keriche* cannot surface during daylight."

"It becomes dark by five-thirty."

"The commander is taking into account that the Tunisian Navy is actively patrolling the coast; he is giving himself a margin of time to maneuver. Are you having trouble with Al Houaranni?"

"One of my men would like to murder him. Al Houaranni is in that corner room on the ground floor. He is blindfolded, so he cannot see you. I ordered that when we heard your car on the road."

Gauthier was impressed. The man was tough and seemed in command; so far there had been no recriminations, and should they come now it augured well that his initial concern was with security and practical arrangements. Gauthier had feared three things—that he would find Al Houaranni dead, the commandos captured or their morale shattered—and of these three, he had feared the third almost as much as the second.

"As soon as I return to Tunis," Gauthier said, "I shall raise headquarters and confirm that Al Houaranni is alive and you are standing by to embark. Is this correct?"

"We'll put him ashore in Haifa harbor. This is what we came to do."

"It is a marvelous thing that you managed to capture him.

In spite of all that has happened, I am very, very satisfied. What do you think of him?"

"A terrible man," said Levanon. "If they put him on trial, he will talk and talk and steal the show."

Gauthier did not pursue the idea; he was aware that he was about to tread on more slippery ground.

"In spite of what they claim, the police cannot be sure that you are still in Tunisia. They may decide to sweep the country-side, but to be thorough will require time. By then you will be gone."

Levanon looked at him thoughtfully, and then phrased his sentence with care. "Suppose *Keriche* does not show?"

Gauthier formulated his reply just as carefully. "Why should it not? The storm has ended."

"Suppose there is a damn good reason?"

"It won't come to that. The Qiryat did not send three experienced agents on a mission to lose them."

"In a war, missions backfire and agents are lost."

Gauthier passed a hand over his forehead and found it slick and cold, as cold as when he had dealt with Ben Larbi. "It is a matter of waiting less than ten hours," he repeated.

"This is quite a long time."

"Whatever happens, you must wait for *Keriche* to take you aboard," Gauthier said curtly.

"That's what I thought," Levanon said, just as curtly.

"I am as determined as you to see this operation succeed. I know you will be aboard *Keriche* tonight, provided that you maintain complete security around the house. Between five and eight you run relatively little risk if you show no lights. No one normally comes up here, and you can get down to the beach without being seen in the dark."

Levanon's eyes were openly mistrustful. "What in hell went wrong last night?"

Gauthier went pink and stiff with angry embarrassment. "I cannot tell you in detail. It was my stupidity. I tried to cancel the operation twenty minutes late."

"Twenty minutes!"

"It was my stupidity; I said that. The Qiryat will take a decision as to responsibility after you are home. I am here now to do everything possible to get you safely aboard ship."

"It is not an explanation," Levanon growled. "We waited until five-fifty, and received no call. This put the entire operation in jeopardy."

"Do you expect me to stand here and begin an argument about what went wrong? Why did you start out without waiting for confirmation—not a very intelligent step, as it turned out. I am telling you to put off placing the blame until later."

"Very well. I am speaking for the others—we will never carry out a mission again in your area."

"Listen, another way of moving you out exists," Gauthier said furiously. "If *Keriche* does not surface, you will double back to Tunis with Al Houaranni. This is extremely hazardous. Do you appreciate why I consider it strictly as a last resort? The rendezvous point will be at this atelier in Sidi Bou Said . . . you will have no trouble finding the place. We'll meet there tomorrow evening at six."

Levanon took the typewritten slip and the small bottle of yellow tablets Gauthier gave him, but said nothing.

"You will administer these to him before you leave; they will knock him out for a minimum of six hours."

"And then?"

"He will be shipped out as air freight under diplomatic

immunity. Yes, I know, it has been done before, but never here, and the Tunisians are unlikely to risk a serious diplomatic incident for the luxury of running a customs check on the Moroccan ambassador's personal effects." For the first time in this strained exchange, Gauthier enjoyed the reaction in Levanon's gray eyes. "The ambassador has recently been unluckier than he likes to acknowledge at the race track—and to pay off debts he is ready to do just about anything."

"In short, Al Houaranni will go like Louk?"

"That is one way of putting it. And the three of you will accompany him on Moroccan passports."

Levanon thought it over and then grunted noncommittally. "Next time perhaps they should book a commercial flight to remove a sensitive target, and there won't be so much hesitation about risking expensive Navy equipment."

"What is wrong with you?"

"I am unhappy with this operation. Whether the mistakes are mine or yours is immaterial. We'll hold Al Houaranni alive as long as we can, but if we have difficulty returning to Tunis, a choice may become necessary."

"You have latitude in that case to make a decision."

"There is no misunderstanding on this? The radioed instructions say clearly that Contingency One is not under any circumstances to be modified."

"Your own safety has priority. After all this trouble it will be a pity to shoot him, but . . . *inch' Allah!*" Gauthier felt that he had said enough, and turned to go. "Is there everything you need in the house? Blankets? Tins?"

"Yes, yes, this is not the problem." He added shortly, "I hope it will not come to the alternative solution. I intend to get him to Tel Aviv alive."

Max watched the station wagon drive away, the heavy tires spurting little eddies of dust from the dry road.

Still frowning, he thought, How would you like to be big and blond and accustomed to giving orders and have to stand there and assume responsibility for a fantastic blunder? This Emir was quite an operator, and had every contingency figured out. Naturally he did not even look or behave or probably think like a Jew. Max remembered a grim ash-blond SS officer who had strutted through their neighborhood in Trier until unexpectedly one Sunday morning he had cut his throat in the barracks out of despair, it was said, at his inability to rise to the demands his country and post made upon his nerves and psyche. It was a disciplined berserkness native to Central Europe, and Gauthier struck him as a moody man afflicted by the same grave, ultimately self-destructive rigor.

For a while Max remained in the forecourt, his fists squeezed together. What he had said contained no play-acting: whatever the last-minute obstacles, he would get Al Houaranni to Tel Aviv. Broad feet planted on the Tunisian earth, he scrutinized the sky with intense attention. Less than ten hours . . . This time not so much as a wisp of white cloud troubled the serene horizon.

## CHAPTER ELEVEN

# The Pursuit

MILLS entered the office jauntily and asked, "Calling anybody I know?"

Preston put the phone down. "You."

Mills wore tinted glasses, against the afternoon glare, he claimed, but everybody suspected him of using the glasses as part of his incorrigible predilection for masks. He removed the glasses and said in his Amherst voice, "Whatever it is it can wait. I want you to hustle over to Kheli's. We've had a riot and the government couldn't control it—or pretended that it couldn't. I want to know which."

"I heard it from here."

Street fighting had a bracing effect upon Mills. He looked dusty, alert and fit in spite of his girth.

"The students started an unauthorized march in the medina with the usual signs, 'Avenge Arab honor,' 'Live Allah's Blade.' When the riot squad tried to stop them, they came around the outer boulevards on motorcycles and began attacking Jewish shops. Then the police did a stupid thing—they split up." Mills sat down and helped himself to a cigarette from the box on the desk. "The prime minister told me this morning he foresaw trouble and had alerted the Army. But for some reason, the Army took its time about showing up this afternoon. I wonder what Kheli's explanation is for *that*. The Army has never sided with the students before. The colonel's a devious bastard; he'll fool you every time. They keep him in the job because he gets around and produces—he really delivers . . . How do I know he didn't organize this on behalf of the government? It's his business to start a fire and see what happens; he works that side of the street."

"Not at this point. His position is too shaky."

Sirens were wailing down the street while the demonstrators' cries died away.

"As a diversion to shore up his empire? Incidentally, the students wanted to break in here. We're starting to get some of the blame for Al Houaranni's vanishing act by every Arab from Rabat to Baghdad."

The phone rang. It was a secretary asking for Mills.

Mills listened unwillingly. He had a dozen facial tics—grimacing, jerking his head with seeming relish, winking—to avoid furnishing a direct answer to questions he distrusted. Finally he said, "The situation is—ahem—full of knots. There's a lot of conniving going on," and hung up. To Preston he said, "That was the ambassador. He always phones to find out what to do when he sniffs a crisis. When the Six-Day War broke out he kept asking, 'What's the latest?' Unless the government produces Al Houaranni's body or an explanation quick, there's worse trouble ahead. I expect a coup within twenty-four hours. You can smell it coming like a snowstorm," he added incongruously on this fair afternoon. "The President has a standing request with the ambassador for asylum, which he updated only this morning—but the old bastard naturally won't put anything into writing. In a way I feel for him—his health isn't all that good. They'll want a full report on the demonstration back home, although Africa has low priority in fiscal '72."

"Do you know Gauthier, the French correspondent?" Preston asked.

"He won't work for us; we tried once. He may be run by the French. I don't see at this point what use he can be to us. From a long-range view it may be different."

"I went over the traces and found a discrepancy in his records. He fiddled with his name and nationality years ago; apparently he's only half-French."

"What does he claim the other half to be?"

"Czech, on his father's side."

Mills was beginning to display well-defined signs of impatience.

"Listen for a moment, Francis. What sort of man assigned to an Arab country would be specially interested in fudging the facts about his ancestry?"

"Gauthier a Jew? I'll buy it, although it's farfetched. Anything is possible. That doesn't make him Israeli Intelligence."

"No, but add this and this . . ." And Preston began to list the various items.

"We'll check him out but it will require time." He reflected. "The Israelis are a weird bunch. I've known them in about a dozen cities. They're quiet but all over the place. A lot are old-time British agents but now they've been unshackled and are doing a better job. Where were you three hours ago when the demonstration began forming up?" he asked abruptly.

"At Sidi Bou Said."

"What the hell were you doing there? Were you with Gauthier?"

"I was having lunch with Gauthier's wife."

"Clever girl, isn't she?" Mills moved a paw over his face and watched Preston. It was impossible to determine how much Mills knew. "Is she Jewish too?"

"No."

"When you start dealing with a Frenchman and a Jew in one package, you need the Mafia for protection," Mills said. "After you interview Kheli, I think you'd better follow up on Gauthier without losing time. Then we can decide what we want to do. I'd take a strong line with the colonel: we're offering assistance, we want to be kept informed."

"I'll be at—"

"I'll know how to find you if I need you," said Mills.


Unchecked, the riot had swept down Avenue de Paris and reached a spot fifty yards from the Embassy, where its progress had been contained. Up to this point it had described a trail of erratic but highly visible damage—overturned heat-whitened cars and charred kiosks lying in pools of shivered glass.

An armed Marine lieutenant at the Embassy gates came up and said to Preston, "You'll have to move, sir."

"All right." However, he apparently wasn't fast enough.

"You getting in or out?" the lieutenant said.

"Out, by all means."

At the entry to the riot area, helmeted police were re-routing car traffic. Preston saw two Gardes Nationals trying to subdue one of the demonstrators, a frizzy-haired teen-ager in a turtleneck sweater who continued to show fight; two sergeants rushed up and helped drag him spread-eagled to a patrol wagon, clubbing him regularly below the kneecaps to make his legs buckle. A veiled old woman who seemed to be his mother swayed on the pavement, gesturing in silent menace at both the boy and the police. Another Garde National pointed a submachine gun at Preston and waved him back. He went down a side street and reached a parallel avenue where he showed diplomatic identification and was let through.

Inside the area of worst destruction, a bald man stood motionless at the entrance to his looted records-and-television store. Trucked-in Army troops swept glass into the gutters and collected smoking debris into trash piles. From upper-story windows faces peered down. Tear gas, prickly and invisible, still floated in the sunny air. Two shattered gray gas grenades lay expended beside a lamppost where they had rolled to a stop; no one had yet snatched them up as souvenirs.

At the intersection with Avenue Bourguiba, Preston emerged, eyes streaming, from the riot area and its unnatural silence into the city's familiar uproar. Trams racketed down either side of the central mall, children screeched like birds in a jungle, a whir of conversation spread out fanlike from cafés and milk bars. Near the Interior Ministry, reserve troops who had arrived too late for the skirmishing sat stolidly, their rifles propped upright between their legs, in armored personnel carriers that were drawn up in a row beside the curb. On the sidewalk, young, intellectual-looking officers waited and spoke softly to one another. They were indifferent and neutral; the riot had collapsed before they were committed; they had neither willed it nor quelled it.

Kheli and Fawzi were together, bending over a large-scale Army ordnance map when Preston entered.

The captain lifted his somber eyes and regarded Preston briefly without greeting. Kheli indicated a chair and said, "We have narrowed down the search to all persons who entered the country in the past week. There is no record of a suspect trio's arrival; obviously they came in separately. We have picked up one lead—a certain physical education instructor from Düsseldorf whose passport date of issue does not correspond to the serial numbers the Germans were using at that time. The address he gave in Tunis has naturally turned out to be false."

The captain took over. "All airports and border posts now have been issued a detailed description of the three Israelis. They will have a difficult time leaving Tunisia. We are patrolling the Algerian frontier on an intensified basis, especially in the north, where it is rough and wooded and illegal crossings often take place. Farther south there is less natural cover and strangers are quickly spotted; furthermore, we have put up aircraft over the entire countryside. At the Libyan frontier the same measures are being applied. The Libyan police offered full cooperation before we had time to ask for it.

"We have seven hundred and fifty miles of coast, but every port is alerted and sailing clearances are being issued only after thorough inspection of holds."

"You are going to object that there are hundreds of beaches along the coastline where a few men can be embarked clandestinely," Kheli interposed, "but we have *avisos* patrolling two miles out."

"They are very efficient—we bought them from the Germans," Fawzi commented with a glitter of triumph.

Preston said, "I was thinking that a small plane can make a night landing in a remote area—"

"Where will the plane come from? Not from Algeria or Libya. Beyond that requires a big plane with a substantial fuel load. If it comes from Europe, say Malta or Sicily, it follows well-defined routes and our radar is monitoring these approaches. The only other access is from the south, but flying up the Sahara is unfeasible for a small plane, I mean all the distance from Mali or Niger. In this case, geography is on our side."

"It is only a matter of time," Fawzi said on a more restrained note. "We will capture them unless they receive help of an exceptional sort."

"What do you mean, 'help of an exceptional sort'?"

For the first time, Kheli permitted himself a frugal smile. "A diplomatic car. A diplomatic trunk. The Israelis have no representation here, but a friendly embassy might provide a helping hand."

"A friendly embassy such as the United States?"

"It is conceivable."

"It is also conceivable," Preston replied tersely, "that Al Houaranni's kidnappers crossed the frontier before your services went into action so efficiently."

Fawzi answered without waiting for Kheli's reply. "Since last night, we have been monitoring Kol Israel broadcasts and have noticed that Tel Aviv has reported Al Houaranni's disappearance without comment. You can imagine that they would boast about it if he were already on Israeli soil. A fact like this can't be kept secret long, even there, and they know better than to deny categorically a story that they may later want to exploit. If he is in their hands, it is in their interest to justify the kidnapping before world opinion as soon as possible. Throughout the night, we also received reports from other capitals where Al Houaranni allegedly landed. Not one of these reports held up this morning. This is obviously a smoke screen the Mossad people threw up for our benefit. I am sure the kidnappers are alive and still in Tunisia. What they have done with Al Houaranni is another matter."

This reminded Preston of Mills's purpose in asking him to call on the colonel. "If Al Houaranni is found dead, this afternoon's riot will seem like an end-of-Ramadan carnival."

Kheli shrugged off the prospect. "Unorganized students brawling with the police and wrecking a few stores—every major capital has it. We knew it was coming. I'm relieved the demonstration occurred so soon and burned itself out."

"Not so unorganized as to be ignorant of how to outflank the riot police."

"Organized tactically, yes; but unorganized politically—without leaders, and above all without support."

"Yet the Army failed to turn out in time to contain them."

"Don't read much into that," Kheli said shortly. He remained silent for a second. "When will your Agency cease asking questions? I hoped that we would obtain prompt practical assistance from you, otherwise what purpose does the liaison serve? We are interested in recovering Al Houaranni and punishing the kidnappers; all you people are interested in is our weaknesses."

Brusquely, Fawzi began to gather up an armful of folders, as though the conversation had become too complex or too foolish, but he paused and said at the door, "Perhaps the Agency is unwilling to cooperate with our present government?"

Preston ignored him and said to Kheli, "It will be a lot easier to supply practical assistance when we know what you really want. Al Houaranni's disappearance represents just one aspect of the problem. For example, what was the second car doing at the Africa? You must know by this time who was in it and what they wanted."

For a moment the colonel gazed down at his stubby powerful hands, then he confronted Preston with a charming equivocal smile. His reaction indicated that Preston's snappiness had at least had the merit of clearing the air. "I don't desire to see passed on what I am going to tell you; this is intended for your Agency's confidential guidance, and I can assure you that neither the British nor the French services are *au fait*. My investigation has turned up the existence of a small Army network—I stress, small; the majority of officers and men are loyal—that, through restlessness over our present policy toward Israel and Arab sister states, has been plotting a coup. The conspirators' objectives are not unlike Al Houaranni's. You can imagine that they sprang at the opportunity of arranging a secret meeting with him during his visit. With his unhealthy faculty for spreading discontent like a disease, he immediately agreed. Yesterday afternoon he pleaded sick and canceled his appointment at the Defense Ministry because he needed a free hour during which he could slip off and meet these officers. To tell you the truth, I had learned about this group's existence some time ago, but their internal security was more efficient than I had expected and we were unable to penetrate their meetings. The fantastic thing is, Israeli Intelligence was evidently better informed than I am, and they shrewdly decided to put their knowledge to use by passing their agents off as plotters and luring Al Houaranni into a trap. This is my deduction."

"Our people had thoughts along the same line," said Preston. "The second car obviously contained the bona fide Army officers who arrived at the hotel too late. You shouldn't have much trouble identifying them, but it won't help you find Al Houaranni."

"I imagine Al Houaranni's disappearance was a big shock to them." Kheli grinned. "They may have thought *I* had something to do with it." He looked out the window where the sky was paling and birds in the trees along the presidential avenue were beginning their evening racket as the sun lost its warmth. He said, this time without reluctance, "You know, I really believe that left to ourselves we can round up a lousy bunch of kidnappers even though our police force is rather amateurish and slow off the mark. Captain Fawzi is right: the kidnappers are here in Tunisia, and no doubt they must be desperate. Something has gone terribly wrong with their operation; I feel it. It is also obvious that they had competent leadership on the spot; the complex logistics could not be organized entirely from abroad. This points to the implantation of a Resident agent; not surprising, of course, although until now we were not one of their priority targets. For obvious reasons he surely does not belong to or operate in the Jewish community, yet he must be a Jew—"

"How can you be sure of that?" Preston asked.

Kheli shrugged. "Who else would Tel Aviv trust? But uncovering the Resident and smashing his network is a long-term proposition, and we have more pressing problems, as you witnessed this afternoon. If I don't produce Al Houaranni soon, the *real* opposition, not the foolish students, will do something irretrievable. Time is playing into its hands. This is why I am in a hurry. We must really retrieve Al Houaranni, and the more life there is left in him the better it will be."

"Your morale seems better than last night, Colonel."

"In a way it is."

Preston said, "Suppose my office were to open a channel to Israeli Intelligence?"

Kheli glanced at Fawzi, who was still standing by the door. The two men considered Preston with a blank, bureaucratic military stare, but it did not require much insight to grasp that they had previously reviewed this possibility. "If Al Houaranni is delivered to us alive and unharmed," the colonel replied measuredly, "I am authorized to say the government will be disposed to furnish his kidnappers with safe-conducts."

"Disposed?"

Kheli read the skepticism on Preston's Irish features and went on. "This means no formalities at the airport; we will pay for tourist-class seats on a flight of the kidnappers' choosing provided it is not to another Arab country, and no questions asked about their contacts here. They cannot export any arms they brought in." He added, "Normally we would not offer this. But it has become a political matter and we must neutralize our opposition."

Preston rose in his severe, dark Lanvin blazer. "We should have something hard soon, Colonel," he said.

"Bullshit! Your Agency has all the money at its disposal it requires, and a global organization. Preston, I am convinced you know at this moment where Al Houaranni is. Your people can help us . . . provided they want to."

"*I* want to," Preston said. "I am authorized to do what I can, but I want a promise from you. No interference in any way from your services with whatever action we deem desirable to negotiate Al Houaranni's release."

Kheli hesitated. "I cannot guarantee that we shall not stumble into each other. We are pursuing our own investigation."

"We can't make a deal with the kidnappers if your people hamper us."

"I'll give orders that they don't."

Bearing his load of folders, Fawzi politely held the door open for Preston and escorted him down the corridor; when they reached the elevator the captain stepped in too. "What is this? Are you going to share a taxi with me back to the Embassy?" asked Preston, who was in the habit of leaving the fourth floor on his own, with a slip signed by Kheli, bearing the time of arrival and departure, which he relinquished at the desk.

"There have been a number of serious leaks that originated in this building. We are tightening up our security measures," Fawzi said expressionlessly.


At 5:30 P.M., the telephone rang in Gauthier's office at the Colisée building, diagonally up the avenue from the Interior Ministry.

He hesitated before answering; there were so many people all of a sudden he had no desire to speak to. Finally, when the phone kept ringing shrilly, he picked up the receiver. It took

198

Gauthier a few seconds to recognize the crisp unfamiliar voice at the other end of the line—it belonged to Preston, the second secretary at the American Embassy.

"I do remember you," Gauthier said, "but I must confess, not well." Preston was proposing a meeting; it had to do apparently with the Al Houaranni affair, but his specific reason was vague.

"It would indeed be a pleasure for me, but I am afraid today is out of the question. As you will appreciate, this story is giving me a great deal of work." It was true; he had just finished phoning Darcy, the night editor, and he still had to return home and raise the Qiryat.

"I looked for you at the Information Ministry briefing," Preston's voice insisted. "What I had in mind was a quiet drink—nothing that will require much of your time. If my information checks out, you may want to make use of it."

"I see. Shall we try to meet at Djilani's café in La Goulette in about an hour and a half? I apologize for asking you to come out of your way, but I am on an absurd timetable and unfortunately I do not live in town."

"That's all right. It's worth my while to see you," Preston said impersonally.

Gauthier hung up. The tactic was so trite that normally it would have provoked a smile. The bait about "information," the elusive wording. Gauthier felt that he was watching himself in a mirror; at any rate, the brief conversation left little doubt about the American's function at the Embassy.

He went to the window and looked down upon the city. The riot had had no effect on rush-hour traffic; it took more than a few banged skulls and shattered windows to interrupt the instinctive Mediterranean outpouring into the streets at sunset. Along the center mall pedestrians passed aimlessly back and forth. Most of the crowd consisted of men; occasionally a girl's miniskirt or an older woman's white *sefsari* moved amid the tight dark groups. If Gauthier remained long enough at the window, he would recognize the same groups returning from one of those twin poles of attraction for Tunis' promenading males, the newspaper kiosk and the tobacco kiosk.

Gauthier wondered what he saw in the city to make him stay: the heat in summer, the moist slipperiness in winter, the poverty, the fatalism—and the cloying smell of spices. The color of putty, Tunis was as rumpled as a sackful of old laundry. If it was a sense of duty, then the duty resembled the city—it too exuded a musty odor.

The only symptom of tension below was a convoy of Army personnel carriers and police jeeps parked at an intersection. If there was more trouble coming, it would break out, thought Gauthier, after the demonstrators had had dinner; twenty-four hours following Ramadan, it was asking too much of any opposition movement to taunt the police continuously on empty stomachs. Al Houaranni's kidnapping had scraped unsuspected raw nerves in an indolent population, but that might prove a blessing. The more troops the government had to commit to break up demonstrations, the less were available to scour the countryside for the fugitives—and in less than three hours the commandos with their prisoner would be gone. Still, the afternoon's fighting had been worse than he had anticipated . . . and the looting was a foretaste of repercussions that would tumble down on the remaining Jewish community. Gauthier shrugged. What counted was the operation's outcome.

He touched the window sill, then gazed at the black

200

smudges the soot left on his fingertips. So his absence had been noted at the Ministry briefing. Who else had noticed it? And what did Preston think exactly? Gauthier stood immobile in the growing dusk, running over lightly in his mind what he knew about the man, and concluded that Preston was bent, to judge by his insistence on an immediate meeting, on obtaining something in a hurry. Gauthier had no desire this evening to drink with him, but he was not overly worried. The two weak links in Operation Flood were Ben Larbi and Anne-Marie. However, Ben Larbi had made the crucial phone call to Al Houaranni's suite when it was needed, and since then he had remained inoperative, as ordered. Gauthier had not seen Anne-Marie since daybreak. "*I won't lie to you, Alex*," she had said, but she had denied nothing. Where had she spent the day—with the same man whom she had seen the afternoon before? Gauthier put his hand on the phone to call her up, then removed it. Ben Larbi's interest lay in saying nothing because of his quaking fear of the police; and Anne-Marie would not turn on him after eight years of shared danger. The only other people who had an idea of what he was up to were the men in the safe-house—and now, seemingly, Preston. Gauthier thought about this American more carefully. He had arrived in Tunisia a year ago, spoke French fairly well, was a personable widower whom one glimpsed from time to time with vivid, dressy European girls at the Tunisia Palace bar. And he was with the CIA. The Americans surely wanted to play a role in an affair that did not concern them. Preston, for all his remote politeness, seemed stubborn. What else was there to know about him? From a half-buried sum of knowledge he did not suspect possessing, Gauthier recalled that Preston rented a beach cottage at

Gammarth, close to the Hotel de la Tour Blanche. Gauthier's blond skin flushed. Suddenly he wanted very much to meet this man.

Immediately after calling Gauthier, Preston left the Embassy in his Porsche. He avoided the center of the city, where traffic was still tied up after the afternoon riot. At a newsstand on Avenue Mohammed V, he stopped to buy the Paris papers and then, seeing that he had an entire hour before his meeting in La Goulette, he entered a corner bar and ordered an Americano. Scanning the papers, he found excerpts from a Syrian Army officer's speech in Damascus, which implied that the kidnapping could not have occurred without Tunisian negligence. It was interesting, thought Preston, that on television and radio the government furnished its people with one carefully tailored version of events, while it admitted foreign papers that hinted at another explanation. In short, disarray within the government was preventing it from doing a thorough job of censorship.

Preston ordered another Americano and found himself thinking of Anne-Marie. Was she in this together with her husband? He experienced, then firmly repulsed, a crazy temptation to call her at home. He was sure that Mills had known about his affair but kept silent for his own purposes. What special game was Mills playing? At times, the notion bemused Preston that all Tunis was simply a whitewashed untidy stage-set for Mills's maneuvers.

He called for the check.

When he came out of the bar, the sinking sun had vanished behind vaporous clouds and a fine clinging mist was seeping up the street. He turned the headlights on and headed for the causeway. He did not often take the lake road out of town; the airport road was the direct route between the Embassy and his cottage in Gammarth. Traffic had thinned out. A girl vaguely resembling Anne-Marie passed by in a car; Preston glanced back in the rear-view mirror—and this was when he became aware of the gray Citroën. He watched it several seconds, then again. It was maintaining steady speed, being careful neither to overtake his Porsche nor fall behind. Two Arabs sat in the front seats.

Preston felt sharp, sudden anger with Kheli. The car almost surely belonged to the Tunisian Sûreté. The colonel had promised a free hand but was apparently devoured by the need to know who Preston was going to contact.

Preston pulled over abruptly to the curb and braked, and got a glimpse of the two Tunisians, who stared straight ahead as the Citroën passed. Wrathfully he let the gray car disappear into the mist, reasonably sure that it would stop a short distance farther on. He could turn quickly and drive off in the opposite direction, but they would inevitably follow and he would lose time shaking them. It was more important to keep his appointment with Gauthier.

At the intersection with Avenue Bourguiba, he swung left. The Citroën had disappeared. No one was following him.

The causeway, a narrow strip of reclaimed land, ran five and a half miles in a straight line over the smelly waters of El Behira. Beside the road ran the tracks of the seventy-year-old La Marsa electric railway, a camp antique that reminded Preston of the Toonerville Trolley. Beyond the rail tracks ran the deep-water channel the French had dredged to permit heavy-draft shipping to sail from La Goulette directly up to the port and customs buildings at the foot of the presidential avenue. Beyond the channel was another strip of reclaimed land, and beyond that, the immense placid bay. The whole formed a complicated piece of geography and man-made engineering that confused newcomers to Tunis.

The rear window was blurred with mist. Preston checked again, and there the Citroën was, directly behind, doggedly maintaining the same prudent distance. He wondered where they had hidden—probably behind a trailer truck he had seen stopped at the intersection. He brought the needle up to seventy miles an hour and heard the changed rhythm of rubber snicking on the damp asphalt.

As if his own speed were a signal, the Citroën leaped to life and began to gain on him. Preston pressed the accelerator down harder. He was damned if he would lead the colonel's men to Gauthier; they could do their own sleuthing instead of violating an agreement. A string of three dirty white railroad coaches came rattling abreast of the Porsche; Arab passengers stared at Preston because he was driving an expensive sporty car. In a matter of seconds the disreputable train pulled away, its fiery round tail lantern shaking and jerking as the wheels clicked over the ties and finally vanishing. And then Preston was alone again with the Citroën.

This was aggressive shadowing, and he noted that no other cars were on the causeway. In the deepening dusk it was difficult to make out traffic until it came upon you at the last moment. The low-visibility gray Citroën had switched to the outer lane and was closing on him fast, and just ahead the shoulder on his right was torn up and a long rectangular ditch bit into the road surface; workmen had placed a triangular yellow warning sign TRAVAUX dangerously close to the repairs. Preston checked his speed. If he tried to move into the outer lane, he was going to slam into the Citroën, at ninety miles an hour; but if he continued straight on he was going to crash into the excavation. He began to brake in hard desperation; then to his disbelief the Citroën was moving laterally toward him, becoming bigger and uglier, only ten feet, then five feet away, trying to ram him into the ditch, and with rage in his soul he slammed the accelerator in. As the right front wheel encountered empty space he felt the car surge in response, and then the body righted itself and shot across the Citroën's path. Barely clearing the front bumper, he thought he heard a brief wicked scrape of metal, he was sure he heard shouts, and the Porsche skidded sickeningly across the expanse of wet asphalt before the tires gripped and the hood faced the long empty causeway ahead, while the rear-view mirror cast back a rapidly receding diminishing sequence of confused movement as the Citroën swerved wildly to miss the ditch, struck an upright tar barrel alongside the sign, skidded forward and sideways, and skated unnaturally and helplessly like a toy toward the center divider before coming to a halt. It had all happened very swiftly; seen from the air, it would have seemed like a fast-paced stunt-driving sequence between two tiny cars streaking down a slender ribbon of road elevated in the midst of a vacant shimmering lake. The Porsche was moving down the causeway very fast, and Preston's knuckles ached with stiffness against the wheel. But that wasn't all. The inoffensive-looking Citroën had borne off before hitting the divider, righted itself and was angrily spurting down the road in pursuit again and Preston knew that it would catch up with him. It was no ordinary Citroën; they had visibly fixed it up with a different motor, and he couldn't afford to play games a second time and let them force him off the road. A dirt lane and a row of stunted bushes on the right were all that separated the highway from the railway third rail. He trusted this car that he had brought down from Paris, and it had just saved his life but he wished desperately that he had the powerful 911 S with which he could reach a speed of one hundred and forty miles an hour. The absolute top speed for a Porsche 914 was one hundred and ten miles an hour—the same as an ordinary Citroën's.

Ahead on his left loomed the spidery pylons of the huge electric plant where the lake ended one mile away; beyond a sharp S curve, he remembered that the causeway narrowed into a badly paved two-lane road without a divider. He thought of the mile in terms of speed, and watched the Citroën. It was still gaining on him. He pressed the accelerator until the Porsche was straining at the top of its capability and the metal was vibrating in protest. He could keep this up only a short distance, but the electric plant now towered solid and nearby on his left, and beyond were the strung-out feeble lights of La Goulette; he had a few hundred yards at most left to cover. The Citroën driver was piling up speed too as he sensed that beyond the plant the Porsche would streak into La Goulette and escape for good. But from the purposeful way he drove, it was obvious that he was wary. Preston thought, I'll show you another trick. They might all end up dead, but if he did not try he was not going to outdistance them. And once on the narrow road, who knew? It would be easy to force him to stop. They had not opened fire, but that might not last if they drew close enough again. What was it all about? He had had no time to find an answer. He was coming off the causeway.

With a vicious quarter spin of the wheel, he sent the Porsche fast into the first narrow banked curve. Ahead he saw the amber lights of oncoming cars from La Goulette. Good!—he could use witnesses. Now through the rear-view mirror he saw the Citroën coming up and its driver, a caricatural mask of black protruding eyes and walrus mustache, fixedly watching the Porsche. The other passenger, who was chesty and blunt-nosed, spoke to him urgently. Preston moved his foot deftly, with a fleeting sense of malice, as he swung the low-slung Porsche, tires squealing, into the second and last curve, knowing that he was lighting up the red taillights. The Citroën swept around the curve and the confused driver hesitated a second because of the oncoming dazzle of traffic on his left, the unpredictable car ahead and the concrete abutment on the right. At the rate of speed at which he was coming, he had to make his mind up fast; he veered out of the vehicles' way and there was a shivering of glass and screaming of metal as the Citroën's right headlight and fender smashed against the retaining wall. Preston had a brief vision of the two men momentarily hurled against each other and of other cars slamming hard to a stop near the scene of the accident. The chesty man raised a slight dark object in his fist, then lowered it as witnesses ran up. A man on foot in the middle of the road was shouting after the Porsche and trying to note down its license number.

Preston smiled sourly to himself. In the night mist that might prove difficult. Why had there been no cars on the causeway when he needed them? Still, they had turned up in the curve; he could not have managed that final bit of flim-flam without the arrival of traffic in the opposite lane. He drove on rapidly. His clothes felt as sticky as if he hadn't bathed. The bitter aftertaste of the two Americanos persisted on his tongue and threatened to nauseate him.

He felt ashamed of his earlier suspicion of Kheli. The two thugs in the Citroën were certainly not carrying out his orders. The colonel might be mistrustful and overprone to spy on whoever encroached upon his territory, even a member of an officially friendly Service, but he did not resort to murder. Was it Gauthier? That was more likely, for he now realized that Preston suspected something. But just what, Gauthier did not know and he had hardly had time to organize a murder attempt.

Who, then, did?

## CHAPTER TWELVE

# The Frontier of Regret

BLUE-DYED trawl nets and starfish adorn Djilani's café, which makes a modest attempt to imitate the nautical motif of the neighborhood's famous restaurants; but no one has ever swept aside the scales of dust that shroud the walls, and the shirt-sleeved owner moves about in an aura of grease. Like every eating place in La Goulette, Djilani's is overrun by hordes of quarreling cats that, when it comes to prowling after scraps, discriminate nicely between tourists and natives. The cats paid no attention to two Arab teen-agers who were concentrating on a pinball machine near a transistor that blared out, in French and Arabic, copious details of the afternoon riot.

Gauthier sat at a small table facing the door and rose interrogatively when he saw Preston.

"The government is offering a safe-conduct to the kidnappers provided that Al Houaranni is released alive." Preston experienced the full weight of Gauthier's ice-blue scrutiny.

"I have been listening to that radio," Gauthier objected in

his indefinable light accent, "and there has been no announcement of an offer."

"I wouldn't expect one until they exhaust other channels," Preston said dryly. He saw that Gauthier had ordered nothing; and although his stomach was churning, he held back, not trusting himself to hold liquor well at this point. Then he changed his mind, summoned the owner and quickly ordered two whiskies. If Gauthier was behind the attack on the lake road, he would at least be denied the satisfaction of witnessing an onslaught of nerves. The owner, two boys . . . Preston automatically counted them up; he wondered whether he had been right in coming to Djilani's unarmed.

"What has convinced the police that Al Houaranni is still in Tunisia?"

"Aren't you convinced of it?"

"They are probably right." Gauthier ignored the question and sized Preston up, making no effort to conceal his curiosity. "But I cannot imagine the kidnappers coming to terms for so little. If they hold Al Houaranni, they are in a strong bargaining position."

"Time may be running out for them," Preston said.

"I should think they would demand a safe-conduct for themselves *and* Al Houaranni as their minimum condition. What have they to lose?" He drained off his whiskey in one swallow. "This is what I would do in their place."

"Were you ever in charge of an Intelligence commando?"

Gauthier smiled broadly. "I'm not so sure that this is my idea of an attractive career."

Preston did not as a rule like Frenchmen; he thought their vanity repelling in its corset of egotism, their dealings with foreigners inept. Gauthier was certainly not at ease in the company of non-Frenchmen; but could Gauthier be considered a Frenchman?

Preston said, "If the kidnappers are still in Tunisia, there will have to be some horse trading."

"Possibly. How is it that the American Embassy is so actively involved?"

"Let's say the Embassy's role is that of friendly intermediary."

"These are the 'other channels' you referred to," Gauthier noted.

"Yes." Preston went on. "I have been empowered to negotiate for the Interior Ministry."

Gauthier watched him with polite aloofness. "But the problem, I take it, is to communicate the offer?"

"I want the right parties to hear about it, yes."

"And you would like to use the press? I can do this for you. There is still time for an add to my story—a trial balloon. It will appear in all of tomorrow's editions, quoting unnamed but reliable sources. Will you take a drink with me?" He turned to give the order, and Preston studied in profile the sturdy Flemish-looking head and clean blond nape.

"No thanks, one is my limit." He did not want to owe this man anything, not even a smudgy glass of whiskey. After all, it was conceivable that Gauthier had suggested meeting in La Goulette on the assumption that he would take the causeway as the straightest and shortest route and thereby easily fall into a trap. Preston shook his head; he had to break the foul mood he was in; he must think clearly if he wanted to force his stolid, overweening man to comply with what he had in mind.

They were alone in the café. The teen-agers had sauntered

out into the uninviting street, and so were not Gauthier's agents after all. It was drizzling in the square, where shopkeepers were boarding up for the evening. The street's emptiness was odd, Preston thought—a misty void out of which imprecise trouble could suddenly emerge. The owner had retreated to the back room, from which floated a faint heady odor of mushrooms and sausage ends simmering in a wine sauce. The radio continued to play, but it was Arab music now, a strident and obsessive chant, a dirge for love's disasters; it or its like echoed down the shore for thousands of miles.

"A story in a Paris paper won't help," Preston said finally. "It will take too long and may not be read here."

"Then how can I be of assistance to you?"

"I'm sure that you know where Al Houaranni is, or where the people who kidnapped him can be found. You're in contact with them."

Gauthier continued to watch him out of opaque blue eyes. "What makes you think this?"

Preston told him the reasons. "Last night, while every reporter in Tunis was keeping a lookout at the Defense Ministry or the Hotel Africa, you were away. You did turn up at the Moroccan reception, but you stayed a surprisingly short time for a correspondent who could hope to interview Al Houaranni. However, I'll concede that any number of explanations might fit. But this morning the entire press corps attended the Information Ministry briefing—with the exception of yourself. This kidnapping is a major story throughout the world, but apparently you didn't consider the briefing important enough to cover. You left your house early and were uncontactable most of the day. No one saw you in Tunis. I've checked."

"And from this you deduce that I am on the trail of the kidnappers?"

"One could conclude that you've developed a lead—"

"It's not a bad deduction. Of course, it is my professional responsibility to try to find out what is happening."

"I haven't finished. There's the matter of daily activity during the past twenty-four hours; now for the background. When you first arrived in Tunis fourteen years ago, you gave false information to obtain a resident permit. You also gave it, in the first place, to acquire a French passport. You travel frequently between Tunis and Europe. A fairly obvious pattern emerges from this."

Gauthier was smiling faintly. "It is not so obvious to me."

"Who represents Israeli Intelligence in this town?"

"You think I do? I wonder you don't inform the Interior Ministry what a dangerous character I am."

"My job is not primarily to clue in the Tunisian Sûreté."

Gauthier was silent for a moment, his state of mind evidently a compound of wariness and withdrawal. Then he said, "What is the CIA's purpose in this whole affair? Where does it stand? Does it even know?" In fact he was thinking that the Americans represented one unanticipated, foolproof way to get Levanon's commando out of the country but fortunately their participation was no longer needed. "You have spent a lot of time prying into old records, but prying after all is your business . . . and mine. I repeat, why not go to the police with your suspicions?"

"Gauthier, whatever your real assignment is, I want to use you as a go-between."

"My answer is no." He rose, acting, thought Preston, as though he held all the winning cards in this ruleless game. To give the man his due, he was delivering a highly professional performance. "I didn't ask for this meeting, Mr. Preston. I am not an admirer of yours; I have less time than you do for drinking and gossiping. I'm not sure now that I would help you if I could—"

"For God's sake! Al Houaranni may still be alive. I'd like you to transmit the offer now, while there's still time."

"Time for what?"

"To assist a moderate government. Somebody in Tel Aviv ought to be smart enough to figure out it's in Israel's interest too."

Gauthier shook his head again. "The fact is, I don't trust you." The Americans, he was thinking, had people like this Preston who worked hard and conscientiously, sometimes effectively, but were lost when it came to flair. What they badly needed were a few dreamers and corrupt individuals to whom confidential information clung like bad breath. Individuals like Ben Larbi. "Moreover, some of the information you cite about my whereabouts can have come from only one source— my wife. I know that you have been seeing her. I won't stand for it. I expect you to stop doing so immediately."

To his momentary frustration, Preston felt an emotion akin to understanding for Gauthier. Preston had an unwanted talent for smelling out arid isolation among members of a pack. He had never been more aware of that scent of hopelessness than in this man; the motives that had led Anne-Marie to be unfaithful two afternoons a week were becoming plainer.

"I think ultimately that's for her to decide," he said.

Listening to his own composed voice, it had seemed to Gauthier that finally he had, after a long, arduous ascent, reached a frontier; he had only reached this point after

difficult journey, across up-and-down country, through vari-
able sunlight and shadow, among faces and voices that no
longer mattered, after losing sight of the beginning and dis-
carding along the way many fine notions. The piercing regret
he experienced was less at the prospect of being without
Anne-Marie in the future than for the enormous waste that lay
like a Sahara behind.

Then he looked down and saw that the American's face
was set and serious, no longer complacent; it bore, in fact, a
wavering gray middle-aged hint of bitterness. This meant that
he was going to give more trouble than a self-assured young
man.

"You are making a surprising fool of yourself," Gauthier
said stonily.

"We can talk about my foolishness later," Preston suggested
with impatience.

"Do you always avoid facing a showdown? I wouldn't have
thought it."

"Listen, my wife became interested in a Frenchman younger
and smarter than you. He wasn't really interested in her, but
he had a track record to keep up. He figured that the husband
could be bluffed easily . . . Frenchmen often reason like
that. My wife didn't like his motivation when she thought
about it and dropped him with a thud that jarred his back
teeth."

Gauthier stared in real astonishment. "What does this have
to do with my wife?"

"Don't confuse me with that Left Bank Romeo," Preston
said.

"Where is the idiotic owner? I must go."

"I'm counting on you to get the message through," Preston

said disgustedly, sweeping up the two individual checks on the table. "A safe-conduct in return for Al Houaranni—it's not an unreasonable offer, considering the situation."

"You have been drinking too much, your breath reeks. Since you are so generous about meddling in people's lives, let me say a word. If you persist in annoying me and running after my wife, you will have more trouble than you seem capable of managing."

Preston knew what else was nagging at his nerves; it was the street's utter silence. There was something unnatural out there, although he couldn't put his finger on the exact cause.

"You're the one in trouble—in spades," he snapped, rising. "It's not *my* operation, she's your wife—"

Gauthier grabbed Preston's shoulder and tried to jerk him forward. Gauthier's dislike of Americans was visceral; he was rattled by their terrifying inclination to insert themselves where they were unwanted, their blundering through a combination of unfamiliarity and cocksureness. Preston knocked down his arm with a grin, but then a weird wail of angry bewilderment stopped them both short.

Gauthier swore and wrenched his arm free.

In the back-room door, where he had materialized like an inglorious jinni, a soiled dishcloth clutched in one hand, swayed the fat owner. Muttering in Arabic, he wagged a finger at the transistor.

The Arab chant had ended.

Gauthier scowled in turn at the owner, then at Preston, as if he suspected them of having connived at a hoax.

"What are you talking about, you old faker?" he asked sharply.

The owner gestured for him to keep quiet and turned the

transistor knob swiftly, passing one station after another, raising fragments of music up and down the Mediterranean. He turned back to Radio Tunis, and this time a man's husky voice read out a long statement in Arabic. Preston realized now that the same voice had, a few seconds ago, broken through the scheduled broadcast.

"What is he saying?" rasped Gauthier. "Have they found Al Houaranni?"

The owner had draped his arms around the set and was listening carefully. Then he straightened up with a solemn worried expression and addressed them both. "There has been a coup d'etat. The Army has declared martial law. The President's palace is occupied. No one is to go outdoors . . ."

Gauthier's face was working queerly. Before Preston could stop him, he made an abrupt gesture of renunciation and hurried out the door.

# PART TWO

*The spy's first duty is to avoid capture.*
—RONALD SETH, *Anatomy of Spying*

*An Arab town is built like a maze: there is the same baffling choice of turnings, the need to remember your way back, the feeling you are solving something, like a riddle.*
—JOHN ANTHONY, *About Tunisia*

## CHAPTER THIRTEEN

# The Gun

THE General said, "We can't abandon them."

"The embarkation time is in forty minutes . . ." the section chief began without finishing his thought aloud.

"No, no, I've given Sebring orders to get himself out of there on the double." The General stared at his subordinate in wary challenge. "Well, isn't it what you sailor types do—whenever possible, sail around dangerous waters?"

"I don't understand your hesitation. Weather tonight is no problem. In the middle of this coup, Sebring can take them off . . . a little imagination and boldness and he'll be homeward bound."

"Committing *Keriche* is out of the question." The General leaned back in his chair and pressed his palms upward with austere judiciousness. "The situation is too far gone now. Of course we could try, I agree, but if we should fail, think of the long-range consequences. We don't want to imperil relations with the incoming crowd. Can you see the headlines if a naval battle occurred? Operation Flood was smash-and-grab at best; it had to be quickly executed or not at all. I must say

Emir persuaded me that he could bring it off, and I always trusted his judgment."

The section chief knew better than to formulate an independent critique.

"I've just heard from him. As soon as he learned of the coup he made a signal to insist that we maintain the embarkation schedule. Coming on his part, the request is rather cynical. Our people will just have to lie low until the worst blows over and we can work something out that doesn't entail inordinate risk. After all, they are safer on Cap Bon than anywhere else."

"Has Emir told them that?"

"I've asked him to relay my orders. The Tunisian Army has imposed a curfew, but he seems to think that with his press card he'll be able to get through. I know, it's a hell of a mess, but they must make the best of a bad bargain. We had some thought of bringing them out, including Al Houaranni, under Moroccan diplomatic immunity, but Tunis airport is shut down."

"So for the moment they're trapped."

"Of course, I am worried on their account, but actually the coup may prove an asset if it distracts the authorities. There is bound to be a shake-up; for a few days the police will have no time to think about Al Houaranni's kidnappers. If it's anything like Tripoli, the government will purge at once and positively encourage informing. Fortunately the talebearing will be directed against their own; foreigners who mind their steps will go unmolested. You know, I once told a chap in this office that killing a man is easier than kidnapping him, but under present circumstances, I believe the reverse may be true. In any event, Emir can help them. He'll have nothing else to do. We're temporarily suspending contact with him; it's in his own interest. The de facto regime may change frequencies, it could become very confused; and anyway, everyone will be watching his neighbor. Emir has a French passport and is in no danger. I've asked him to fly up to Paris as soon as air traffic resumes."

"He's in no danger unless one of your commandos is caught."

"The only one of the lot who can positively identify Emir is Levanon, and Levanon makes a specialty of bulldozing his way out of scrapes—in fact, on some he has turned a profit. That's why I picked him."

The section chief thought that the General was being sanguine.

"Isaac, how are they going to skip the country in the middle of a revolution?"

"If need be, they have a valuable hostage whom they can trade for their freedom. It is not an ideal solution and I hope we shan't resort to it, but my responsibility is to get these three fellows out—we need them back here, they're useful—and without Al Houaranni they will find it easier to fend for themselves." The General's aged hands fidgeted a bit. "Emir's considerable part in Flood's failure is a worry to me; I'll have to deal with it of course once all the loose ends are accounted for. He sent an absurd explanation linking his blunder to his young son's health."

"His son? I didn't visualize Emir with a family."

"Oh, yes, very much a paterfamilias he is. His wife is the daughter of a famous old man in French politics. When I met her, I understood how Emir could be wildly taken. It was years ago. She's probably changed—we all do, you know."

Some time that same night—police later ascertained the exact hour to be eight-twenty—a station wagon with Tunisian plates careened around the corner of Rue Didon in Carthage and came to a jolting halt a short distance away at a road-block on Avenue de l'Amphithéâtre that had been set in place by a company of soldiers belonging to the First Armored Division, which had sided with insurgent elements of the Tunis garrison.

The driver, a heavy-set blond man, leaped out, showed the officer in charge a press card and made an energetic plea to be allowed to proceed to Cap Bon in spite of the curfew. The company commander, a captain, refused to make an exception in his favor. The vehicle thereupon turned around and departed for Carthage.

From then onward, Gauthier realized that no further hope existed of carrying out Operation Flood—it was over, unsuccessfully terminated, washed up. He also had the feeling that God was peering over his shoulder and laughing at him in vexed bewilderment.


They waited on the beach, but this time there was no storm and the moon's dead glow illumined a tranquil expanse of shore and sea. After the storm the stars sprang out with purged brilliance; on a distant point a sharp white light blazed like a torch. They saw clearly the low round outline of the Qelibia lighthouse standing up on a hilltop near the old Spanish fortress.

"It will be more dangerous than last night," Marston objected.

"How do you mean?"

"The *lamparos* are out tonight."

"I don't see their lights."

"Neither do I, but they missed last night's catch. They must be around the point."

"Well? If they see the signal flare, what can they do? They have no radio link with shore. Assuming one of them is prepared to sacrifice two hours of fishing to do his patriotic duty, by the time he puts in to Qelibia we'll be out of these waters. Once *Keriche* submerges, the *avisos* will be unable to plot our course."

Al Houaranni was following their conversation in Hebrew with hostile attention, but Max spoke freely because he no longer feared what the other might learn. As the afternoon had worn on and no police had turned up to besiege the safehouse, Al Houaranni's talkativeness had subsided; finally, when it had grown dark and they had led him shackled to the Peugeot, he had obeyed in sullen silence.

Black said, "*Keriche* had better show—or God help Emir."

"I am sorry to disappoint you but nothing at all will go wrong this time." Max glanced at his watch. It was eight-ten —five minutes before embarkation time. He heard the sea's soft, insistent lapping at the edge of the beach and he smelled the tepid breeze off the calm Gulf.

"While there is still time, I want to propose a bargain." Al Houaranni cleared his throat with an attention-drawing rasp and turned toward Max.

"Move back," Black said at once—his lips were white with

225

strain—"or my gun could go off. Don't step around unexpectedly like that."

"Try to be a little less nervous," Max told him and addressed Al Houaranni. "I am not interested in striking a bargain with you." He stared intently at the moonlit sea on which no boat had appeared.

"A bargain to ward off the deaths of five hundred Jews?" Al Houaranni was warily watching Black's Beretta, as if indeed it might go off without warning. "I think you misunderstood my wording—'while there is still time.' Not later than tomorrow your people will suffer horribly. Do you catch my meaning? A new operation is scheduled against Israel; if it is not canceled, Haifa will experience a catastrophe."

Max glanced skeptically at the slender captive figure on the beach.

"What is new about this? We know that your tactics are murderous."

"Arsenic will be found in wells—"

"What sort of amateur blackmail is this?" Max shouted. "Haifa? I'll alert them from aboard ship."

"Listen to what he has to say," interrupted Black. "I don't think he's bullshitting you."

"He has nothing to tell me. He's consoled himself all day with a vision of five hundred deaths." Max's bad temper was aggravated by the glib, confident voice at his side.

"Not just Haifa is targeted. Do you think we are turning up all our trump cards? But I can promise that the poisonings will be coordinated and kill many Jews—"

"Unless we free you immediately."

"Yes, this is the condition. I can cancel the operation, provided that the order reaches Damascus before dawn; afterward, it will be out of my power."

"Here we have a dedicated idealist and national leader who this morning bragged of his readiness to die so that a sacred objective could be achieved—"

"Your show trial cannot help my people. Why should my life be lost for a nonessential purpose? If you are a realist, keep me here and give me a chance to contact my aide in Tunis."

"The dumb man?"

"Yes." Around Al Houaranni's feet the moonlight described shadowy arabesques on the sand. "He will transmit a priority message to Damascus calling off the operation. Then he will contact the Tunisian Sûreté and make it clear that in return for three safe-conducts you are ready to free me. Once you are aboard a plane of your choosing, the Sûreté will go to a mutually agreed-upon place and find detailed information about my whereabouts. The Sûreté will agree to this plan. What can it lose? It can easily check that I am not aboard the plane. That I have been murdered? This is admittedly a risk, but one the government will gladly run to terminate an affair that is a daily embarrassment."

Impatiently Max stared at him. "Why should we do all this when we hold you?"

"To abate terrorism. Isn't this why you came to Tunisia?"

Without Al Houaranni, Max was thinking, they would not be waiting on this beach for a small, inflatable boat to emerge providentially out of the dark sea; with him they were prey to recurrent irritation and fear. He was an undernourished gadfly, a woebegone oddity thrown up by the Middle East's sick taste for sonorous rhetoric and self-destructive frenzy.

"Why are you smirking?" Al Houaranni asked him.

"The Haifa operation is a hoax—"

Al Houaranni quivered and moved brusquely forward. "Not a single one of our operations has been a bluff—"

"Shut up!" Black cried.

"—it is you who are bluffing. Where is your submarine?" he hissed, when a dull loud report cut the question short.

As his words petered out into a cross whisper, there were two more shots, bunched together so that virtually no time elapsed between them.

Al Houaranni wheeled partly around in a balletlike movement of refusal and defiance, and then pitched face forward to the sand. Nothing broke his fall, and his intelligent angular features scraped pebbles, then settled gradually into an expression of indifference and repose.

"I warned him . . ." Black began, but basic untruthfulness seeped into his fractious voice. In midsentence he changed his mind and snapped half-aggressively, half-aggrievedly, "Goddamn good riddance."

Max leaned over the sprawled body, feeling the pulse. Then he rolled Al Houaranni over so that his dark eyes stared expressionlessly up at the sky. The grouped black wounds in his chest were visible. Looking up, Max said, his voice trembling with barely controlled rage, "It is you we ought to get rid of."

Black still held the Beretta pointed vaguely at the recumbent body.

"Put the gun down."

Black obeyed automatically.

Max had straightened up. He inhaled in great gulps, as

though fearful of going under into some terrible tenebrous deep from which no stubbornness or effort of will power could rescue him. Under the black sack suit his shoulders heaved abruptly. He was angrier than at any time since landing in Tunisia. He was aware of the weight of his own pistol tugging clumsily at his inside jacket pocket. When he was like this, he could be dangerously rapid. He crouched, ready to draw the Beretta if there was any further insubordination on Black's part.

"Give me your gun."

The second order roused Black from his stupor. "You can't use two guns," he said, hesitating.

"Are you going to give me it when I ask?" In one recess of his mind, Max was conscious that perhaps he should beware of Marston, who had not moved or uttered a word since the shooting.

"Give it to him, Noah," Marston said.

Without taking his eyes off Max, Black removed the magazine by touch and handed the Beretta over quickly, as though he wanted to avoid contact with Max's fingers. The magazine he put defiantly into his pocket.

"Someone is sure to have heard those shots, damn it," Max bawled. "*La'azazel!* Go to the devil! Why did you do it?"

"He was about to——"

"Yes, he was about to disclose information we need. When I called the Haifa operation a hoax, I was trying to goad him into saying more. You don't grasp much at all, Black. Now we will never know what he intended to say. All right, before they start investigating where the shots occurred, we are going to dispose of him and get aboard."

"*Keriche* isn't coming. Once again this is a trick Emir played on you," Marston said.

Max did not reply at once. On the moonlit sea he saw no movement that could indicate a boat's approach. He felt the warmth of high anger as blood moved up to his bull neck.

"We'll give Sebring a little more time; meanwhile, keep your pessimism to yourself," he said. Without emotion he glanced at Al Houaranni. "The body must not be found for a while. As long as his followers think he's alive and can be freed, they will hesitate about carrying out the Haifa operation; certainty about his death, on the other hand, will surely provoke more terrorism. We can bury him there without trouble." He indicated the dark shore.

Black stood a little way off, not participating in the discussion and conscious of being shunned.

"Face the facts—we're better off without that killer," he muttered.

"What do you consider yourself to be, Black—a humanitarian from the Bronx? What difference is there between you and Al Houaranni?"

Max studied the Black Beach's topography and pointed to the rock ledge, where the night before they had waited forlornly in the pelting rain. "There," he said. "From that height he'll sink at once."

"Are you sure?"

"Don't try my patience tonight," Max growled.

Shrugging irritably, Black secured the corpse by the armpits while Marston lifted the legs off the sand. They carried Al Houaranni up the overgrown slope and set him down on the ledge. Here they could smell the black lane of water; even by moonlight the sea represented a greater darkness than the

230

land; the sea at night was the incarnation of a vast and latent malevolence.

Black began to grope inside the dead man's battle dress. Aware that he was being watched, he explained, "We need proof. Without his papers those smart-asses at the Qiryat will say we kidnapped the wrong man—"

"He's worrying about the situation once we get back to Tel Aviv," Marston observed.

"Black, do you understand what will happen if the Tunisian police capture you with documents that belonged to Al Houaranni? We don't remove so much as a postage stamp from his effects." Max turned to Marston. "Is there anything in the car you can use as a weight?"

Marston nodded and disappeared, making no noise, in the direction of the Peugeot.

As Max waited for him to return, he was intensely aware of the night on this alien shore, with its cryptic lights and sounds. Only nights in one's own country are meaningful, he thought. In one's own country one imagines what goes on behind the gate, what is being whispered inside the house silvered by moonlight. A pine nearby creaked, an owl hooted. For all his worry, he refrained from speaking to Black, who stood silhouetted against the sea—a bumptious, immobile figure.

Marston was soon back, a short coil of rope in one hand. He had run the entire way and was panting. "We have to get rid of him right away. There are car lights on the highway moving toward us."

Black whistled softly in the dark.

"Toward us?" Max repeated.

"I can't be sure but I think so." Marston was already busy

searching through the underbrush. He brought back two flat mossy rocks and placed them beside the body; then he took out a pocketknife and sawed the rope into two even lengths. Squatting, he circled one length twice—widthwise and lengthwise—around the bigger of the two rocks. To keep the rope from slipping, he made a bowline knot from which he ran out the bight around the corpse's ankles, drew it taut with a half hitch and tied another knot.

"Will it hold this way?" asked Max.

"Long enough to drag him down to the bottom. We'll attach the other rock to his neck; there's enough rope for that."

Black was at work with the length of unused rope Marston had handed over to him. He raised Al Houaranni's head and passed the loop around the neck. Black pursed his lips as he lowered the dead man's head, which stared past him with blank disregard that might have been construed as playfulness. Black avoided letting his hands drift near the dark, coagulated eruptions of blood above the heart. No one spoke. When the rope was secured, he sprang to his feet briskly.

"Take off the handcuffs," Max said. "Why leave an identification clue for the police?"

Black muttered an inaudible comment but complied.

Then together the three men lifted the body, sharing the inert, leaden weight, and carried it to the side of the ledge. Twenty feet below, black water glittered in a deep natural pool strewn with half-submerged rocks.

"Avoid the rocks, straight down," Max urged them. He was supporting the base of Al Houaranni's spine, finding the contact vaguely repellent, but thinking that if he were to find himself in his enemy's position, a burial by the seashore, under the stars, was not a mean way to be disposed of.

"Now!"

The body slid from their outthrust arms, then plunged toward the pool. Just clear of the boulders, it crashed sideways into the water and was immediately swallowed up. The water churned white and frenzied for a few seconds but was soon calm again. The corpse did not reappear.

Max glanced out at the open sea. It was now eight-forty. More time had passed jettisoning Al Houaranni's body than he had wished. Were *Keriche* nearby, it would have put a boat into shore by now. Marston's pessimistic forecast was correct; they could expect no help from the inimical expanse of water out there. Apparently, from start to finish, the embarkation plan had been a spectacular lie. But to what purpose?

Max stamped back toward the Peugeot, aware that Black and Marston were docilely following him. Without breaking stride, he said over his shoulder, "How is it the rope was available?"

"I found it this morning in the garage."

"So you put it in the car trunk?"

"With our Arabchik friend you never knew what to expect." Marston's flat, skeptical voice floated ahead in the night.

"Where are these lights you threatened us with?"

"Just a second and you'll see more than you want."

They had reached the clearing where the Peugeot was parked and—exactly as Marston had promised—through the trees they glimpsed, advancing steadily toward them, the outspread yellow beams of grouped headlights that danced up and down the distant horizon.

"Police—but on another assignment," Max said promptly. "Do you think they would advertise their presence in this way if they were looking for us?"

Black murmured, "That's a heavy police concentration for a Cap Bon road at night."

"I want you to reconnoiter—no, wait, you stay here with me, let Marston go. Keep off the highway. Down the road there is a village—enter it only if absolutely necessary to find out what is happening." He had no qualms about allowing Marston to use his own judgment.

The small, restless figure vanished soundlessly down the stone track in the shadow of the giant cactus hedges.

After he had gone, Black broke the silence and said, "Why did you send Marston?"

"Because I have no further confidence in you."

"I don't have a loaded gun anymore—why can't you trust me?"

"You were warned earlier about disobedience. This murder you cold-bloodedly committed destroys the operation's entire purpose. What do you expect—a citation? Black, why did you get into Intelligence work? For revenge or the sake of adventure? Either is an unacceptable motivation."

Black snorted and gave him no time to continue. "Al Houaranni was a committed terrorist; on trial he would have proved an embarrassment. So what have you lost?" Whenever he became worked up by a sense of injustice, his voice rose to a rebellious squawk. "What did you plan to do—feed and entertain him until that no-show submarine turned up? Where is it, anyway? I could murder Emir without a gun—"

"You won't do any more murdering, is that clear?" Max yelled. He glared at this violent American who acted on linear

234

assumptions of virtue and reward, crime and punishment. For the first time on this assignment, Max felt weary and old—and, in consequence, at a disadvantage in handling this unruly subordinate. Nonetheless, tomorrow at the latest, he would have to do something about him; no more than a restive watch-dog could Black be permitted to break discipline whenever he pleased.

A few minutes later, Marston emerged out of the track's shadows. Lightly as a highwayman he advanced upon them, then he paused, lit a cigarette and produced a tight, self-satisfied smile. "The Army has seized power—would you believe it?" he said, and triumphantly exhaled a ring of white smoke.

Max gripped his elbow. "Are you sure? How did you find this out?"

Marston was basking in an aura of unique achievement. "I'm not putting you on, believe me! A coup d'etat took place two hours ago, and it changes the entire setup. The headlights we saw—do you know what they were? A convoy. Twelve tanks passed within ten yards of where I was standing. When I decided to walk into the village, no one paid attention to me but I overheard what they said. The battalions from the back country are driving into Tunis to support the new government."

Max was somber. "The coup is the reason why *Keriche* did not surface."

"Perhaps," Marston conceded, but his tone was doubtful.

"If all this is true, the Army will make a special effort to capture us—to prove that it is more efficient than the preceding regime."

"And no sign of Emir," Black said. "Obviously he has

orders to stay away. We might jeopardize Emir's cover at this point, so the General made his choice and is writing us off; Emir is of more long-term value than we are."

"Don't be ridiculous," Max retorted. Watching the starry horizon, he waited until the convoy's lights had entirely disappeared behind the hills. "Later, more Army vehicles are bound to be on the road; we had better return to the house while we can and review the contingency plan. For the time being at least, we'll be safe there."

After the others had gotten in, however, Black made no attempt to enter the car. He stood beside the door and said, "Listen, we can slip into Qelibia before it gets light and requisition a boat. Pantelleria is closer than Sicily; I studied the map—it's a four-hour run. Once we enter Italian waters, they automatically intern us. What's wrong with that?"

From behind the wheel, Marston jeered, "Spaghetti dinners, Mafia has-beens, but no belly dancers like here. Do you think you could stand it, Noah?"

"Better than a firing squad."

"How do you 'requisition' the boat?" Max asked.

"With three guns," Black said. "Once aboard, I take responsibility for setting course to Pantelleria. The direction is due east. It's simple."

Max looked at the tall, rawboned, distressed figure—instinctively he had expected Black's proposal to involve an escape by sea—then shook his head. "If *Keriche* did not surface, it is precisely because Tunisian patrol ships are watching the coast. The same danger applies to us; we would be run down within minutes of clearing port."

"The safe-house is a trap."

"What makes you say that?"

"It was intended for use as a temporary hideout. Sooner or later we'll have to clear out of this area."

"Yes, but this involves reasonable risk; going to sea is not reasonable." The car motor was running, and Max added, "We cannot stay here indefinitely. What are you waiting for?"

Sullenly, Black climbed into the rear of the car.

Max glanced at Marston covertly. He was moving about, making sure that the living-room shutters were fastened and blankets draped at every window. Throughout, Marston had obeyed orders automatically—but where was the breaking point? If Marston cracked, the consequences would be far more worrisome than a revolt on Black's part.

"I think you should try to get some sleep," Max said.

"First get the work done, Captain." Marston checked a window latch, then he sat down in an attentive position in a straight-backed armchair. Beside him, Black sprawled on the couch. The silence inside the house was oppressive, accentuated by the dry click of date palms in the garden.

"My intention," Max declared softly, "is to stay here till morning. This will give us all a chance to get some rest. Then, while the Army's attention is diverted, we make our way back into Tunis. I want a showdown with Emir. If he is clean, he can send a message about the Haifa operation and request a new escape plan; he is our sole link with headquarters and we should not underrate this advantage. Don't worry, I no longer have blind confidence in him, but unless proved otherwise, he can help us. No one else can or will do so. Why let him side-step his responsibility?" Max presented his plan with misgiving. He realized that discipline and belief—the General's famous "belief"—no longer would suffice to drive these two men. It was possible that both Black and Marston might turn on him simultaneously in this isolated house—not likely but possible. "What do you think?" he inquired.

Marston smiled wryly. "I appreciate that you asked us. Look, Captain, I am simply grateful to be still alive at the end of this awful day. So many mistakes in forty-eight hours! Excuse me, but his has been a lesson to me, even though it may do no good. Probably you are right; who knows? It is your responsibility. So why ask me?"

"Am I entitled to an opinion?" Black snapped.

"Unfortunately, yes."

Black's liquid eyes met Max's, then swerved off. "You already know what I think. There's one way to get out of this dead end . . . not two ways or three." Angrily he rose and left for the kitchen. "I'll stand guard until six. I don't need any goddamn rest."

Max sat stock-still on the couch and stared at the cheap wicker furniture. For once he sympathized with Black's outrage. It seemed ages since Emir had driven up the sunken road in his big station wagon and delivered his solemn worthless promise that *Keriche* would rendezvous on schedule.

"Then two to one my plan it is," Max said tersely.

"That's right, Captain."

"If we are going to return to Tunis, you'd better try to change the car's license number even though the new number won't match the registration papers. Is there paint in the garage?"

"Yes, and I'll do it now so it will be dry tomorrow morn-

238

ing." Marston looked embarrassed and added unnecessarily, "And then I am going to get that rest. The beds upstairs aren't bad. Why don't you turn in too?"

"Probably I will. Good night, Marston."

Max removed his jacket and folded it over the nearest chair. Then he stooped down and untied his shoelaces. A sudden flush of heat mottled his temples, and he wondered whether he was running a fever; to be ill at this stage would be a crowning mishap. There were probably aspirin in the bathroom. With care he unhitched his belt, then recalled the two Berettas, loaded and unloaded, he had stuck into his jacket. With a grunt he got up, retrieved the pistols and concealed them behind one of the pillows on the couch. He would go upstairs later, but first he wanted to think the situation over. He should have urged Marston to keep an eye on Black, but he had forborne from doing so for he was uncertain to what extent Marston was reliable, and besides, he had no idea how to admit him into his confidence. The old worry about discipline wound tight around his throat. He would lie prone but awake for a while—all night if necessary. Black's plan bothered him. It made some sense—not much, but at least it possessed the virtue of action; perhaps he had been unfair in his reaction. To himself, Max conceded that his distrust of Black was so great that it completely warped his judgment. Still, the distrust was founded in fact. Because of Black, Al Houaranni was dead, and it made that Palestinian cutthroat posthumously right. There were other confused thoughts spinning about in Max's sluggish mind, but he did not resolve them, for, in spite of his determination to remain awake, in a few seconds his swollen eyelids shut and he was fast asleep.

CHAPTER FOURTEEN

# The Village

MAX came awake suddenly and unpleasantly. He knew at once that Black was gone. The sound of light footfalls prowling the corridor (Black was always astir at dawn) was missing. And there was a smell missing, too—Black's persistent, acid odor, which he had developed as soon as he stopped bathing.

Max reached under the pillow and his fingers encountered two long steel barrels. Both Berettas were still there; he grunted with relief.

Then he heard a dull, repeated thudding somewhere in the back of the house; this was the noise that had awakened him and he suddenly realized its significance. On bare feet he hurried up the flight of stairs and stared at the locked bedroom door. Inside, Marston muttered indistinctly. Without hesitation Max threw his full weight against the flimsy panel but it did not yield. Cursing, he ran downstairs, seized the loaded gun and hastened back up. He shouted to Marston, "Stand back," and heard his choked exclamation of assent. Then, aiming downward, he fired twice above the lock and heard the wood splinter. This time, when he shoved hard, the door ripped a gash in the jamb and flew open.

At the far end of the room Marston was gagged and hand-cuffed to a chair, against whose leg he had been kicking steadily. Max undid the gag without trouble, then found the tiny handcuff key where Black had thoughtfully left it on the night table.

"Where is he?"

Marston stared at him with reproach. "You heard him mention Pantelleria."

"And you did nothing to prevent him?"

"For God's sake, he had a gun on me—*my* gun. I couldn't stop him and I couldn't talk him out of it."

"Can we intercept him?"

"I doubt it. You took a long time to wake up."

Max nodded and went to the window, unfastened the shutter and looked out. It was just past dawn and the sky was a faint patchwork of gray and salmon. The sun was beginning to tint the barren slope; the sea that was of no assistance to them shimmered pacifically far below. The house was eerily quiet, rid of the preceding day's tension but uncomfortably empty after Al Houaranni's death and too big for only two men. Max turned around and said in a sudden fury, "He flagrantly disobeys orders, shoots a man and deserts. The stupid, spoiled horse's ass will lose us all."

He studied Marston's sour, obstinate, dutiful face. "Why didn't you go with him?"

"To be honest, I thought about it—but in my opinion he doesn't have a chance. Where is Al Houaranni, the Tunisians ask themselves. Not in Tel Aviv. Has he been found else-where? No. Then maybe he's still in Tunisia. In such a situation, what is the simplest escape route? By sea. So they patrol the coast, wait offshore for us to venture out, and then run the boat down."

Max studied his thick fists and asked, "When did he clear out?"

"Almost a half hour ago. What about you, Captain. Do you think he was right?"

"Do *I* think so? To try to navigate fifty miles of open water—" Max checked himself. "Perhaps. It may be that he is right and we are also right," he added with unwonted humility.

"I'm sure that killing Al Houaranni was getting to him. He stayed up all night alone in the kitchen, thinking about it and figuring out reasons for skipping. When he came upstairs, I told him to shut up but he wouldn't."

"I know why he skipped—that crybaby was shitting in his pants."

"Listen, he's only doing what he believes in. He said you told him the operation was over; he said it wasn't desertion, that he was going to do his best to reach Tel Aviv."

"If he does, I'll have his perfumed ass." Max smacked one fist against another in utter frustration. "He could be anywhere now—including in the hands of the police. If they capture him, he'll accuse us of shooting Al Houaranni—he's the type."

Marston screwed up his left eye into an outraged squint. "Not yet, with his luck he's not under arrest; it would surprise me very much. But watch out when that character becomes convinced he has fooled the whole population into taking him for a fedayee—I hope to God by then we're out of the country." Marston's facial contortions put Max in mind again of

242

the monkeyish artful taxi driver he had recognized in the General's office and almost immediately trusted. "Noah didn't get any sleep, so he won't get far—but he has that gun."

"He's a moron. He's found out that a gun works. He won't stop using a gun now until someone kills him." Max lit a cigarette and inhaled deeply. He let it burn down between his fingers and felt the companionable blue smoke coil wispily around his wrist. To say what he had to say now, he faced Marston with a scowl. "Due to Black's violation of orders, we no longer have a hostage and we may not get away alive. Therefore, in good conscience, I cannot order you to return with me. If you want to try your luck like Black, I'm authorizing you to do so."

"Unless you object, Captain, I'll stick with you. You're doing fine, given the circumstances. It's stupid to split up. Personally, I don't think I can find my way out of Tunisia alone."

"It's true, but I didn't want to influence your judgment," Max grunted. "All right, then that's decided, but listen to me." It was cold in the house, and the puffiness was still lodged behind his eyeballs; this time he was sure that he was running a fever. "I gave Black's plan a lot of thought last night. Although I am convinced that it cannot work, I agree with him that we cannot stay here without pressing our luck. Somebody is bound to discover our presence. I have no idea what game Emir is playing. Either he is one of our people or this operation was a trap from the start, but I do not believe this. Perhaps he can simply do no more—"

"Emir may be under arrest."

"Certainly. If so, we had better know about it and no longer count on him. For us, obviously nothing is safe—least of all, however, letting others make decisions first, which is what will happen if we foolishly stay here. At any rate, Emir is not coming back to this house; the contingency plan calls for us to fall back to the address he gave me in Sidi Bou Said, so this is what we must do."

"When do you want to leave?" Marston asked.

"Now."

"The police got a good look at us at the Africa. We'll be stopped at the first roadblock."

Max shook his head. "No we won't. The Army, not the police, will be watching traffic into Tunis, and they won't be looking for us; they will be looking for political enemies. The police have other problems; most of them are trying to prove they never collaborated with the old government, and this will distract them from their real work. Marston, all the rules are reversed during a putsch. *I* know. Provided that a man knows what he wants, keeps his head down and moves fast, he can get away with anything during the first twenty-four hours of a coup." He read the eternal skepticism on Marston's homely face. "If we are stopped, the Army at worst will be looking for Al Houaranni and three men who like like Tunisians and speak fluent Arabic; there will be no Al Houaranni, and only two foreigners who do not speak Arabic and whose papers in no way match the kidnappers'. We'll take back roads on Cap Bon, then abandon the car outside the city. If this proves impossible, we'll use other means, including our feet. How far is it to Tunis? Sixty miles? We'll hitchhike. It's risky, but there is no choice."

Marston half closed his left eye—the squint twisted his seamed face—and then pressed the palms of his stubby hands

244

together, as though he had something more to say—perhaps a prayer—but was encountering trouble formulating it.

"What other complications have you thought of?" Max asked him.

"Until we reach Tunis, the mere fact of being European will make us conspicuous."

"Do you prefer to have the Army come here?"

Marston grimaced. "I think risk is preferable to doing nothing. The car is ready. We can leave whenever you want."

Max was satisfied. In the split second that followed a decision you had a gut reaction that told you whether it was right or wrong. He felt absolutely sure that returning to Tunis was the right course of action.


For the first hour they encountered no sign of danger. It was a dry, clean winter morning, and the white back roads of Cap Bon crossed rolling country picked bare by sea winds. Flocks of sheep grazed on rocky downs. In the fields young Arab girls bore jugs of water. In this unchanging landscape it required an effort to believe in the reality of the coup or, come to think of it, the kidnapping.

They passed somnolent hamlets where burnoused men squatted in sunny doorways. The inhabitants lifted bilious yellow eyes as the Peugeot churned up dust from the unpaved streets and sped away into the distance.

Then it was open country again, brown and green, like figs, the monotony broken by stone wells and rows of eucalyptus trees. It was like Spain, the leopard skin of earth sloping off successively into long, tilled valleys, then rising again to meet the foothills of bluish mountain ranges. Along the road the young eucalyptus trees rippled and shimmered like silvery sardines in the flowing, honey-clear wind. Presently they drove past a citrus cooperative. Max watched the dark-green orange groves pulsating in the sunlight.

He asked curiously, "What did you think of Tunis, Marston? After all these years?"

"Just another scurvy Arab town." Marston glanced at the trees without interest.

"This countryside is like Emek Hefer."

Marston grunted but did not respond. He was, Max thought with disappointment and pride, as practical as a camel trader. Past a certain point, who knew what moved Marston? Few emotions—and these, neat and austere—sparked that frugal heart.

Finally, Max tapped Marston's shoulder. Ahead, for the first time, was traffic: pickup trucks, donkey carts, gray little burros on which jounced Arab women and children, pedestrians making their way beside a ditch. Thirty yards farther on, the road curved out of sight. Through an olive grove could be glimpsed square whitewashed houses.

Marston brought the car to a gentle stop on the dirt shoulder.

"Give me ten minutes," Max said. He got out and started on foot down the road.

He adapted his pace to that of the men who were ambling in cheap shoes under the eucalyptus trees, looking neither to left nor right, displaying Arab indifference to their surroundings.

He came around the bend past the last row of feathery olive trees and saw the village in its entirety—a white blot set in the midst of tawny tableland stretched over dry folds of ravine and gully. The unrepaired road wound between houses of uni-

246

form height, then described another curve and disappeared beyond the last habitation.

Nothing singled out this village from a dozen others, but his instinct had been right. Halfway down the road was erected a primitive barrier of felled tree branches, boards and oil drums. A scarlet Tunisian flag fluttered from a pole propped upright between two drums. A space at either side of the roadblock permitted vehicles and pedestrians to pass after being checked out. Young soldiers in battle dress were doing the checking. An altercation was going on with an old, emaciated man in burnous and sandals who had no identity papers. From their windows village women enjoyed the dispute, while screaming barefoot brown children darted scot-free around the roadblock. Finally the old man was allowed to proceed. Max lingered a few seconds longer, watching the way the Army was running the checkpoint. No one bothered with him—a balding, stolid figure in dusty jacket and pants, he fitted into the street scene. Motor traffic was light, and the soldiers were letting each vehicle pass after a few cursory questions. The mood was as excitable and friendly as at a country fair; the villagers obviously approved of the coup. As Max had expected, no gray uniforms of the Garde National were in sight.

Upon returning to the car, he told Marston what he had seen, then added, "They're not looking for us."

"Still, we have to get past that checkpoint."

Max studied Marston's unmemorable, sallow face and felt reasonably certain that he could get past the soldiers. As for himself, there was a danger that he might be recognized, but about this eventuality he was fatalistic.

"We'd better separate for the time being. I'll take the car

247

through and wait for you on the far side of the village."

"The car's been my problem ever since we came to Tunisia, Captain."

"Are you sure you want to?"

"I don't want to, but I'll take the chance."

"You don't have a gun any more," Max said worriedly. "I can give you Black's and half of my ammunition."

"Either I get through or I don't. A gun won't help. What about you?"

"If necessary, I'll shoot and try to make it to the car." As a final precaution he asked, "Have you destroyed everything that connected you with Flood?"

"Everything but my face and my fingerprints on that policeman's throat."

A few seconds later, Max watched the dust-smeared Peugeot with the phony number pick up speed down the road past the olive groves and disappear around the bend into the village.

It was nine o'clock now. By the time Max re-entered the village, traffic had grown heavy and vehicles were backed up along the main street, waiting their turn at the roadblock. The inspection procedure was taking longer than before. The sun beat down on the broken street and blanched houses. As the congestion grew, the mood became less friendly. A truck driver sounded his horn long and wrathfully; another imitated him. At first, the soldiers took no notice of the caterwauling, but then suddenly a broad-shouldered sergeant spat into the dust, strode up measuredly to the truck that had begun the racket, wrenched the cab door open and ordered the driver to climb out and follow him. Instantly the other vehicles fell silent.

On foot, Max approached the row of oil drums where pedestrians were being checked out. He was close on the heels of a family of three men and four women who were stolidly toting a miscellany of indefinable junk in wicker baskets and voluminous cardboard boxes. Deliberately he prepared the green passport in his pocket for inspection. Suppose the soldiers expressed surprise at his presence alone and without transportation in the middle of the Tunisian countryside. He knew that his voice would come out right—forceful and guttural, a bit on the overbearing side, the tone a German businessman adopts among inferiors—and his explanation was ready: his car was laid up for repairs in another village. It was unlikely that they would want to go to the bother of verifying that harmless story.

Two soldiers with slung rifles had approached the Peugeot. One accepted Marston's French passport, leafed through the pages and was about to wave the car on when the burly sergeant who had silenced the truck driver came up and, indicating Marston's passport, motioned to him to step out of the car. Over Marston's protests the two soldiers began to search him. Max's puzzlement turned to relief. What could they find that was out of order? If they suspected that Marston was in reality a Tunisian, they were barking up the wrong tree. Marston looked Arab, to be sure, but the passport was his, at least so far as the Army could prove, and he could put up a convincing demonstration of being a Frenchman. Then, with a feeling of hollow, sick helplessness, Max saw the first soldier frowning over the contents of Marston's wallet. The second soldier came around and frowned too. Marston vigorously shook his head in denial, but the two soldiers, their faces dark with distrust, were no longer in a mood to listen.

The sergeant stabbed his finger accusingly at something they had discovered—a small plastic-sheathed square. Max swore violently under his breath; he quickly went down a mental checklist of his own belongings. No, he had torn up the Interior Ministry pass Emir had provided, but Marston—Marston, who was a model of meticulousness and foresight—had forgotten to get rid of his. It was a self-sprung trap. The revolutionary soldiers could not know—and Marston could not admit to them—that the stamped and countersigned pass was unauthorized, useful only for kidnapping a Palestinian terrorist; in their eyes, it was bona fide and the bearer was a police officer of the old regime who inexplicably possessed a French passport. Or, if he was French, what was he doing with an Interior Ministry pass? Either discrepancy was enough to hold and interrogate him. Running ahead, the sergeant brushed past Max and shouted in his excitement a few incomprehensible words; behind, Marston was escorted at rifle point to the police station on the near side of the roadblock. Max caught a glimpse of his white face before he disappeared into the building; the fierce, friendless eyes stared straight ahead, seeking out no one in the street.

The village was aboil with excitement. It was the first time that the soldiers had detained a suspect. The startled crowd did not understand why the slight dark-skinned man had been taken into custody, but it had formed an inquisitive semicircle around the Peugeot. Only one sentry remained on duty by the oil drums. The family with all their belongings and baggage were checked out. Max moved forward. A soldier had sat down behind the Peugeot's wheel and begun turning the ignition on and off, trying to move the car to the side of the road. The sentry at the curb had turned to watch what was happening. Swiftly, Max stepped past his broad uniformed back. He expected someone to shout after him but no one did, and when he glanced up he was past the checkpoint. In a moment he had caught up with the family who were struggling with their clumsy loads in dispersed order up the street; to anyone who gazed in their direction it would seem that Max was part of the group. A hundred yards farther on, the village ended. The scarred landscape dotted by dark tufts of pines and lighter flecks of silvery hoary olive trees resumed.

Max hurried out into the open country, the blood beating furiously at his temples. He had not stopped to think; he had moved forward instinctively because the guard's attention was diverted and the opportunity existed of escaping. For the moment he could not dwell on what had befallen Marston; he must concentrate on his own safety. He had a grinding head-ache, but one essential fact stood out stark clear in his mind: ever since the moment they had landed at the airport—in fact, still earlier, perhaps on that morning when he perceived the scrap of unattainable sky from the General's window—he had realized that they were blundering into a maze. They had done so, as one did most things in life, deluded by appalling ignorance, without sufficient distrust. But he remained per-uaded that, as any mathematical problem contains its own solution, a way out of the maze existed. Only he had not found it yet.

The family had disappeared over the horizon.

Max broke into a run.

## CHAPTER FIFTEEN
# The Boy of Splendor

B LACK stole into Qelibia an hour after dawn. He struck off
from the main road and found himself in a labyrinth of
side alleys that twisted back crazily upon one another. He was
intent upon making his way unnoticed to the port. However,
he had not the faintest idea which turning to take, and he did
not dare ask directions. Shortly he came upon an empty lot
from which could be seen the ultramarine sparkle of the sea.
He plunged down a narrow passageway.

To reach Qelibia, Black had skirted the coast highway,
moving within a fringe of eucalyptus woods that bordered the
road, striding easily on the long serpentines of papery bark that
littered the ground around the tall, ancient sweet-smelling
trees. He came to an unforested stretch of road, where he
paused and listened for the sound of approaching vehicles
when he heard none, he ran in the predawn cool to the next
clump of eucalyptus. Once, as he trotted past a mud-walled
farmyard, a chained dog yelped at him, but after a while the
querulous barking died out and was not taken up by other
dogs in the vicinity.

252

Black had a supple, rangy gait; he moved fast on his tall body and he enjoyed the dash through the fresh, winter dark. He did not feel particularly tired. He had slipped out of the house with a walletful of Tunisian dinars in his pants pocket, the false German passport buttoned into his shirt breast pocket, and Marston's Beretta stuck into his belt under his jacket. Whatever else he needed could be requisitioned en route, he thought, and felt the Beretta's reassuring weight against his belly.

As he picked his way through the wood, Black experienced an abrupt sensation of freedom and his heart lifted. Levanon's ghetto fretfulness and Marston's inbred submissiveness were receding into the past. He had had enough sense to part company with two *meshuggeners*, two born dreamers who were cornered by their illusions into a desperate situation. Marston was handy and tough but hamstrung by his sense of duty; Levanon had a bolder imagination but he was disabled by middle-aged caution. Running out on them was not desertion; it was a measure of self-defense.

Black hurried unchallenged down a long, powdery street, overflowing, it seemed, with Tunisian school children, caramel-colored little girls in pink smocks, clay-colored boys in blue smocks. Impoverished huts drowsed in early-morning silence. An open drain reeked in his path. Then under an archway he came into a square that resounded with cheerful activity. A bearded old man haggled over a pan of sardines with a grocer. From a cavernous stall came the tap of a carpenter's hammer banging nails into a board. A weaver squatted in a doorway before a round loom; at his feet a teapot bubbled on a *kamoun* heaped with embers. Here, in this sensible neighborhood, all was normal; the coup had not yet

253

interfered with daily life. As Black hastened around another corner, a naked child stared at him with curiosity from a fetid courtyard, then disappeared brusquely into a dark interior.

Emerging from the warren of passageways, he looked out for the first time upon the harbor. The sun rode low like a fiery apple in the wan sky and the last stars had vanished. The *lamparo* fleet was long since in, its lights extinguished, but a few fishermen were walking up the jetty three abreast carrying trays of sardines and mackerel. Black sniffed the wind blowing from the southwest and thought that it was going to be a fair, bland day.

Through the window of a waterfront café near the Fisheries Office, he saw Arabs seated about a radio set turned full on from which tumbled an avalanche of guttural announcements. Black recognized the news. He smiled sourly and went on.

At the docks, he counted up the fishing boats. There were all together, several dozen; none was of Italian registry. He was sure that Italian boats did cross to Qelibia, but the sailing times must be subject to weather and inclination, and always at the mercy of abrupt cancellations. To reach Pantelleria, he would have to make his own arrangements.

Black walked past the docks where the *lamparos* with their twin oil lanterns were tied up. Two late boats glided into the harbor as silently as swans; only as they cleared the break-water could you hear the purring of their engines. A boy stood up in the bow of the lead boat, ready to make fast. Farther along the quay, a Swedish crew was noisily making repairs on a freighter from Göteborg. A Sudanese boy dived into the viscous water and reappeared grinning alongside the bow

Black squatted on the pier, smoked a cigarette and examined the green, blue and white fishing boats. Their gunwales were as gaily painted as Sicilian carts. Fish boxes were stacked forward to dry; nets were folded and ropes were coiled neatly above the cabin houses. The crews were off somewhere, except for one old fisherman in a straw hat. He stood midships in a lateen-rigged boat whose cords were frayed and whose triangular sail had been patched too often; the boat was small, but nonetheless it looked seaworthy, and it boasted a 40-hp outboard which was canted out of the water. The old man was stumpy and bowlegged, and in the ravined face the sunken eyes shone with bad temper. He wore a checked shirt and faded khaki shorts and a wide-brimmed straw hat almost as high-peaked as a sombrero. The hat, together with a black, flourishing mustache, gave the old man a fierce Mexican look. When he removed the hat, his hair had the flat shiny quality of hammered tin foil. His forearms were tattooed with stars and burned to a toast-brown, like a lifeguard's. Black noted that the wrists were hairy and powerful. Slowly the old man wrung out a pair of black pants and an undershirt in a pail of water and hung them on a line. Then he wrapped a bluefish in a newspaper, clapped his hat back on, seized a wicker basket and clambered onto the pier.

Black followed the old man down the dock past the Swedish freighter and the tied-up *lamparo* boats. The old man cried out something unintelligible to several fishermen on the pier; when he reached the waterfront café he made for the beach to the right and plodded down the shore. The insignificant tide was running out; worn rocks slumbered in the sun like old lions and on the spongy gray sand lay exposed a carpet of seashells. The foreshore was littered with rusting

cans and misshapen pieces of driftwood from which rivulets
of machine oil dripped and formed shiny viscous black pools
that seeped into the sand. The old man proceeded stolidly past
a row of untidy bungalows, then the silted-up garden of a
two-story brick house with broken windows, whose cracked
concrete walk led down to the water. Soon, although they were
less than a half mile from the harbor, the shore grew uninhabited and wild. Abruptly, the old man turned around and
stared at Black. Black flapped his hand in desultory greeting.
The old man turned and shuffled onward, paying him no further attention. Black waited for him to proceed; he stooped
and selected a flat, smooth stone, which he sent skimming
across the water's surface, watching it skip forward three times
before it sank with a plop for good. It reminded him of
August vacations on Long Island. A gull cried overhead and
flew on its way toward the open sea.

After a few moments, Black shook the sand from his shoes
and resumed his pursuit. The old man was already far off, and
Black had to lengthen his stride to keep him in view. In the
distance there was a single habitation, a clapboard shack with
a roof of palm fronds built back from the beach on a sandy
rise strewn with dune grass. Without a backward glance, the
old man disappeared behind the tar-paper door.

Black gave himself five minutes. He saw no one coming up
the shore. Gripping the pistol under his jacket, he pushed
open the door without knocking.

In the gloom of a small room the old man was bent over
a wooden table on which was spread out the newspaper containing the fish. He had removed his hat.

"What do you want? Why are you following me?" he
snarled, eyes fierce, stupid and yellow.

Kicking the door shut, Black pointed the Beretta at the old man's heart.

"Cry and you die a merciful death," he said with effortless transition to Arabic hyperbole. His eyes were adjusting to the semidark and he distinguished the cot, the shelves, the Coleman burner, which comprised the old man's possessions. No sign indicated the presence of another human being in the shack.

"You must take me to Pantelleria for nine hundred dinars," he said simply.

As he had intended, the sum struck off a brief, incredulous spark in the old man's sunken malarial eyes.

"Then why do you point the gun at me?" he muttered.

"To make sure that you accept."

"It is forbidden to leave port today." The eyes were dull and disinterested again, and the old man made an upward tossing movement of his head, in Arab fashion, to reiterate negation.

"Stand up straight," Black ordered him. "Face me without flinching and tell me it is impossible. Recite the reasons and make them plausible. I disbelieve every word you utter."

"The harbor master . . . the Navy . . ." he recited, scowling in powerless fury.

"The Navy is nowhere near the harbor entrance, as you well know. Why are you lying?"

"There is a heavy fine," the old man moaned, exhibiting sordid uneven teeth.

"And more dinars than you earn in a year to pay it with. Do you never break the law, old scoundrel? I am giving you an opportunity to enrich this dried-up, miserable, cheating body. Put your hat back on; make sure to bring enough drinking water—it is a long, thirsty crossing."

The old man did not leave his safe position behind the table. "When the harbor master discovers a boat is missing," he whined, "I will be shot."

Brusquely, Black waved his gun, and the old man bleated.

"Nine hundred dinars—everything I have! Old man, did you hear? I could compel you to do it for nothing," Black observed.

When he spoke, the old man's voice had lost its burr of stiff rage. "You have this much money, or is it a mere promise?"

"One-third of what is due when the breakwater is cleared; one-third when no land is in sight; the rest when I land. You will earn all this in a few hours," he emphasized.

"We will be prevented from sailing."

"Tell this tale to children. The harbor police are busy elsewhere today."

"I have gas only to clear the port."

"You have a sail and the wind can be caught off the point. See? If you do not handle the boat properly, I will be aware of your treachery."

"How am I to get back without gas?"

"You will buy gas in Pantelleria with the money I give you, and pray that the wind holds. What makes you such a coward?"

A snakelike black gleam of animosity showed in the old man's pupils. "I am no coward but you are a foreigner— perhaps it is a trap?"

Black pointed with grim coldness to the door.

Grumbling, the old man put his hat back on and stepped out, pausing to gather up two earthenware jugs of water that stood cooling in the shade under the overhang of the thatched roof.

Black covered him with the gun carefully as they descended through the silky grass in the direction of the port.

The old man asked without turning around, "Why do you—a foreigner—want to sail secretly to Pantelleria?"

"Damn you!" snapped Black. "Do as you are told without asking so many questions. And when we come to the port, be careful not to try to trick me. You will not be the first Arab I have shot."

During the first hour aboard the boat Black learned that the old man's name was Ahmed, that he was sixty-three and a widower whose children were inattentive to his needs and lived far from him. Black listened to these domestic details without enthusiasm, but the story helped while away the time, which, after the tension of clearing the harbor, he found to be long. Ahmed volunteered information about himself in declamatory gesticulating sentences that collapsed in midpassage when he lost the train of thought and were eked out by steadfast savage spitting.

Black stood midships and kept an eye on the old man, who was in the stern, steering. The sea was listless, traversed by a mild westerly breeze that drove scraps of cloud rapidly across the sky. Black balanced his body against the boat's gentle roll, his luxuriant somber whiskers prickling in the salt-flecked breeze. From time to time the breeze propelled Ahmed's faded almond smell his way, and he sniffed the odor curiously. After a while, Black thought of the red-haired girl in Rome, whose mane whipped about her soft, nervous features as she writhed complacently on the dance floor; he would have enjoyed planking her right now, on deck. Then this pleasant fantasy was spoiled by a peevish query from the stern.

"Sidi, where is the money?"

Black glared at the old man's brick-hued neck. "How much longer to Pantelleria?" he snapped.

Ahmed turned up the whites of his furious eyes and tasted the spittle on his gray lips. He muttered, "Three hours if no storm comes."

"Bullshit! The horizon is clean." Black was beside himself at the old man's cantankerousness; he was ridden with as many grievances as fleabites. With reluctance Black fought down a keen desire to choke him there and then. "Sail now, pay later," he mumbled.

Ahmed wailed in dismay. "I do not understand. Can you not pay? Have you no money? Are you dishonoring your promise?"

"Forget it." Black kept the gun trained as he searched for his wallet and clumsily extracted part of the much-rubbed and -folded bank notes. He crumpled them into a ball and watched the old man narrowly. Propping his brown splayed toes against the tiller to keep it firm against the swell, Ahmed used both hands to unfold and count out the notes before buttoning them into his shirt pocket. "This is only one-third," he objected surlily.

Black was enjoying himself. "Do you deserve more for being so unreliable? Have we lost sight of land yet?"

"In a moment's time, Sidi; I solemnly promise it!"

The old man made no further request and began to croon

an Egyptian love song to himself in a reedy senile singsong.

Black shook his head, bemused. In these countries money really did smell; the bank notes were slippery from being manipulated by so many unwashed callused fingers, and a packet gave out a faint odor of grease, stomach-turning if you were on the alert for it.

Clearing the harbor had proved to be child's play. When they had returned to the docks, the last of the returning *lamparos* had made fast and the fishermen had sold their catch and trudged off to the waterfront café. Over the idle port brooded winter-morning silence. They had boarded the boat without witnesses; the old man had lifted anchor, then the boat glided, its outboard sputtering faintly, into the middle of the basin. The harbor master's office, from which sprouted a tall, needlelike radio aerial, stood directly opposite. Black's grip tightened on the Beretta as he watched for signs of activity around the patrol launch moored in the berth alongside, but no one took notice of them. Then they had slipped down the channel toward the harbor mouth, the old man grunting unremittingly but his brown wrist steady on the tiller. For good measure, Black nudged the Beretta into his rib cage. Abeam of the harbor lights Ahmed suddenly stood up and Black just as quickly ordered him to sit down. Then his heart stopped when he saw a boy on a bicycle speeding down to the docks; at the last moment, however, the boy braked sharply, dismounted and strode off without a glance in their direction. In no time at all they had rounded the cape and were out of sight of the port. The last Black saw of Qelibia was the crenelated ocher fortress on the crest of the hill.

The silver-blue water smacked gently against the keel; the wind filled the triangular sail and drew it taut. It was nine

261

o'clock. As far as the eye could see, they were alone. By noon, at latest, they should make landfall. Levanon had erred in not staking everything on an escape by sea. With an ounce more daring the commando would still be together, but after Al Houaranni's death it had been impossible to communicate with Levanon. Black stirred and shifted the pistol from one fist to the other. Interrelated images dissolved through his mind of Al Houaranni in the hotel elevator, shackled to the bedpost, then finally on the dark beach. Operation Flood's main objective had been achieved, whether or not in a manner the General would approve. And it seemed, now, to Black that Al Houaranni's murder had been inevitable; had he not squeezed the trigger, another avenger would have: retribution had buzzed about that scrawny neck like a tenacious wasp.

A grin softened Black's features. Here he was, the Blade of Allah's executioner, in a small boat beside a Tunisian fisherman, bound for a semitropical Italian island, with the entire outraged Arab world in pursuit. There were classmates in New York who would be devoured by envy.

The coast was invisible; the safe-house, the Peugeot, the tank convoys had dropped beneath the horizon. He wondered where Levanon and Marston were at this moment and how they were faring. In field operations men of varied competence were flung together, shared intense experiences and underwent common danger, then were separated; if they were realistic, they made no attempt to extend the brittle relationship. He thought ahead to what he would tell the Italian authorities on the island when he landed as a baggageless tourist. His claim to American citizenship would be difficult to reconcile with a German passport; of course, once the

Consulate became involved, he would have to tell part of the truth—a very small part, he decided.

He heard the sudden drone of a motor and, looking up, saw that it was a yellow plane with civilian markings coming in low, buzzing the boat. Then it flew off and did not return.

"If that happens again, wave to it as though you have nothing to hide," he instructed the old man.

Ahmed kept silent for a while, then asked abruptly, "Are you a Jew?"

"Or maybe Russian? Or Chinese? No, for your information, my name is Horstmann and I am from Düsseldorf." He found it hard to tell whether the old man believed this.

Imperceptibly the sun had climbed high into the vaporous sky and Black stifled a yawn. He had not slept in two nights. By now they were well out of territorial waters. He sat down and reclined his head against the cockpit. Nothing alarming was happening abroad, and since the plane's departure it was very silent in the Gulf. He was becoming bored.

For the past hour, Ahmed had covertly studied this foreigner's movements and appearance—the raffish oily head, flaring nose and dark, sorrowful Arab eyes. French and Arabic newspapers from Tunis, sometimes recent, sometimes weeks old, drifted into the old man's possession, and were precious; as a rule he smoothed out all but the greasiest and foulest copies on his plank table and painstakingly read the contents, pausing over the difficult words in both languages. He was curious about what went on in the capital, and from his dutiful reading and listening to café conversations he managed to be relatively well informed. He knew, for example,

263

that several days earlier in the heart of Tunis three Zionist terrorists had kidnapped an important and powerful Arab chieftain from the Mishrak lands. That this action could be carried out with impunity provoked in him less a sense of patriotic indignation than sheer wonderment, for he had a respectful opinion of the Tunisian police. Then this tall, unshaven, nervous foreigner had, as though in a bad dream, bullied and bribed his way aboard his boat. It did not take much concentration to link the two developments in the old man's irritable mind.

Yes, his passenger was a kidnapping, gun-brandishing *Yhoud*. And so desperate was he to sail illegally from Tunisia that he was ready to pay a ridiculously high sum for passage. This was the detail that disturbed Ahmed most. Had the foreigner merely poked a gun into his side and ordered him to sail to Pantelleria, he would have fatalistically complied; it was a crossing he had made often as a younger man, and there was no arguing with a weapon such as the Italian gun. But the mention of money was unfathomable and had set demons to work in his mind. Everything else beside the money dwindled into insignificance. At first, he had suspected the *Yhoud* of outright lying. Who but a madman carries a fortune of nine hundred dinars in his pocket? Then, to his stupefaction, he had received one-third of the promised sum. Now he was no longer so ready to transport his unwanted passenger across the Gulf. The old man set no stock in the *roumi*'s promise; experience taught that a *roumi*'s promise tended to be elastic. Upon making landfall there was no guarantee he would hand over the remaining six hundred dinars. Ahmed groaned inwardly with repressed longing and cupidity. Nine hundred dinars represented a half year's hard work, rising in winter before dawn and rousing his aging body into life over the heatless glow of a bed of charcoal embers; then, after six hours at sea, often returning to port frustrated, arms and shoulders aching, while other, younger men slipped into the café and gulped a glass of raw fig brandy. The money was there, tantalizingly close, in the *Yhoud*'s pants pocket, but how to grab it? The gun was in the way. In the man's fist, it looked enormous and ugly.

Ahmed stared miserably at the horizon. His mind was riveted on the gun and the money. It was obvious that to secure one he must seize the other.

After a while, hearing no sound, he glanced about and his yellow eyes widened in astonishment. The foreigner had sat down and fallen asleep. Or was it another trick?

Very carefully the old man brought the boat about and trimmed the sail. For several breathless seconds he considered his passenger. When he was satisfied that the drowsy figure presented no danger, he abandoned the tiller and crept toward him on bare feet. The gun gleamed slick and tempting in the sunlight and Ahmed put out his hand tentatively, as a baby does for a toy. But just then, as the boat rolled to meet a long, lazy comber, the *Yhoud*'s hard-featured, sunburned head snapped upward and his wrathful eyes glared devilishly at Ahmed.

Black sprang to his feet and glanced wildly about. The old man crouched in an awkward stoop ten feet away.

Bracing against the boat's easy sway, Black took deliberate aim with the Beretta and announced, "I am going to kill you."

"Sidi!"

"What sort of fish will eat your insides out in these waters?" Black shouted.

"I could not resist. I wanted to be rich and splendid like you and die in comfort!"

"Die you will, and soon, but when, I will decide. Get back to the tiller, son of a bitch!"

With a terrible expression and a crablike sideways movement the old man rapidly scuttered away, groped for the tiller and undid the rope.

"Keep an eye out where you are sailing, *Kelb*. I can shoot you in front or back!"

Black was quivering with rage, and his lips were white and strained as when he had opened fire on Al Houaranni. He must have dozed off a few seconds; he sensed a fundamental change aboard and regretted that he had not handled the tiller himself. Suspiciously he glanced up: the boat's rig was the same, the sail—

"Where are you bearing?" he screamed and pointed at the sun. "You are sailing west!"

The old man was trembling uncontrollably, and a prolonged, doleful moan escaped through his bleached split lips. The trembling was not caused by the reason Black suspected. Ahmed had formed an unflattering opinion of the foreigner's manliness and thought him incapable of perpetrating cold-blooded murder that would leave him helpless in the empty sea. If the old man was trembling, it was because his birdlike greedy eye had roamed over the deck and lit on an object that lay next to the *Yhoud*. Ahmed knew exactly what he must do to separate, once and for all, the money from the gun. But he had to do it just right and the idea was actually inducing nausea.

"Not west, Sidi!" he screeched, finding his voice. "Look again at the sun!"

Black glanced up and was momentarily dazzled by the glare. With a curse the old man shoved the tiller out as hard as he could. Black dodged the boom but it struck him a violent blow on the shoulder. He shouted and automatically fired, but the shot went wild and thudded into the planking. Bitterly Ahmed yanked on the end of the rope that lay coiled serpent-like at the *Yhoud*'s feet. Black stumbled, the Beretta rolled down the deck and Ahmed swiftly snatched it up. He squeezed the trigger deliriously and, flabbergasted, watched the foreigner clap his hand over his forehead and topple headlong to the deck. Then Ahmed kept firing point-blank with accumulated ferocity at the thrashing figure until it moved no more. He rushed forward, knelt and began fumbling greedily through the foreigner's clothes, ignoring the blood that was running over his wrists. Finally his groping fingers encountered a flat, leathery thickness alongside the dead man's hip. Disregarding the proximity of the *Yhoud*'s head, he unbuttoned the pocket and withdrew a limp cheap billfold. Inside the vent were dinar notes. Ahmed counted them, frowning; he repeated the addition, to make sure, then rapidly stuffed the money into his shirt pocket. What was left amounted to no more than one hundred dinars.

Quickly rising, he looked about. The horizon was gray and empty. He seized the sunburned dead man by the armpits and propped him in a sitting position against the gunwale. He stepped around, lifted one of the foreigner's stiff legs, examined the scuffed shoes and decided against removing them. Instead, he swung the legs about so that they hung overboard. Then Ahmed paused to wipe the sweat from his brow. He was conscious of the flapping sail and the boom swinging to and fro. Attacking the powerful back, he pushed and nudged it upward until finally, with slow, dignified solemnity, the body leaned forward and plunged overboard in a heap.

*Allah yarhamou*, God have pity on his soul!

The boat was drifting eastward. Without pausing Ahmed tacked and passed the spot where Black had vanished. For a moment, when the doubled-up body crashed out of sight, the water had seethed as brown as when the great springtime killing of tuna took place up north, at Sidi Daoud.

But now the water was deep blue and unsullied again. Before setting course for Qelibia, he would bring out the scoop from the cockpit and rinse the circles the blood had made when it spurted into the wood. On the way back, he would invent a tale for the authorities to justify his going to sea that would omit all reference to money.

Ahmed set to work. His lip curled in disdain. Four hundred dinars altogether . . . from start to finish the *Yhou* had lied.

## CHAPTER SIXTEEN

# A Tunisian Love Affair

No names of the Committee have been made public; we have an informal idea who they are, but no confirma-on." Mills leaned back in his chair and stopped typing. It's all the more pity under the circumstances that your good iend the colonel is out of circulation; he could have pro-ded some of the answers."

"Would he have?"

"I think so. A few seconds ago, I was wondering whether tried to reach the Embassy—"

"From what I've been able to reconstitute, he wanted to get the presidential palace; but it's really immaterial at this age."

And that was Kheli's only epitaph.

Upon speeding back to the Embassy the evening before, eston had briefed Mills on his conversation with Gauthier; en he had telephoned the colonel's office, but by that time the terior Ministry was no longer accepting calls or furnishing formation about its personnel; then Preston had tried neli's home number, and a woman's voice had replied in broken French that the colonel was absent, then she had hung up.

All they knew of the colonel's movements was that at six forty-five that evening he had telephoned the Embassy, and in Preston's absence left a brief, cryptic message. The message said simply that he had received important information that needed to be verified at once; he had promised to call again later, but had never done so. The time-group indicated that the colonel had learned that the coup was about to take place. What had happened at that point? The colonel had been seen shortly afterward leaving the Ministry escorted by three young Army officers with whom he entered a waiting car and drove off; then he had been seen no more.

Throughout the remainder of that unpredictable night Mills had worked. He had started typing a report that gave facts and eschewed prophecy. Pat brought in a thermos bottle of hot coffee and stood beside his desk waiting for each take, which she bore to the cable room, from which it was radioed encoded on a Flash Number One priority to the Watch Committee at Langley. In the Political Section, lights were likewise on and typewriters were clattering. Numerous cars drove into the compound; among the arrivals were several foreign ambassadors who had come to seek an American reaction and interpretation before drafting a report on the coup for their own governments.

Now it was a half hour past dawn, and the sky was brightening rosily over the city.

Preston said, "I've asked for an immediate meeting with Fawzi."

Mills nodded and continued to type. "Did you get it?"

"No luck so far."

"What did Fawzi tell you?"

"Someone in his office said they'd get back to me when it's practical."

"Keep after him without making commitments. If his heart's in the right place, which I doubt, he'll want to make it perfectly clear without losing time that new friends can be as valuable as old ones."

Looking tousled but durable, like a girl who has spent the night winning steadily but with difficulty at poker, Pat stepped into the office. She said, "The British are on the line. Do you want to talk to them?"

Mills picked up the phone. It was not a long conversation; Mills mostly listened, nodding. Then he said to Preston, "They've found Kheli's body in a ditch beside the airport road .. machine-gunned to death."

At that bleak postdawn hour, Preston thought of the colonel with whom he had worked and relaxed throughout a difficult year; now, his expertise was missing, which was the sincerest tribute one could pay him. However, there was the still unsolved riddle of the lake road attack; had it been the colonel's final, unaccountable move before he fell victim to the coup? Preston hoped not.

Mills was honestly appalled. "It's just sheer murder. Of course, as Secret Police chief, he was a prime target. Eric Morton said he thought I would want to know at once."

Pat re-entered the office. "I'm getting through again to the Interior Ministry."

Preston took the phone. "Captain Fawzi?"

There was rapid, frantic breathing on the line, followed by

a series of clicks and guttural shouts, then a man's voice said with pronounced coldness, "This is Fawzi. What is it?"

"We understand that Colonel Kheli is dead. Are you replacing him?"

"The colonel is in custody and will account for his actions before a democratically constituted court. His death is a rumor spread by Western newsmen. Meanwhile, yes, I am in charge."

"Under the Liaison Agreement I should like to meet with you as rapidly as possible."

"You will have to wait your turn, like the other services. We are giving priority to liberating the ministries of unreliable, counterrevolutionary personnel."

"When do you think our turn is likely to come? This is an official request."

"I am aware of that. Perhaps this afternoon—certainly not before. The Committee has denounced the Liaison Agreement; it is no longer valid."

Mills had been eavesdropping on the conversation on the other receiver. "They're aping the Libyans," he said equably. "It's no worse than I expected."

"He probably has the Chinese attaché in his office right now."

"The Chinese won't buy their olives." Mills brushed back his thick hair with the flat of his hands. "Well, we'll have to deal with the captain from now on. He asked us once for training in G-2 and was turned down—then he became assistant chief of Secret Police. When you have one of those, it's an uphill struggle all the way."

"He's smarter than I gave him credit for—from captain to

colonel overnight isn't bad. Maybe," Preston said, "the job will prove too big for him?"

"Don't nurture that idea. This place is a paradise for conspirators like Fawzi. On the other hand, I don't take too tragically the annulment of the Liaison Agreement. If the Committee starts to play that way, it could hold up recognition, and I seriously doubt whether they want *that*."

"At least, he said that Kheli isn't dead. I still don't understand the colonel's role in the Al Houaranni affair."

Mills looked at him curiously. "Forget Al Houaranni. Fawzi has, I'm sure, and we were never terribly interested, except insofar as it affected the previous regime's life expectancy. Al Houaranni could be a red herring. Concentrate on the Army—they're the group we'll have to do business with in future."

It was a translucent hour of the morning when Preston's imagination stirred. "I wonder what happened to Gauthier's agents? Sweating out a bungled operation, with an entire country baying at their heels and no one really giving a damn . . ."

"I've been in that position myself," said Mills, without further explanation.


Raouad Beach has coarse sand but the view is marvelous— along this wind-whipped shore the thunder of the sea seldom ceases and the offing is vast. Anne-Marie had moved her car off the road and parked it on a sandy path that led down to the shore. From afar Preston saw her, slim, outwardly serene. She wore a tweed coat thrown over her shoulders and stood alone. When she turned, he saw that she was smiling.

She held him by the waist and looked up critically into his eyes.

"Did you have trouble driving out?"

She shook her head and continued to scrutinize him.

"I saw Alex yesterday evening," he said.

"He told me. Does it still matter terribly to you, finding Al Houaranni?"

"Finding out what happened to him, yes." As they descended to the beach together, his eyes went pale and humorless in the way she had noticed the summer before.

"For all your air of detachment, you're devoured by ambition. I suppose that it's a quality," Anne-Marie said doubtfully. Then she added, "I may not be able to leave Alex as soon as we planned."

He stopped short in his tracks, examined her face and saw that she was making an effort.

"Oh, I wanted to ask him for a divorce; I really tried," she exclaimed. "I was brought up that way. 'Never shirk a challenge'; my father drilled it into me as though I were a boy. I had it all so carefully prepared in my mind, just what I was going to say. From the moment I had lunch with you at Sidi Bou Said, it was all I thought about, and what I was going to do and say and the idea of being together with you for good afterward made sense and was absolutely right and just what I wanted. When I heard about the coup on the radio, I sensed that it was going to spoil my plans, although I told myself that was absurd. Then Alex came home, but he went out again right away and came back. I braced myself and saw the right moment—"

274

Preston did not like to dwell on disappointments. "There'll be another opportunity, Anne-Marie."

"No, listen, you don't understand. When he came home, he began by saying, 'Guess what? Earlier this evening I was drinking bad whiskey with your lover.'"

Preston shrugged.

"Then he continued: 'It is important, of course, but not so important as other things.' He was not angry, otherwise it would have made things easier. I literally did not know what to answer; you see, I had promised not to lie about us, and I had no wish to.

"'Have you heard the news?' he asked.

"'What difference does it make to us? Alex, you are over-committed——'

"He sat down on the sofa, stared at me and shook his head.

"'Why is it so important?' I asked. 'The coup is dangerous, I'm not minimizing that; but our lives amount to more, much more, than information.'"

Preston interrupted her. "You don't have to call it 'information.' I know about Alex's work; he knows about mine."

Anne-Marie smiled faintly. "Yes, he said to me: 'The CIA has become interested in my activities——'

"I asked: 'Is that what you are worried about? Is that what you mean by more important things?' Contrary to what I had intended, I was beginning to lose my poise. I thought that he was going to walk out of the room; instead, he sat there quietly for a while, smoking and looking at his hands. Then he said: 'Of course not. The essential fact is that the operation is a disaster. I am out of contact with the commandos. They are going to be captured or killed resisting capture, and it will be a memory I have to endure for the rest of my life. Do you understand why, under the circumstances, your American matters less to me than you?'

"'What is going to happen to us?' I asked him.

"'For the moment I am worried about their safety.'

"'Can't you do something—try anything—to save them?' I asked.

"'No, it is too late for neat little improvisations,' Alex said. Then he went up to bed. I never mentioned the word 'divorce.' How could I?" Her nails gouged Preston's palms. "What is happening to us? Why did it have to happen all at once in this way?"

"Don't overdramatize it."

"What is wrong with me? Why don't I do as I intend?"

"You'll tell him next time."

"I don't know." She stared at him. "I'm tied to Alex by the kidnapping. He wasn't responsible for what went wrong; I was. How do you think I feel?"

Anne-Marie shut her eyes. The beach was out there, glittering, blinding; so were Gammarth's white solid houses and jasmine-scented byways, but she saw how Tunisia's white could become black, as light and dark are reversed on a negative. Even the sun-filled lunch at Sidi Bou Said in retrospect seemed a preparation for a nightmare. She reopened her eyes.

"Better now?"

"Mmm."

"Do you know what I'm thinking?"

"If you're angry with me, I don't want to hear about it."

"That you don't love him but don't want to leave him."

"You're wrong." She stared at him as though he had uttered

a monstrous falsehood. "More than anything I want to go away with you." When she was with Preston, it was a sharp, fretting, painful happiness, as though her body no longer entirely belonged to her and could not be trusted; she liked the feeling, but when she thought of Alex her pleasure fled. "I do love you and nothing has changed, and I wish it had."

"I was also thinking that no two people could be closer than we were day before yesterday afternoon at my house."

"Then yesterday at Sidi Bou Said was not the same, is that it?"

"Yes."

"You were trying to be *malin* and find out things about Alex, and I was already nervous wondering how to tell him about us."

It struck Preston that summer was their inherent style; winter had not brought either of them much in the way of fulfillment. Like Tunisians they drew in upon themselves and hibernated, waiting for the advent of real warmth. "This is a Tunisian love affair if such a thing exists . . . everything in this country turns to sand."

"It's not true!" she exclaimed, disengaging herself from him.

## CHAPTER SEVENTEEN

# An Alien Shore

G AUTHIER sat trying to compose a lead for his paper about
the coup. The city was beset by cryptic rumors of
requisitions, internments, reversals of policy and repudiation
of heroes, but try to confirm the reports . . . The politics
were all wrong here: you tried to look through the show window and found your own reflection staring back from a
tarnished mirror. How could you cope with a streak of cruelty
that cropped out in the treatment they practiced on enemies, a
simple goodness that sometimes bowled one over, and an in-
eradicable flair for intrigue? They're always conniving, the
whole bloody lot, Gauthier thought, and so they can't imagine
your not conniving too. They can never accept an explanation
at face value, he concluded with rage—for never before in his
life had he so badly wanted his own fragile explanations to
go down without fuss.

The telephone rang. He hesitated and then finally lifted the
receiver.

"I am coming back." It was Levanon's voice, oddly streaked
with levity, as though he were sick or not in his right mind.

"Why?" It was the last thing Gauthier desired. There was no reason or need for the commando to return to Tunis; he had expected it to stay put at the safe-house—then he recalled giving Levanon the address of the atelier in Sidi Bou Said. Twenty-four hours ago it had seemed unthinkable that it would ever be used. He remained seated in his office, staring at the wall. "Yes, I suppose that is all you can do now. I am not trying to dissuade you, but you will have trouble entering the city. Troops are stationed at every approach and they are screening all incoming traffic." He made no attempt to suggest sympathy. When the Qiryat had informed him on the second night that the submarine would not surface, he had felt a sudden wrench of pain, as though someone had twisted a member and left him breathless with frustration. His faculty for inspiring others and communicating a sense of leadership had seemed to dry up forever at that moment.

"There is absolutely no choice," the voice insisted. "I am alone. Wave is dead."

Gauthier was far from sure that his telephone was not being tapped. He hesitated again, then asked unhelpfully, "Was it avoidable?"

"What do you think? I shall see you at the place we agreed upon this afternoon at four. Do you understand?" There was no further truce in Levanon's tone.

Gauthier clasped his hands and sat stock-still in the silent office. Levanon's information throbbed like a diseased tooth in his head. If Al Houaranni were dead and Levanon alone remained, what of the other two? Were they captured or dead? And how long would it be before Al Houaranni's death became known? Levanon had not made it clear. Presumably he would when they met. It promised to be a grim get-together darkened by one-sided recriminations. But who can blame him? Gauthier thought. His conduct is not at fault. If I had attended to my work and treated my son's sickly qualms with more composure, we would not be caught up in this disaster. What had been intended as solicitude was in effect a symptom of weakness. He understood that now. Each person harbored an invisible fissure—love and affection, for example, or pride—into which a dormant but destructive strain penetrated one day and did mortal damage. Was it just possible that in his case the moment had occurred without his realizing it?

Quickly he rose, grabbed his jacket and prepared to leave the office. He felt an overwhelming need to talk to someone, anyone, and drive the unhealthy notion from his mind. Then the telephone rang again and this time it was Darcy, the night editor, who was still on duty although his shift was over. "Do you know that the President has delegated his entire authority to the Committee? The wires are carrying it."

"Are you surprised? He had a choice of doing that or being shot; as it is, he's under house arrest."

"Under house arrest?" Gauthier could hear Darcy's labored, asthmatic breathing as he typed out a lead. "Why haven't you been in touch? What else is new down there?"

"I'll have a complete story for you in a half hour if I can get through. Outgoing calls and cables are temporarily suspended," Gauthier said dourly. But, he thought, his report would not include the news about Al Houaranni's death. What a fantastic story his paper could have had under different circumstances!

He struck off down Avenue Bourguiba. The tramways were stopped and few cars were in evidence. Tunis was dazed and apathetic after the night's disorders. Families had brought their children to inspect the damage; there was an instructive, graphic quality about the gutted window displays of Fath ties and *frivolités*, the derisory little piles of cobblestones hoarded in doorways. The Army had shown more competence than the demonstrators; it had struck at nightfall, maneuvered tanks up to a dozen key buildings and seized power with a minimum of agitation. There had been no speeches, no marches. It was ·a modern, computerized coup d'etat. But an Arab rising always has elements of a fete. Gauthier passed a weapons carrier whose idle crew were licking ice-cream cones and dangling their legs indolently in the sunlight against the armor plate. Down the avenue, soldiers were firing rounds of ammunition into the air with contagious enthusiasm, their excitement feeding on itself. The soldiers struck Gauthier as being drunk on that most potent of Arab alcohols, rhetoric. He saw few Europeans in the street. Tunisian women gathered outside a shut pharmacy muttered as he came abreast. A moment later a stone banged at his ankles. He whipped around but saw no one whom he could accuse. The stone had been flung contemptuously, as though to chase off a stray dog. This time they had made sure the stone did not hit him, but if the current mood persisted he knew that would change. The carefully learned lessons about courtesy to foreigners were swiftly forgotten. Xenophobia too was always an element of Arab coups.

A crowd was gathered around the Information Ministry, where two blue-eyed soldiers with submachine guns motioned passers-by away. The steel doors at the main entrance were bolted. Around the corner, Gauthier came upon a squirming, perspiring group of men and women who pushed forward and fell back with a tidal motion at a narrow side door. Using his height to advantage, he unmercifully nudged and prodded and forced his way up to the front rank. In the doorway, a lieutenant aided by a civilian in shirt sleeves was scrutinizing identity papers. Gauthier flourished his press card and was promptly admitted.

He clambered up a back staircase and hurried to the Press Department. Stillness and desolation engulfed these premises; the main corridor was dark. In the building's forlorn silence his heel clicks rang out too loud.

Then at the far end of the hall he heard a typewriter's brisk, sane clatter. He went in that direction and found installed in the Press Chief's office Zaki El Bahi, a loose-limbed, olive-skinned young man whom he had known in former days as a minor but helpful employee. El Bahi looked up from his typewriter and waved amicably. His shins were awash in overturned files; messages arrived in jerks and fits on a telex machine in one corner.

"Monsieur Gauthier, you are the first foreign correspondent to call on me. I am running the department singlehanded while we mobilize some secretaries. Help yourself to what is in that refrigerator—whiskey and fruit juice, I think. The swine who occupied this office made off with virtually everything else, but he was arrested last night at his brother-in-law's." While Gauthier brought out a bottle of Scotch and poured a measure into a glass, El Bahi finished his report, signed it with an elaborate paraph and sealed it into a Ministry envelope. Then he looked up intently. "I must tell you first of all that organized resistance has ended. At nine A.M., an hour ago, the Palace Guard, who were barricaded in the President's garage, surrendered. You already know about the Letter of Withdrawal from Office; this has permitted a group of responsible officers to assume transitional executive power in a legal manner." His voice skated fondly over the word

"legal." "This is obviously a temporary measure until the people can, in a free and worthy manner, with the proper safe-
guards, express their own will. The movement to which I
belong has no yearning for a military dictatorship."

Gauthier's eye drifted over the plundered room; he had
heard it all before. "Who belongs to the Committee?" he
asked.

"You understand that there is no point in attempting to
identify all of the patriotic officers at this stage? This information will become a matter of public knowledge soon enough,
but it is quite secondary. The officers form a staff, or, if you
prefer, a Coordinating Committee." It was the first time
Gauthier had heard the new term. "None has individual ambition or a desire for personal publicity; they are working closely
together on behalf of the nation. Will you print it if I tell
you that some of these junior officers have never been in the
capital before?"

Gauthier detected no glint of irony in the brown protu-
berant eyes. "What is the situation with respect to censorship,
and when will international telephone facilities be restored?"
he asked.

"Monsieur Gauthier, what a question! The answer is, in no
time at all. We are lucky to have in this country a fine,
trustworthy and efficient communication cadre who were
among the first to pledge unconditional allegiance to the new
national and popular government. There is no censorship but
newspaper dispatches will be read, merely to assure that a fair
image is being presented to the outside world of what we are
accomplishing here. In the same nonvexatious spirit all phone
calls abroad will be monitored. I think this will be a positive
measure; it should prove no hardship for you, Monsieur

Gauthier. You have made your home here for many years and know us and sympathize with our true aspirations. I am sure you will realize where to draw the line. What else is there I can do for you?"

Gauthier decided that it would be unwise to ask directly about what was uppermost in his mind.

"During the night the airport terminal building and one runway were hit by tank fire. Two Boeings of Middle East Airlines are grounded." Gauthier told this lie in his sturdiest manner. "What other damage was done?"

"Utterly untrue. Who spread that tale? The Army"—he amended this—"the Transportation Ministry is re-establishing normal flight schedules as soon as possible."

"Can I enter the airport area?"

"I doubt it." He rose from his seat. "I would appreciate your mentioning in your first dispatch that a special flight to accommodate stranded travelers with priority status will take off this evening. Tunisia's foreign friends are being looked after."

"Is this correct?"

"Would I say so otherwise?"

"This is of personal interest to me. My son requires medical attention in France." The essential had been accomplished. Gauthier had discovered that a way out existed for Anne Marie and his son.

"The Tunisian Health Service is perfectly adequate—there have been no complaints to my knowledge."

"The recommendation comes from a Tunisian doctor," he lied again.

El Bahi shot him a skeptical glance. "Perhaps by applying immediately to the Transportation Ministry you will obtain a eat. I think, however, it must be very difficult. A great many foreigners have suddenly remembered maladies and business that need looking after on an urgent basis." He asked, "Are you contemplating leaving with your family?"

Gauthier shook his head. "You can't get rid of me that easily—"

"We don't want to."

"The end of a story has always had special fascination for me." It was true, he thought, and finished his whiskey. "At least, thirst won't be a problem. I am relieved to see this is not a Libyan-style revolution."

"Not in the superficial details like prohibition of liquor that provide you journalists with so much colorful copy. As for the end of the story, Monsieur Gauthier, I think it will be a happy one."

Out in the street, Gauthier drew a long breath and cleared his mind of all that verbiage. The new Press Chief's parting handgrip, emphatic and monkey-cold, still caused his fingers to tingle.

He walked stolidly away from the Information Ministry—all, Nordic, clever and cold. No one who saw him would have guessed the panic that suddenly assailed him. A nightmare, thought Gauthier—that was how Anne-Marie described his existence here; well, if so, it was a private nightmare suspected by few. "*Are you contemplating leaving with your family?*" What did El Bahi's query conceal? Were they already distrustful of him? Gauthier cast back to the conversation. He could not disregard the threat in the light, glib voice.

was possible that he had waited too long to get out. They were surely getting ready, at the very least, to introduce exit visas. Exit visas had always ranked among the occupational

hazards of his career; they could be devices as lethal as mines.
He remembered applying for an exit visa from Syria after the
war, when they were isolated and unsure of themselves, and in
consequence suspicious and cruel, and how he had very nearly
been refused one.

Gauthier looked about the street sourly. The past clung to
him like a repugnant secretion, a jellyfish. He had come
fourteen years ago to this languorous country of the feline
gesture and the cactus-prickly pride. He was fed up with the
fatalism, the flies, the homely commingled stink of plaster,
dust, spices, stagnant water and goat dung—*des odeurs
pauvres*, as Anne-Marie had put it. He'd spent fourteen years
here and had nothing to show for it, nothing except a boat he
would feel true regret at giving up when he left someday.
Tunisia was not a country but a long coast; the deeper you
traveled inland, the drier and more desperate the land became,
petering out in salt depressions. All Tunisia lived, struggled
and perished on the coast. His life had been played out on
the coast, an alien shore on which his world managed to leave
no lasting imprint. But how could he and Anne-Marie and
others hope to take root in this clayey soil? It wasn't only the
commandos who had found themselves on an alien shore. We
are all in that fix; they are only an extreme case, he thought.
He passed a tobacco kiosk around which a crowd had
gathered. The Committee had issued handbills cautioning the
population against enemy *provocateurs* in its midst. Probably
he was reading too much into El Bahi's query. They could not
possibly suspect him yet. Over fourteen years he had succeeded
at his work for the Qiryat because his nerves were strong, his
sense of measure unimpaired and his self-confidence remarkable. Now he was experiencing an overdue attack of nerves. He

came at an awkward moment. Get a grip on yourself, he thought; put things in perspective; you are not a helpless old man.

Gauthier paused before the Colisée building. "*Are you contemplating leaving with your family?*" Moodily he passed on. The question had cast a shadow over his day. He had no will to return to his office; he had no ambition to file a story on the consolidation of the Revolution.

Later in the morning he called at the Transportation Ministry and happened upon a division chief he knew who was well disposed. The division chief made several lengthy telephone calls, then turned with a bleak twitch of his lips. "I do not believe your wife will be on tonight's flight," he said apologetically. "Unless, that is, you can furnish a medical certificate."

"I think we can arrange that."

When Gauthier drove home at midday, he found Anne-Marie in the kitchen listening to a special radio bulletin.

## CHAPTER EIGHTEEN

# The Safety Margin

"*Ça y est.*" Gauthier's face was sickly white. He was becoming more frightened than he had ever been. "I'm blown."

"It can't be true! Are you absolutely sure?"

"You heard the radio—they've caught one of my men. I know the fellow."

Confronted by his enormous fear, she tried to cling to a shred of faith. "He's a trained agent; he won't break down—"

"Do you think that this new regime will hesitate to use torture? Marston will talk; he has no alternative. They'll make him vomit out everything before he's hanged." Gauthier's face was like that of a man trapped in an earthquake. "Naturally he won't crack right away; that's where his training will serve. But when he does, he will furnish my description—he saw me yesterday—and the names of two other men. One of these men, the commando leader, is still alive—I just heard from him—and he can identify me."

"How much time is there left before they find out about you?" The question had a slippery metallic taste on her tongue.

"Marston must be undergoing interrogation at Sûreté head-quarters. Perhaps they have captured the other man, too; I have no idea. I didn't expect this, at least not so soon. To break the story, they must be very sure of themselves; usually they hush up a capture until they can roll up the network. Of course it may be partial bluff, publicizing sensational news to bolster their position—"

"How much time?" Anne-Marie repeated.

He looked at her expressionlessly. "A half day. With luck, till this evening. Prizing information from a strong-willed man takes time; evaluating it, more—this is the safety margin."

"This evening . . ." Her mouth was working uncontrollably. She was not prepared for so short notice; at bottom, she had been bracing during two days and nights for the collapse of his abnormal career, but not this quickly, not with such meager forewarning.

"The one solution is for you to be far away from here to-night." He told her about the flight, conscious that he was uncertain whether she would consent to go. "First, we must pressure the doctor into furnishing a medical certificate that confirms the need for medical treatment in France; this will be your responsibility. It should not be overly difficult to obtain—"

"That's secondary," she said. "You're the one who has to get out. They won't bother much with me."

"I wouldn't be sure of that."

It was worse than anything Anne-Marie had supposed, and his unruffled voice made it still worse. She had an abrupt vision of the hangman's shadow falling upon them all now—an imprecise but terrifying vision. Suddenly her sole desire was to flee. "What about you? A medical certificate isn't going to provide you with a seat."

"It never occurred to me until this moment to leave; I was trying to arrange your departure. I can't leave—not as long as even one man of the commando is still alive. It's unthinkable."

"Has your headquarters ordered you to stay?" Anne-Marie asked.

He was astonished by so much pertinence. "On the contrary, I am no longer operational; they want me to fly out whenever possible. But that has nothing to do with it."

"Would the commando leader do as much for you?"

"Perhaps not. That also has nothing to do with it. I planned Operation Flood; the moral obligation to remain is clear—"

"I thought morality didn't exist in Intelligence work."

"Surprisingly it does for me."

"I don't know what to tell you, Alex. The choice is so inhuman, and I'm afraid of being a calamitous influence."

Isolation was inherent in a Resident's functions; he had always made decisions in silence, alone, without support except from an abstruse organization at the distant end of a single side-band transmission. "First, I shall do whatever can be done to safeguard our rear—that is, for the commando leader —then I am going to leave," he said. "If I rely on the Transportation Ministry and the Information Ministry, I won't get aboard; they'll find excuses for delaying. They've made it clear that I'm a hostage of sorts for the Revolution—a correspondent who will write favorable copy. However, I have one hope. In this situation there's a fellow who can help me. He's utterly untrustworthy."

She cried, "Why do you deal only with people like that?"

"Is there a choice in this sort of business?" A sentence he

had read in recent weeks slipped into his mind: *Is it necessary or indispensable for a man to touch rock-bottom at least once in his life to be wholly a man?* His own life here was coming apart; there was no sound of identifiable breakage but none-theless it was happening. He had expected to leave someday, of course, but, like Anne-Marie, not soo soon, and unconsciously he had avoided setting a date. In his mind's eye he saw the Cercle Nautique's cheery white clubhouse at Sidi Bou Said gleaming with a fresh coat of paint in the morning light. But summer was far off; the new season, when the seaside restaur-ants reopened and special buses ran out to Gammarth, would not begin till mid-June. And no self-respecting Tunisian would dream of waddling out into the warmish safe green waters of Raouad Beach before early July . . . Gauthier shook his head. It was all nonsense; his duty was to deal with the immediate problem. Let the past rust, partly submerged like a damaged hulk, where it could do only occasional harm; he was willing to settle for that. He said, "I think I know a way of making sure this fellow stays loyal—temporarily at least, which is all I need. Even more than wheedling money, he would like to cease being a spy. I'm going to exploit his eagerness to get rid of me."

"We'll never see this again." Anne-Marie looked about, contemplating the garden, the view, recalling the amphithea-ter, the ruins, the disgraceful lake, the lights of Tunis on cer-tain evenings shining weakly through the mist. "We'll board the plane with a couple of suitcases and the clothes we happen to be wearing, like refugees."

"You don't have to tell me what being a refugee is like."

"If I start to pack the slightest souvenir, the maid is going to suspect something—"

"You will simply have to go about your life as on a normal day. Tell the *khedima* that you are going to the doctor's to fetch Marc's prescription; that's plausible enough. Then, when you come back, send her home as soon as possible without arousing her curiosity. I shall return here at four-thirty and we shall leave immediately afterward."

"Have you thought about your boat?" she asked, impervious to how incongruous the question sounded.

"What of it? I'm writing it off, like the house and my work for the paper. I'm in a corner—don't you understand how strange that is? I always wanted to get people out of corners." He had never put so much blazing anger into a single outburst.

Anne-Marie thought that his disillusionment showed through his violence like ribs sticking out of a crushed thorax, but she could discover no coherent response to console him.

As he went into his study, Gauthier shouted, "Do you appreciate that an ideal has been betrayed?"

Indignant, she cried after him, "What ideal, in heaven's name? By whom?"

"Dedication to a cause . . . betrayed, or, if you prefer, neglected, by me. My work here was valuable. We got rid of that filthy terrorist. They won't find a replacement for him so soon!"

Gauthier dialed the Interior Ministry number. At once a shrill feminine voice replied. The Committee had put a new operator on the line, and she had answered, probably following strict orders, in Arabic.

Gauthier spoke in French, carefully enunciating the extension number.

"*Parlez dans la langue du pays, s'il vous plaît!*" The Revo lution's effects were making themselves felt in a hurry, he thought.

Gauthier swore and repeated the number in French.

After a moment, the woman's sullen voice said, "*Ça ne répond pas.*" He began to protest and the line clicked dead.

Now there was no alternative but to call Ben Larbi at home, a procedure he had avoided in the past as a violation of security.

When the receiver was lifted, Gauthier said, "Where have you been? There are a number of urgent things we must discuss."

"I haven't heard from you in days! Not that it possibly matters."

"I'll meet you at sixteen hours," Gauthier cut him short. The code meant an hour earlier—fifteen hours, or three o'clock—and since he had failed to specify a new rendezvous site it automatically implied the last place they had met, at Maurice's in La Goulette.

"I can't, I'm sick" was the overprompt reply.

"What is wrong with you?"

"My nerves are fluttery. The doctor says I shall have a *crise* if I continue to overtax my mind with worry."

Gauthier listened with chafing impatience and finally said, "At our mutual friend's. I expect to find you there." It meant Ben Larbi's own apartment. He hung up in exasperation.

Anne-Marie had followed him into the study and overheard the close of the conversation. "If you go," she said, "he'll set a trap for you."

"He would love to, but first he has to find out what I'm up to; it will take him time to decide how to betray me without destroying himself. Our relationship consists of a balance of terror, like that of the famous two scorpions in a bottle: neither can sting the other without being stung. Of course," Gauthier added, summoning up a smile without warmth, "it's a pity the flight doesn't leave earlier. Still, I believe we will be gone before he can make serious mischief. *Inch' Allah . . .*"

Anne-Marie caught herself half agreeing and realized with a shock how much the last few hours had transformed her responses. Before, submission to fatality had not been one of the guideposts in her life.

"I still don't think you should go."

"I have to run the risk; after all, I am an 'illegal.' I agree that I am not meeting him under secure conditions"—he had lapsed into Intelligence jargon—"but for once this can't be helped."

"There must be some other way of obtaining a place on the flight."

"Unfortunately I do not know of any."

From the moment her husband had raised the possibility of fleeing Tunis, the thought of Preston had intruded insistently upon Anne-Marie; he stood out clear, demanding, troublesome, yet outside and apart from her life. She felt angry at her changeability, yet it wasn't her fault, she thought. It was a matter of unmistakable priorities.

"I thought of leaving you, Alex," she said. "Instead, I'm running away with you, and it's not only to save myself as you may think."

"If that is not the reason, then why are you?"

"I don't honestly know. Maybe I'm a coward."

"I doubt that is the reason. At any rate, we are leaving together. This in my view is what counts."

"But I may not stay with you afterward."

"I realize that." He avoided the unwelcome subject and nodded in the direction of their son's upstairs bedroom. "There is no problem about his being able to travel?"

"No, why should there be? The sulfa pills worked right away, and the fever is over. Anyway, it's a short flight to Paris."

Gauthier barely listened. Another thought had occurred to him. He glanced sideways at his wife and said noncommittally, "Should a man called Levanon phone in my absence, tell him simply that he must be on time at our meeting, otherwise I cannot wait."

"Is he the commando leader? Aren't you planning to help him?"

He faced up to the question's implication. "When he returns to Tunis, I shall give him money and a friend's address; then he will be on his own. There is simply no more I can do for him, and I am going to explain this to him. It's a terrible thing, I know. But to stay is suicide. It won't help anyone if I lose my life; in fact, it will endanger others." Then, as though in partial extenuation, he muttered, "Emir no longer exists."

"Who is Emir?" Annie-Marie asked candidly.

Gauthier went into the garage, removed the oilskin and rubber boots, lifted the tarpaulin and found the transceiver where he had left it. He carried the suitcase out and deposited it in the recess of the station wagon. Then he walked through the garden and retrieved the antenna from its hiding place and placed it in the car too. Finally, he returned to the garage and examined a toolbox on the shelf for all the other objects that could spell trouble and had to be disposed of—note pads, two receipts from Ben Larbi, an onionskin slip of paper bearing coded winter frequencies, and a small blued 6.5-mm. Walther PPK dusty with disuse. He carried these odds and ends to the car, but after a slight hesitation he slid the gun into his jacket pocket. It was preferable to be armed for the unfinished business he had to conduct later with Ben Larbi.

He drove down the hill toward Hamilcar. The suburbs drowsed in winter heat. Seemingly the revolutionary Army was heavy with torpor after last night's excitement and over-feasting; he encountered no patrols and in the distance saw only one column of half-tracks proceeding sluggishly as a caravan along a back road in the direction of Tunis.

At Hamilcar he turned toward the shore and parked the station wagon close to a brackish small pond near the beach. At his back, a sagging barbed-wire fence enclosed an abandoned excavation site littered with chips of sculpture and shards of amphorae strewn in the sand amid pellets of goat dung. Gauthier bore the transceiver to the pondside, set it down, wiped his forehead, then prodded the suitcase with his heel until it slid down the grass and toppled into the green cloudy water. The pond was six feet deep; he had ascertained this long before. Gauthier dropped the aerial and paraphernalia from the toolbox into the water, cast one bitter backward glance at the green ripples, then strode back to the station wagon. Someday an archaeologist or fisherman would come upon the queer treasure, but not for a while, and at any rate no one could ever connect it with him. He got into his car and drove away.

"Were you followed? Did you get rid of it?" Anne-Marie asked as he re-entered the house.

"So far there are no problems."

"Are you absolutely sure the man you're going to see can really help you?"

"He'll have to," Gauthier said inflexibly.

Anne-Marie shivered. She had a dizzy sensation of nearing a void with no barrier to restrain her if she tripped. "Suddenly I feel we have so much to lose."

"So much to win, you mean. If we manage to leave this country, there is still a chance everything can right itself. No, that's wrong. I don't mean everything, only a few essentials. We *must* be on that plane—and we shall be!"

His terse phrase "the one solution" tolled in her mind. "How can you be so optimistic?"

"This morning I went through a rotten time; I'm better now, although I'm still very worried about the commando leader." He looked at the disorder in the garden and the larger disorder that spread in green scarred circles on the hillside: the ruined basilica's decapitated stone columns bleaching in the sun, the styleless Cathedral metamorphosed into a neutral museum. "The commando leader will be all right if he stays concealed at the address I provide; later we can organize his escape." He turned around. "I was becoming fed up with this place. The thing about Tunisia is that, except for the Arabs, everybody is on temporary assignment; no one has roots here, no one belongs. We all live in rented houses and buy the same things, rugs and blankets and bird cages. It isn't anything but one assignment among others—"

"You're saying all the things I said last summer," Anne-Marie told him.

"They'll have to get a new Resident."

"No." Anne-Marie reproved him sharply. "You need a new purpose; this is what matters."

Ten minutes later she saw him leave for his meeting. In a French forest she had once surprised two wild boars, immobile, at attention, scenting a hostile presence in their area, tusks needle-sharp and dangerous but their shaggy flanks large and vulnerable to a sudden blow. As Gauthier stood in the driveway, he reminded her of one of those boars.

She watched the heavy station wagon sway in the curve, then right itself on its shock absorbers as it gathered speed down the steep road. Behind rose the ambiguous hill of Carthage, dun, faded, brooding in the mellow afternoon light. Anne-Marie roused herself. She had to get to the doctor's and obtain the certificate.

## CHAPTER NINETEEN

# The Strong Man
# of the Revolution

JUST a half hour earlier, Preston had received a telephone call to present himself at three o'clock sharp in Captain Fawzi's headquarters.

He discovered a transformed atmosphere at the Interior Ministry. The Army was ubiquitously in charge. Suntanned young field officers brought by the Revolution to Tunis from primitive, arid billets thronged the narrow, bleak corridors, and newly recruited teen-age secretaries darted to and fro at their behest. In the main hall, civilians milled about, giving vent to outbursts of worry and fright. Through the commotion Preston ascended to the fourth floor, where he shouted his name to a rabbity *chaouch* who was on duty and was perspiring from the strain of trying to maintain order. Preston was led to an antechamber and was kept waiting—not unreasonably long as it turned out. Soon a burly, dark civilian with a walrus mustache appeared in a doorway and beckoned to him. Preston found the man's profile familiar in a hazy, disquieting way, but failed at the moment to associate his face with a name or a place.

Fawzi sat behind a polished rectangular desk in what had been Colonel Kheli's private office. A blank space on the wall marked the place from which the President's official portrait had lately frowned down. Fawzi did not rise and his greeting was austere.

"Mr. Preston, we have some urgent arrangements to discuss. This is why I summoned you—"

"Let's set the record straight right away, Captain. The United States Embassy requested an appointment with the de facto head of Counterintelligence. I was not summoned."

"The two *démarches* must have coincided," Fawzi answered distantly. He tapped the desk with his fingernails and assumed an air that managed to be both aloof and reproving. "In spite of the Liaison Agreement's cancellation, we shall count on your Agency's full cooperation in all current matters. I wish that you would tell Mr. Mills this. Obviously we shall assign new personnel to coordinate efforts in an area that is so sensitive. It is also obvious that in many specific affairs our interests are not likely to be the same as the preceding regime's."

Preston sat, with some amusement, taking the measure of the captain's rococo bureaucratic style. What the statement meant was that until recognition was granted by Washington the Committee wanted an ad hoc working partnership. The offer was disingenuous. It implied that the burden would fall upon the Agency of providing intelligence and conforming to its obligations as a presumed friendly Service; as for the Committee, it could decide what information and facilities it wished to supply on the basis of its undefined "new interests."

"I am not empowered to make a commitment," Preston said crisply.

"I understand that. However, you can communicate our view—you are the Liaison Officer."

"What are the 'specific affairs' you referred to?"

Fawzi smirked coyly. "I expected you to ask. We are not going to be very demanding, if this is what you fear; on the contrary, the new relationship will require rather less than more immediate cooperation. For example, we shall no longer seek the Agency's assistance in the Al Houaranni case. M'hamed Kheli's decision to enlist your help—a mistake, in my opinion—must be considered null and void. We are capable of handling this affair on our own; why should your Agency be bothered?"

"To put it plainly, you are ordering us to mind our own business."

"I have some recent news for you that should explain our attitude." The captain's round cheeks glistened with excitement; his skin was glabrous; whenever a vein fluttered beneath the epidermis, olive oil seemed to course through the pores of his face. "We have received a report from Qelibia, a port on Cap Bon, that a foreigner—a Jew—forced his way aboard a fishing boat this morning and compelled the owner to take him to sea, apparently with the notion of reaching an Italian island, in spite of the temporary ban on sailing. The fisherman patriotically resisted. There was a scuffle and the Jew fell overboard and drowned in circumstances that are unclear. Does this suggest anything to you?"

Preston sat erect in his seat. "Yes, that the Mediterranean has probably done your work for you and eliminated one of the kidnappers."

"Not one but two are neutralized. Doubtless you have heard

about the other, related development. At roughly the same hour this morning, another foreigner pretending to be French attempted to brazen his way through a checkpoint some forty miles from Qelibia. He was careless enough to be carrying an Interior Ministry special pass—a pass valid for access to the Hotel Africa during Al Houaranni's stay—and this led to his arrest. He is being interrogated at present and has already confessed that he and the Jew in the boat belonged to the Ha Mossad commando that kidnapped Al Houaranni."

"He's admitted a surprising lot in a short time."

Fawzi's mouth was unhumorous. "I can't say he's been very cooperative. There is still much he is obviously holding back. But once in our hands for a while, these fellows crack. We have determined that a third man is at large in the same area. He will be caught shortly. The commando is in complete rout. You see, we really are able to solve a crime when we put our minds to it."

"Then where is Al Houaranni?"

"We shall supply the Agency with a full case summary as soon as feasible."

"Is he alive or dead?"

Fawzi's somber fretful eyes turned opaque, and Preston knew that the last thing he was going to obtain was a straightforward account.

"He is probably dead. It's atrocious, of course, but in this affair the important consideration, from our point of view, was to reassure the world that Ha Mossad's terrorists could not operate with impunity. Don't you agree that this has been accomplished?"

"I think that the lesson would be clearer if your police had managed to retrieve Al Houaranni alive."

302

The captain said with a tight, bogus smile, "It is probable that the whole affair could have been better handled."

The reply, Preston thought, dispelled any illusions about the Committee's interest in Al Houaranni's fate. Al Houaranni had been ill-advised enough to become the pretext for a coup . . . and one major requirement in this thieves' game was to avoid becoming a pretext for any move.

Fawzi relaxed in his predecessor's chair, front teeth even and yellow in his flabby large face, khaki tunic ballooning over his corpulent torso. There was something distinctly un-Tunisian about his ponderous solemnity. Preston realized, interested, that it was sham, a pose adopted to convey serious-ness, an attitude he had probably misinterpreted and copied ignorantly during a temporary training assignment with Western security officers. Fawzi's gravity was as implausible as a young boy's. Behind it lurked an itch to smirk. Neverthe-less, for all his artificiality, this fat junior office with the elephantine bottom was impressive. He had spent five years in daily contact with the colonel and had helped him run the country's entire Counterintelligence operation. It had to be assumed that Fawzi had picked up a fair number of his chief's techniques. Now he held a key post for enforcing his own views. In short, Preston was dealing with one of the new regime's strong men.

"While we're at it, I think the world wants to be reassured as to what is happening here—to the extent, of course, that Tunisia is of interest." He had not been able to resist the taunt, for the captain's overweening conceit badly needed pricking.

The captain again displayed the same tight, parsimonious smile. "Never fear, we have no exaggerated sense of our own importance, even in the Arab world. We are merely trying to push through a number of overdue reforms; our aims are no secret." His brown eyes flashed with undisguised self-righteousness. "Why do you think I joined the Committee? Have you ever asked yourself that question? To steal the colonel's pips? That is a schoolboy's interpretation. No, I will tell you —because of shameful abuses and inexcusable hypocrisy at the very top. For instance, the President had a Jew in his Cabinet. How could you reconcile that with genuine support for the Palestinian cause? I am no anti-Semite, but a believer in our strength, our future."

Preston ignored the diatribe and asked brusquely, "What has happened to M'hamed Kheli?"

Fawzi's expression altered; he couldn't repress a glint of vindictive triumph. "The colonel is under arrest and will shortly face a special military court, as I already informed you this morning. He has a great deal to answer for."

"Then who was the man found machine-gunned on the airport road?"

"An enemy of the Revolution—a man who vaguely resembled M'hamed Kheli."

"What are the charges?"

"Why is your Agency so concerned about the colonel's fate? Or are you personally involved? In this business it's always a mistake, you know."

Preston was in no humor to accept lessons from this half-baked fleshy officer. "Gathering information happens to be our business. Isn't it yours?"

Fawzi shrugged with disdain. "The charges are, among others, abuse of power, withholding of confidential information from his superiors, financial irregularities, questionable dealings with a foreign Service—"

"Could that mean us?"

"Also, criminal negligence of Al Houaranni's security. I concede that the man in this post cannot foresee every wild move of the enemy, but just the same . . . the kidnapping made a laughingstock of us."

Nauseated, Preston said, "Better than anyone else, you know this charge to be untrue. The colonel did all that was humanly possible to protect, then rescue Al Houaranni."

Fawzi nodded briefly. "Yes, later he tried to recoup his mistakes, but in the first place he dawdled and dispersed his efforts. Don't forget that Ha Mossad obtained the timetable of Al Houaranni's stay in Tunis through an agent planted in this Ministry. The colonel's slipshod supervision of his own personnel was to blame for that state of affairs." The sudden hoarse note of grievance in his voice was genuine.

"The kidnapping's success gave you a pretext for the uprising."

"Yes, that is true"—Fawzi planted his hands palms down on the shiny desk in a movement oddly reminiscent of the colonel's—"but you realize that public opinion demands an identifiable culprit for the Al Houaranni affair. Would it be very different in your country?"

"It could well be the same. But I liked and respected the colonel." Preston got up. He was hot and tense and very angry. The conversation was getting nowhere, and if Kheli was still alive, the charges Fawzi had just ticked off amounted to a death sentence. "I've just remembered where I saw your aide," he added. "I mean the numskull with the

305

mustache who showed me in. He tried to assassinate me on the lake road last night. Was that the colonel's responsibility too?"

"Sit down, Mr. Preston, for a moment; let's not start off the new relationship on the basis of a misunderstanding." Fawzi scrutinized him without embarrassment. "I will try to explain from the beginning—" When he saw that Preston made no move to resume his seat, he rose, too, and stood with his back to the wall.

"For some time, the Inner Committee had planned a coup, but we were unsure of civilian support and decided that it must be a purely military effort. The target date was far off.

"Then the Israeli commando kidnapped Al Houaranni. For us this was a near-disaster. Why, after all, had we gone to so much trouble to organize a clandestine meeting with him? He could be of tremendous assistance to us if he wanted to—with tactical advice and in other practical ways, notably by sponsoring our movement and putting us in touch with like-minded reformers in other Arab capitals. Imagine our frustration when he was snatched out from under our noses!

"As it turned out, the kidnapping had the effect of angering the entire population. Popular resentment culminated in yesterday afternoon's student demonstration. We had nothing to do with that; it was entirely spontaneous. To the extent that it undermined the government, however, we welcomed the demonstration, and we did what we could to abet it by delaying the arrival of Army units. As you know, the protest march then escalated into a riot. By afternoon the over-all situation was deteriorating; we had almost no choice but to move up the date of our coup, otherwise we ran the risk of being outmaneuvered by civilian movements. In a political vacuum, this threat, let me tell you, is far from imaginary.

"However, there was another, disturbing aspect to the problem. Ha Mossad's agent had obviously infiltrated our movement, participated in our secret meetings and knew our identities. This implied the strong possibility of a trap, a provocation. If we set a specific hour for the coup, it was certain that Ha Mossad would receive precise advance information about our plans. In a move to destroy us it might decide to alert the government, preferring a known, moderate leadership in power to an unknown, radical one. We felt quite vulnerable. As a result, all yesterday afternoon the Committee wavered over the decision to strike—wrongly, I think, for sometimes you must boldly improvise.

"Then you turned up in this office and acted as though you knew the kidnappers' whereabouts and were on the verge of striking a deal with them. Naturally the colonel encouraged you; he saw this as a respite for the regime. But from our point of view—the Committee's, that is—the last thing we wanted was Al Houaranni's release. It would make the President a hero, strengthen the government and oblige us to postpone the coup indefinitely, a prospect that was not only frustrating but dangerous. Why? Well, you remember that the colonel already had an inkling of the Committee's existence. Although he played down its importance in a conversation with you—a 'small Army network,' he said!—he knew that it represented a definite threat to the regime. He told me as much! He had realized at once the significance of the second car that drove up with several officers in plain clothes to the Hotel Africa. It meant that an Army group was in secret contact with Al Houaranni. He went to the President with his findings and a crackdown on all ranks was about to start. Given enough time, it was likely that the colonel would uncover our identities and smash our organization.

"In short, either we had to act or he would. As soon as you left this office, I gave orders—without the colonel's knowledge, naturally—to have you followed. The men in the Citroën were in permanent touch with me by radiotelephone. Of course there was a temptation to let you lead us to the kidnappers, but it was even more important to prevent you from negotiating Al Houaranni's release—otherwise our pretext for the coup would collapse. When I learned your general direction—that you were taking the lake road—I decided to arrange an accident for you, not necessarily fatal, but one that would put you out of commission for a long while. But then thanks to your *Mabrouk*, your luck, the 'accident' backfired and, worse, you vanished into La Goulette. At this point our hand was really forced. For all we knew, you would contact the kidnappers and Al Houaranni might be freed within hours. We quickly moved up the time and date of the coup, sent word to unit commanders and struck at nineteen hours— and it succeeded! Through your interference, you, in some ways, are responsible for the coup," he concluded with glittering malice.

"Why not justify it by saying the CIA rides again?"

Before Fawzi could reply, the phone rang. He listened, let his eyes dwell without expression on Preston, then murmured his agreement and hung up.

Preston glanced automatically at his watch. It was three forty-five.

"Contrary to your suspicions, we are actively following up

the Al Houaranni affair. Kheli's investigation into that area was not all stupid. I hope to give you more positive news later today."

The captain's manner had changed following the call—it was less leisurely and betrayed a basic tenseness—and Preston wondered what the message was really about. He had never liked Fawzi, and liked him still less now.

" 'Not necessarily fatal'—just 'out of commission,' " he snapped, reverting to the captain's lengthy explanation. "Are you out of your mind? Do you call this a new relationship? Do you expect recognition if I send a cable on this?"

"Let's be thankful the attack miscarried. When the need arises, you people play dirty tricks too." Advancing, Fawzi said briskly, "I can show you letters from your own ambassador thanking me for past help. No, Mr. Preston, there is no cause for complaint. If you should do so, you would be the first American to disappoint me."

He extended his warm, pulpy hand, but Preston knew that in the future, on whatever business brought them together, he would have to reckon with the captain's implacable hostility.

## CHAPTER TWENTY

# The Balance of Terror

B EFORE entering the apartment house on Rue Ibn Khaldoun, Gauthier made a rapid check of the approaches.
No car had followed him on the way in from Carthage and he
saw nothing untoward in the street. The stocky, taciturn men
who operated out of the Interior Ministry's fourth floor could
not yet have picked up his trail—but when they did, it would
be too late to flee.

At the door, Ben Larbi bade him a grudging welcome.
Gauthier stared at his agent's tight black velvet slacks and
tasteful lemon turtleneck sweater in featherweight cashmere.

"You don't look very sick to me."

"I would utter any lie so as never to see you again!" Ben
Larbi hissed, with what amounted to a lover's ire. Peevishly
he indicated a divan and flung himself into a wicker armchair, crossing and drawing up his legs like a fashion model's.
"They have announced the capture of one of your unspeakable
thugs. Objectively I am delighted, although, of course, it
doesn't make my future brighter." He observed Gauthier's
frown and said dourly, "Don't worry, no one has entered thi

place in days—during a coup one ceases to have friends. The room is safe; you can speak up. What has happened to Al Houaranni? Obviously he never reached your scheming country. All this insane risk for nothing! How could you let things slide so badly? I don't want to hear about it," he added with strait-laced disapproval.

Gauthier glanced about, taking note of the cozy gimcrack French furniture, the Moorish pieces and German record player—for all of which the Qiryat had paid—visualizing the prancing assignations that had been consummated here. Candy-striped chintz curtains filtered the sunlight, which entered in golden diagonal bars. The room was as secretive and garish as a harem quarter, but draw the curtains back and the apartment, Gauthier suspected, would turn out to be like Ben Larbi himself—as slick and synthetic as linoleum.

"I suppose that I must offer you hospitality," Ben Larbi remarked moodily. "There is nothing whatever in the buffet."

"Whiskey," specified Gauthier with intentional nastiness. "You must have put in a case or two for Ramadan."

Ben Larbi set out a bottle and two unclean glasses and shot him a sulky, sidelong glance. "For my part, I carried out your instructions punctually and loyally. You can have no complaints whatever; I more than earned every miserable dinar."

"Did I receive forewarning from you of the coup's exact timing?"

"I waited and held my tongue so as not to compromise you! Besides," he added with a limp attempt at conciliation, "it is likely that you learned about it as soon as I did; the Committee acted at the last moment."

"Why is it that you are not at the Ministry, working?"

311

"Because I am truly horribly sick," Ben Larbi cried, his husky voice rising as though the question had scraped a raw nerve end, "sick with tension for which you are entirely to blame!"

"What does the Inner Committee think of a conspirator whose nerves are unequal to the strain of achieving the Revolution?"

"The Coordinating Committee—get the name right, for heaven's sake—has enough difficulties without attending to my nerves. It is preparing to settle many scores—I think one of them will be with you. From now on, you are a lost man."

*"Tu es vraiment con,"* Gauthier said coldly.

"Don't play arrogant with me! Fourteen years is too long to be Resident! Vanity is your Achilles' heel; the time has come when you are going to topple over like a false god."

"You'll be crushed underneath in the ruins."

"Why is it that you came to see me exactly? Is it to make my life still more wretched? What justifies your hate and contempt? Why don't you go away for good so that I never see you again—while you still can?"

Gauthier lifted his eyebrows but detected no hint of clairvoyance or irony in the other's thick, shopworn features, only a deeper than usual pool of self-pity.

"Stop blubbering so and listen to me. There is, in fact, a special flight for Paris that leaves at ten tonight. Only passengers with priority status are allowed aboard. I must have a seat; this is what I want to fix up through you."

Ben Larbi had moved his armchair out of reach with alacrity and was glaring at Gauthier in genuine alarm. "Do you think it is like the old days when a bureaucrat could manage any dishonest trick because no one inside or outside the government cared? Those humiliating days are over, thank God. The Committee has ordered each Tunisian held responsible for his actions——"

"That's an excellent idea."

"What will happen if I request a priority travel order for a French journalist who is a notorious snooper and probable Deuxième Bureau agent—and, heaven knows, even then they don't suspect the whole sordid truth about you! I don't understand your asking this of me. Are you losing your mind?" he asked hopefully.

"We'll leave here together. From you office at the Ministry you'll make the *démarche* on my behalf."

Ben Larbi moaned. "Do you know what you remind me of, you and your whole unhappy race? A disease carrier who infects everybody he comes into contact with."

"By procuring a travel order, you get rid of me. Isn't this advantage worth a little risk? You must realize that once I am aboard the flight they'll make endless difficulties about allowing me back in."

Ben Larbi shook his head stubbornly.

"I am escorting you to the Ministry," Gauthier announced. Long ago, he had grasped that on the day this sleek, avaricious little southerner ceased to wail, further manipulation would become an insuperable task.

"My conscience no longer belongs to a *Yhoud*. Haven't I made this clear? We are divorced."

"I am escorting you just in the event that you should experience a change of heart——"

Ben Larbi rose as though stung by an electrical discharge. "You have lost your mind. I am being tortured and persecuted by an *afreet*, an unholy demon who sucks on my being

313

like a leech. What crime did I commit to deserve this punishment?"

"Are you ready?"

"If I turned you in, at least I would die with a good conscience—"

"And a broken neck." Gauthier asked ominously, "Have you attempted to do any such thing?"

Ben Larbi seized the whiskey bottle and replaced it inhospitably in the sideboard. "Would I be so suicidal?"

"Would you?"

"On my sister's virtue—I know it signifies nothing to you —I have spoken of your shabby intriguing to no one. You never appreciated what a help a trustworthy agent could be, but now this is over and done with, terminated. The Revolution furnishes even someone like me with an opportunity to start afresh."

Gauthier nodded gloomily. "Yes, it will, once I am gone. But in the meanwhile we are losing time and you have to carry out a final assignment." He drew his gun and trained it on the stately figure.

Ben Larbi wet his lips. In his erratic career no gun had been brandished at him before; he was used to meaner behavior—being slapped and spat upon.

"Obviously you are concealing some additional nastiness. Otherwise the Information Ministry would fix you up with a seat."

"You know better than to pry into my business, Ali."

"If I help you, what am I to get out of this? Money, I suppose—it is all you were ever capable of offering."

"I can provide something more useful than money. When

you need a fallback position, as you undoubtedly will—abroad, in the near future, for example—I shall help."

"Do you think I am going to pick beets on a kibbutz?" Ben Larbi shouted. He was increasingly disturbed, daunted less by the gun than by the prospect of the ruin of the blissful garden of pleasure he had so meticulously cultivated in this apartment; nothing Gauthier might have said could have cut him more to the quick. "You are really a disgusting person," he observed.

Gauthier moved the gun so that it was level with the heart, and Ben Larbi felt the thrill of wholehearted surrender. "If I am mad enough to accept, it is understood that this will be the last—the very last—service I ever render. Or have you sunk to being a permanent professional blackmailer?"

"Why don't you stop talking nonsense?"

"At any rate, you must wait—"

"Wait?" Gauthier repeated the word irritably.

"So that I can change my clothes! Do you expect me to flounce into the Ministry got up like a beachboy?"

In five minutes he was ready, dapper in elegant navy-blue, hair neatly brushed and oiled; in deference to the Revolution he had forsworn tie and breast-pocket handkerchief and wore his collar open, militant-style.

Hips waggling a bit, he trotted nimbly ahead of Gauthier down the broad stone stairway that was dark as Ali Baba's cavern in midafternoon. Once outdoors, Gauthier was momentarily dazzled by the street glare. Then each detail came into focus sharp and perilous. Two men in business suits stood in full sunlight on the opposite sidewalk. They began to come toward him. Another man advanced down the street, hugging the side of the apartment house, taking long flexible strides, like a heron. For a second Gauthier considered retreating toward the stairway, but he distrusted what might be lurking there.

By this time he had a grim armlock on Ben Larbi's neck and was prodding him with the gun away from the doorway, down the pavement, away from the advancing man, toward the corner where the station wagon was parked. Windows were opening in upper stories. An Arab street crowd had gathered —shopkeepers, old women, urchins were scurrying now for cover. Ben Larbi was squealing and thrashing like a puppy against the unbreakable armlock; spittle in semiliquid threads ran onto Gauthier's knuckles. On the opposite sidewalk the two men were running parallel with Gauthier. One of the men was moonfaced and wore a drooping walrus mustache; he ran with his gun hand held high and shouted at Gauthier in Arabic. The words meant nothing to him. Absurdly an image of ambiguous felicity—his lunch at La Goulette—swam into Gauthier's mind; he squeezed down on his agent's neck and Ben Larbi squeaked. Gauthier sniffed a dust-ridden breeze that blew grit into his eyes and closed his throat. Why had they failed to post a fourth man at the corner to bar his escape? Was this a trick, too? With a growl he clenched the armlock tighter, stifling Ben Larbi's yelps. All three men were dog-trotting in silent pursuit, heads down, economizing their breath, switching from one sidewalk to another and between themselves to confuse him. Abruptly the man with the mustache darted forward and crouched behind a delivery van. Gauthier fired at him immediately but the shot went wild. Clutching Ben Larbi's quivering body, he jabbed and kneed him toward the station wagon; they were within less than a yard of the rear fender when the mustached man sprang up and sprinted for the corner. Gauthier pivoted to give his gun arm a clear field of fire, and in that instant Ben Larbi bit his finger to the bone and wrenched free. Gauthier saw him bolt for safety into a barbershop but withheld fire. Waste ammunition on that lily-livered informer? He fumbled at the door handle and slid in across the front seat, trembling. His throat was raw and ash-dry. A shot thwacked against the fender, another thudded into the left front tire. That would be the mustached man again, who knew his job. The two others were out of sight across the street. Where were they? He had to make it somehow out of this ambush, out of the city, then he could decide where to hide. Ignition, accelerator . . . The blood drained from Gauthier's head at the metallic scraping sound; he stared incredulously at the pedal: the motor could not be stalling now . . . A blue police minicar was approaching down the street, its siren wailing.

Gauthier swiped up his gun from the adjoining seat and fired; at once a burst of dry shots replied. The station wagon settled brusquely like a camel on its deflating front tires. Men rushed past; their bodies converged and seemed to overflow the car. They were all about him, avid and bloodthirsty. He spat into a downthrust abstract face that materialized as an invisible fist pounded and shook the door. Suddenly the left side window shattered under the impact of a swiftly withdrawn pistol butt and flying glass flew at his lips and nicked his nose. He swore in German and tried to fire into the formless eager enemy, but outstretched hands were already clawing at his eyes, his mouth.

## CHAPTER TWENTY-ONE

# A Hiding Place

THE Gauthiers' maid was a dumpy woman with clever, luminous eyes set like black olives in a sallow moon face. Outdoors she hab ually wore a flowing white robe over a pink cotton blouse and black skirt; beneath, her body was plump, round and fluid, and there was not a touch of henna in her black smooth hair. Her voice was light as a young girl's but she had a tendency to screech. On this afternoon she was alone in the house with the Gauthier's son. The *khedima* sat on the back terrace, shucking peas into a saucepan and watching the boy bend over a jigsaw puzzle. She did not care much for this frail blond boy who was too quiet and polite, but the *khedima* was a conscientious woman who fulfilled her duties without grumbling. She was also, within the limits of her illiteracy, an astute woman. She was aware of the sprung tension between husband and wife in this household, and she did not expect them to remain together. The *khedima* inclined to side with the wife, despite her pampered ways, for she was lively and mettlesome; the husband's self-absorption repelled the *khedima*.

She heard a swift, furtive movement behind her back and frowned. In the suburban midafternoon stillness it had sounded like feet trotting in haste through the house. Or it might have been the creaking of the garage door, whose wood was warped from last summer's heat.

With a soft grunt the *khedima* waddled across the terrace and stared down. The garage door yawed open. When both Gauthiers were out, the door was normally left shut. She had understood that the husband was not due back for another hour, and the wife's red Triumph was certainly nowhere in sight. The *khedima* stood very still, watching suspiciously and debating whether to go down into the garden and inspect. After a while, detecting nothing unusual, she padded back to her chair on the terrace.

It had grown windy outdoors and the sun no longer lit the flagstones. "Marc, we must go in now," she told the boy.

Anne-Marie had listened to the doctor's views about child care, smiled with tact and finally come away with what she wanted. The signed certificate lay in her handbag. Flattering the doctor had taken about as long as she expected.

She parked the Triumph and leaped out. When she was gone forever from Carthage, she thought, the absence of this small red car would strike home hard—harder than the loss of most of her clothes and furniture.

From the driveway she saw that the sudden overcast had driven Marc and the Arab maid indoors. Tunisian winter afternoons were treacherous; most of the time it was warm enough to sit outdoors, but if the sun vanished for even a second it instantly grew bitter cold.

Anne-Marie let herself into the house through the front door. As she started to remove her coat she heard a light footstep in the hall closet. Before she could turn, a thick hand snatched her wrists, crushing them together; damp fingers imprisoned her mouth and nose, and a leg firmly pinioned her ankles. She couldn't see who the man was, but she felt herself losing her wits as he dragged her back hard against his broad body, and becoming sick as she caught the vile stench of his sweat and fear. Writhing and clawing desperately, she encountered a muscular forearm and really thought that she was going to faint. "Stop it, you hysterical idiot!" a voice rasped in her ear.

She thought of biting the fingers, but the clamp on her mouth was too tight. The man twisted her right arm and she arched forward in pain, lips flattening against his moist palm.

"Don't try to scratch me or I will break your arm. I am a friend of Alex's, and I have a loaded gun. Will you be sensible?"

Anne-Marie jerked her head up and down wildly. For an awful, incoherent moment she had feared that Marc was being kidnapped in some new, odd twist of the Revolution; if the man was not after her son, she was less afraid of him.

Releasing her arm, in one rapid movement he had prodded a steel barrel into the small of her back. The fingers of his left hand still lay in an airproof gag over her wet mouth.

Anne-Marie fought back the temptation to scream. She remained backed up against him in the closet, quivering and disgusted. If he hurt her, she planned to bring down her heel with full force on his foot.

He edged around fast and replaced his hand on her mouth, just as firmly but somehow less painfully, and she saw a short, homely man with a crown of black curls around a bald patch and a high, rotund forehead and dark eyes as trustful as a croupier's. He was training an ugly long-barreled pistol on her.

"I had to make sure you didn't scream," he said, with a trace of apology, in a German-accented voice. "Where is your husband?"

She pointed to his fingers and he removed them from her mouth reluctantly.

"I am here to see your husband. Where is he?"

"He went to Sidi Bou Said to see you—if you are Levanon, that is. Are you?"

"Maybe. My name should not concern you. You—or he —may be telling lies. When do you expect him to return?"

Anne-Marie bristled at this casual assumption of her untrustworthiness. Her mouth smarted less; she could talk back to this ruffian now. "What are you going to do to him when he comes back?"

"Don't worry. I need his cooperation," the man said unsmilingly. "It is quite simple."

Should she tell him the truth? How much more brutal would he become if he learned that they were planning to leave Tunis? "Alex will be back at four-thirty," Anne-Marie said finally.

Levanon stood very close and spoke in a grating whisper. "Who else is in the house?"

"My son and our maid." Anne-Marie glanced involuntarily at the ceiling and he frowned. "Did she see you?"

"How would I know? I don't think so. The garage door was open and I entered that way. A woman was talking on the terrace."

"She's upstairs with my son now. Can we go into Alex's study? She never sets foot in there without being asked to."

Levanon nodded and, with surprising softness of tread for a man of his stocky build, followed her into the small room.

Anne-Marie carefully locked the door, then turned on him.

"Are you looking for a hiding place?"

Max appraised her and did not lower the gun. He did not know to what extent, if any, he could trust this woman. However, her behavior so far reassured him; he was glad that she had struggled fiercely to break free. He profoundly mistrusted females who sobbed and pleaded for mercy to escape the slightest flick of pain. Gauthier's wife was self-possessed—it was far easier than trying to control a nervous, fearful hostage.

"Yes," he grunted, "I need a hiding place."

"I thought so. How did you get here without being caught?"

"Don't ask so many complicated questions. Weren't you trained not to?" He gazed around the room. The study had only one entrance, which he could cover with ease. He motioned to Anne-Marie to move aside from the window that overlooked the garden.

She did so with deliberate lack of haste. "Are you going to keep me a prisoner here until Alex returns?"

"Unless I have a better idea. I can afford no more errors; this must be obvious to you."

"Why did you come here? To make trouble?" Anne-Marie burst out hotly. "Don't you realize this house may be unsafe?"

"Do you think I had a choice? The submarine did not come; the Army and police were everywhere—" He broke off, seeing that her attention had wandered.

"Will you let me go upstairs and tell the maid to stay where she is? Do you trust me enough? Usually, as soon as I come home, I go upstairs to see my son. If I don't, she'll wonder what is happening."

He shook his head emphatically.

"Why not?"

"To use the upstairs phone and call outside for help?"

"There is no other phone but this one. Anyhow, do you think I want to let people know that you are here?" Anne-Marie was persuaded that he would refuse. She was partially lying. There *was* an extension in the master bedroom, but she had no intention of using it, for she had no idea whom to call without becoming ensnared in dangerous explanations, and, moreover, she had no stomach for exacerbating further this roughneck who had broken into her house. "I can't afford to let the maid find you here," she pleaded in a taut whisper. "If you would only admit that we all have the same problem!"

Abruptly Max made a gesture of assent with his free left hand.

When Anne-Marie had left the room he sat down. A tide of fever flushed through his head, rushing up to the roots of his hair. Fever made him unduly conscious of other things—of the tooth decay festering under one of his gold crowns, of the garland of black strands woven wetly around his belly button. All day he had been on the run; now, under a sheltering roof, he experienced an overpowering urge simply to shut his eyes and wait.

Anne-Marie found the *khedima* stolidly storing the boy's ironed shirts in his dresser.

She looked up and announced, "There was a noise in the garage."

"I heard it too," Anne-Marie's son said. "It was like a cat. Do you want to come and see?"

"I'd like to but not right away; if it was a stray cat, it's gone by this time. Can you dust the guest room and take down the curtains? Do not polish the silver, it can wait; you have no time for that this afternoon." The maid had to be sent home firmly but tactfully, in a way that started no questions in her inquiring mind. Anne-Marie was aware that once home the *khedima* told her husband everything of interest that went on in the house of the well-to-do French family.

"I can stay longer today if you want," the *khedima* said.


"Make as little noise as possible. She suspects nothing for the moment, but I am having a hard time sending her away."

"Why is your husband taking so long?"

"He went to Sidi Bou Said to meet you," Anne-Marie replied sharply. "In order to help you."

"I don't trust your husband," Levanon scowled, sitting up, the gun within easy reach in his lap. "Perhaps if I had distrusted him further, the driver in my commando would still be at liberty."

Anne-Marie had never before heard a man speak with such matter-of-fact dislike for her husband. "He is risking his life to save yours," she whispered angrily.

The reply did not seem to impress the squat, desperate man in the armchair.

She experienced an obscure need to overcome his distrust and force him to amend his judgment.

"In the first place, what happened to the commando was not Alex's fault—" Anne-Marie fell silent, fascinated and repelled by the man's snakelike fixed black gaze. She did not specify whose fault it had been.

"The time is up. You said four-thirty. Why is he not back?"

"I have no idea," she retorted truthfully in an anguished undertone. Time was dragging on terribly. In spite of her efforts to remain composed, her imagination was beginning to run away with her; she visualized a half-dozen explanations, all of them dire. Anne-Marie rose nervously, went to the window and surveyed the empty garden as though she were staring out from behind bars.

Levanon had picked up the long-barreled pistol warily. "When I came here, I wondered whether I could trust you. I decided that I could. Now I am again no longer sure," he grumbled.

"My God! I encouraged Alex to help you."

Watching her, he realized that she shared his fear. "You haven't told me the full truth, have you?"

Anne-Marie bit her lip. If Alex was not back in ten minutes, she had decided that she would confide in Levanon and tell him about the meeting with Ben Larbi. Curiously she studied this plain, rumpled Israeli who held her prisoner. Now that she was becoming accustomed to his presence, she had revised her opinion of him. He had had the gall to talk his way into Al Houaranni's heavily guarded hotel suite and spirit him to the far end of Cap Bon, then turn about and bolt back alone into occupied Tunis. It required some quality besides sheer bullheadedness to do that.

"You are going to have to trust me more than you thought," Anne-Marie murmured.

Levanon began to growl in reply when he was interrupted by the noise the *khedima* made on sandaled feet as she moved about upstairs.

Anne-Marie caught herself waiting tensely for another, closer sound that would signify the maid was coming downstairs.

"That is why you must trust me," she said starkly. Her mind was made up; in Alex's absence she would act by herself. She was unsure what to do about the certificate in her handbag, but she had decided that first and foremost she must get Levanon out of her house—for his sake as well as her own.

Mills listened to Preston's report of the interview and commented with a glint of asperity, "The captain is a provincial bore on the make. These types are the same everywhere; they'll lick your ass or kick your ass. The sort of cooperation he's blathering about amounts to zero. I've already talked with the Committee. They don't number more than a half-dozen officers and some are all right. We can do business with them. In the lot, Fawzi is the bad apple. There are three possibilities: he may do as he says and break the Liaison Agreement; or he may say that's what he's doing but in fact do the opposite; or he may already be in bed with the other side and this whole offer is a provocation. However, that's unlikely."

Preston exhibited a tiny smile. "I came close to walking out on him."

"That was pretty silly. It would be terribly unfair to the guy. After all, he told you where he stands. Furthermore, it would be the surest way of driving him across the street to the other side."

"Sometimes, with these people, you have to shout to make yourself heard."

"Not too loud—not in this business," Mills said. "There are other ways of gaining cooperation." When he talked in this vein, Mills's face turned stony; only his eyes sustained a life of their own, watchful, uninfluenceable, coldly waiting. "I think I had better brief Washington—then we can decide how far we want to trust him."

"What do you think the Division will do if he refuses to uphold the Agreement?"

"Bully or intimidate him, you mean? I think it would be an idle threat."

"Do you think we can work up a deal to save Kheli?"

"I doubt we can save anybody. The truth is, at this point Fawzi has no need of us. Later it's bound to change, naturally."

"I think he's lying and that Kheli is dead. But since it doesn't look respectable for his predecessor to be found machine-gunned alongside the highway, with bullet holes in his back, he's concocted this fable about another victim."

"If he lied about that, he'll lie about everything else in the future; in dealing with him, you can never afford to forget it." Mills looked serious for once and said, "You'll have to watch your step from now on if you become involved in anything operational or risk expulsion. Your impression is that he's cracked the Al Houaranni case by appropriating the colonel's leads?"

"Some of it may be bluff."

"Do you think that Fawzi in his entire career ever sat down and bluffed? The Committee's coup succeeded because it lacked bluff and imagination; the whole bunch are literal-minded, which is what renders them so unattractive. Fawzi himself is idealistic, pious, virtuous, opinionated. What could be more dangerous for a chief of Secret Police?" Mills stood up and braced his shoulders; he was putting on too much weight but he bore himself with the snappy assurance of a Guards officer on parade. "I'm not looking for a sparring partner at the Interior Ministry. I need a fighter who can last fifteen rounds and win on a decision to run this country's Intelligence Service. So let's have a little headwork from now on, please." Suddenly he hunched his shoulders and passed a large, freckled paw over his mouth as though repressing a roar of laughter: this was his lazy and effective way of simulating amusement. "I hope they don't chuck us out. I just had a year in Washington and I don't like to move around too often. We're settled in here, the ambassador's been good to me and the beer isn't bad in this place."

Preston returned to his office upstairs. He found an urgent telephone message Pat had left on the desk. Anne-Marie Gauthier would be at his cottage at 5 P.M., it said. There was not a single word of explanation. Preston glanced at his watch and saw that it was already quarter to five.

## CHAPTER TWENTY-TWO

# A Cold House

ANNE-MARIE said to the *khedima*, "I must go unexpectedly to see Madame Chateaudun. Since you are in no hurry, will you stay with Marc until my husband returns?"

"I can stay until seven."

"He or I will be back long before then."

Legs flashing impatiently, Anne-Marie left the house by the front door and walked down to the red Triumph in the driveway. She backed the car far enough into the garage so that it could not be seen from upstairs and stared through the rearview mirror. Levanon stood immobile in shadow behind the warped door. A few minutes earlier she had led him in silence down the servants' staircase to the basement, attentive to any sound that might alert the maid. As far as could be judged, the *khedima*'s vigilance had not been aroused. Anne-Marie waited until the shadowy figure had scrambled into the rear and was huddled out of sight on the floorboards, then, taking care not to accelerate noticeably while the house was in view, she drove away, her heart beating wildly.

Several unpaved back roads crisscross the neighborhood

between Carthage and Gammarth. These roads, which bisect parched fields of corn and beans and patches of oasislike greenery marking out new, uncompleted residential developments, attract scant traffic. Anne-Marie encountered only two or three cars, as few as when she had driven—heart likewise beating wildly—to her twice-weekly rendezvous with Preston.

By the time she turned off the beach road, the dying sun loomed red as a giant apple over the hills of Sidi Bou Said and Gammarth. The sunset glow lasted only a few seconds but it splashed the wide sky with garish color. Such dusky tints elsewhere might seem stagy; here they appeared African and natural.

Preston was already waiting for her in the doorway.

Anne-Marie turned the headlights off and ran up to him. "I have someone with me—it has to do with Alex," she explained hastily.

"I thought your message might have to do with us and our conversation on the beach."

"How could it?"

"No change of heart? I'm sorry. Bring him in. No one can see you over the wall."

Preston led the way into the long, impersonal living room and then turned and inspected his guest. The chesty, curly-haired man who trudged into the house on Anne-Marie's heels had a wrestler's shoulders; sweat sprang out in little onions on his sunburned temples; the tiny veins in his eyes were red and inflamed. He seemed utterly unconcerned by the cloud of dust and sourness his rumpled black suit stirred up.

"This is Kaleb Levanon, the leader of the Al Houaranni commando." Anne-Marie made the introduction tartly. "I found him in my house hiding from the police and waiting for Alex. Finally I lost my nerve. I didn't dare keep him longer with the *khedima* about. I called your office and now I've brought him here. I told him who you are and what you do. There was no one else I could turn to."

"Wait here a moment," Preston said and went outdoors. When he returned they were standing stiffly in the center of the room without speaking to each other.

"I've parked my car in front so that it hides yours. Where is Alex?"

"He went into town." Anne-Marie made no effort to hide her panic. "God! I don't know what's happened to him. He was due back at four-thirty."

She told Preston about the evening flight and the meeting with Ben Larbi.

"Half an hour is not very long to be overdue."

"I know it. But do you think he would be late today, of all days, if he could help it? 'We *must* be on that plane,' he said."

Preston considered her for a while. "What have you done about the tickets?"

"Nothing yet," she replied tersely. "While I waited for Alex, I kept wondering whether to go on my own to the Transportation Ministry and get a travel order—but I wanted your advice." She indicated Levanon without joy. "Can you hide him here for a while?"

The squat man interrupted her. "Gauthier was a fool," he growled. "Why does he need to be aboard that flight? What is he worried about? Unless I am caught, his cover cannot be blown . . . and I am by no means ready to be caught." He stood planted on the Kairouan rug, legs apart, truculent and attentive—resembling, Preston thought, a thick, immobile beetle.

Anne-Marie disregarded him and went on. "If Alex came home now, he wouldn't understand why I had left."

Preston took up the telephone and dialed the Carthage number. It rang for a few seconds, then an Arab woman's voice replied. Immediately a stream of words swarmed over the wire like bees. He had to strain to understand the disjointed sentences in guttural French. He asked a few questions, then ended the conversation abruptly by saying, "No, I don't know where either of them is. But stay with the boy as long as you can."

Preston turned and encountered Anne-Marie's pale stare of interrogation. He said without amenity, "Your instinct in clearing out was right; the police arrived just after you left. They searched the house, terrified the maid, waited for you, then finally returned to Tunis, posting one man in the street. The maid is out of her wits. She told them you went to see a friend; she's afraid they want to arrest you."

"They must have arrested Alex." Anne-Marie stood petrified with blank horror. "I'm going back——"

Preston forced her to sit down, and she looked up at him, haggard. "Will you help him? Can you do something for him?"

Calming her, he thought, had instant priority. "We're not even sure that Alex has been arrested——"

"Why else would they have come to the house? They have nothing against *me*."

"The police will trace the call here," Levanon said.

"No they won't. I didn't give the maid my name."

Preston calculated the time. He had left Fawzi's office at about three-fifty; a few minutes earlier, the captain had received the call that had led him to brag about "positive news" and "actively following up the Al Houaranni affair." Was that an allusion to Gauthier's arrest? When had Gauthier gone to his meeting with Ben Larbi? At two-thirty. In the interval of one hour and twenty minutes it was certainly possible that the police had set an ambush, arrested Gauthier and informed Fawzi. Enough time had then elapsed for them to cover the distance to Carthage. Their main purpose had obviously been to search the house . . . which implied that they needed incriminating papers to document a case against Gauthier.

Preston said to Anne-Marie, "You can't return home and I can't keep either of you here, except temporarily. Assume that Fawzi knows about us; he may not dare raid this house too, but he'll put it under surveillance. I have to move both of you to a safer place."

"God, Alex is missing . . . my son is alone with the maid—" Anne-Marie was trembling uncontrollably.

"She is going to be sick." Max came forward with a clumsy gesture of assistance.

Swiftly Preston filled and handed her a glass—a liqueur glass, the nearest to hand. She tried to refuse but then ended by accepting it.

She swallowed the fig brandy and grimaced. "I *was* going to be sick; it came over me all of a sudden. Do you remember when I once said that this is a cold, cold house—well, it is. I don't know why I came here."

333

"I can't let you go back. It's too late for that. If you're arrested, it won't help Alex."

"How can you be sure the police are holding her husband?" Max addressed Preston. "Probably he smelled a trap at the agent's home and fled. He is no beginner at this business—no more than you or I."

"Are you trying to cheer us up? If he's on the run, they'll catch him soon enough."

The shrill ringing of the telephone, echoing through the house, startled them into silence by its abrupt intrusion. As Preston answered, he made a conscious effort to avoid Anne-Marie's gaze.

It was Mills. He was speaking calmly but quickening his delivery and his prep-school intonation was more noticeable than usual. "You'd best plan on another long night. The Israeli agent arrested on Cap Bon has committed suicide by jumping from the Interior Ministry's top story—at least, that's the official version. A helpful push has been known to occur in that building, but of course we're told those practices ceased when the French left. He was 'undergoing an *interrogation poussée*,' it seems." In spite of his size, Mills's voice was soft. Close up the articulation was clean and precise, as befitted a man who could not afford misunderstandings; but on the telephone, or even at a short distance, one sometimes had to strain to catch his meaning, for he did not seek to be overheard in public places. "There's more. Gauthier is in custody and the Ministry is acting as though it's landed a big fish. The gossip is that Gauthier was the Resident Director, which would confirm your suspicions. At any rate, lots of coming and going, talk of a secret trial, an emergency Cabinet session. The correspondents are being called in later for a briefing."

334

"I've heard the news," Preston said succinctly. "Has the Committee made an announcement yet?"

"No." Mills was being very careful now over the phone; he was obviously attempting to convey a warning. "I think they'll wait until they can round up the others."

"People who leave the ball game before the ninth inning are optimists."

The blood was roaring obscurely in Preston's ears; it had been ever since he spoke to the Gauthiers' maid and realized that he would have to act on behalf of Anne-Marie's husband. "I'd like to have a frank chat with you—as soon as possible."

"Am I finally getting a little headwork? Why don't you drop in for a hamburger—you haven't seen the kids for a long while—or do you want to come back to the office?" Mills was trying to find out how urgent it was. Mills's stately house in La Marsa fronted the sea and presented certain advantages. When he led a visitor down to his private beach, no one could eavesdrop with accuracy on what was said. The beach was a good deal more security-proof from long-range microphones than was the Embassy.

"Yes, I'll come to your place. Expect me in about fifteen minutes," Preston said. It was urgent, all right, urgent enough to warrant a side trip to Mills's house. He poured some fig brandy for himself, sat down and regarded Levanon and Anne-Marie.

"Unfortunately the news is confirmed. Alex has been arrested."

She had set her glass aside and was staring at him intently with complete concentration, but the panic, Preston saw, reassured, had yielded to a healthier, tougher strain of resistance.

"I've an idea—a risky one admittedly, but I think that we can finesse the captain, provided no one loses his nerve, particularly you, Anne-Marie."

Her green eyes glowed in her pale face. "Where else can Alex look for help? *They* can't help him." She meant the Qiryat, which had no open allies, no avowable influence. "To try to save an Israeli here is worse than anything; it's the kiss of death."

Levanon stirred, as though she were wasting time in pursuit of an unprofitable truth. "Are you just now discovering this?" he rumbled.

"Whatever you want, I'm willing to do," Anne-Marie said in a level, unemotional voice, "if it can help save Alex."

"Maybe it can, maybe it can't; don't become overconfident. I'm giving you the trickiest part of the plan to carry out. The man you'll be coming up against is stupid, obstinate and hard. We'll do our utmost to back you up."

"But will it work?"

"We'll be putting a lot into it."

She sensed Preston's reservations. "Don't you realize that Alex is in deadly trouble?" she cried. "He's mixed up; he no longer knows whether he's Israeli or French—and he's found out that others are cleverer than he is."

"I realize all that, Anne-Marie."

"He walked straight into a trap because he was trying to do his damnedest for a sick boy and an unfaithful wife."

"This is no time to weep over that—or to go to pieces on me, either."

"I won't if you don't."

"I'm trying to save Alex from his own errors." Preston rebuffed her with cold-blooded disapproval that inwardly he did not really feel. In their trade, after all, an attitude of smugness was a distinct luxury, but one way or another he had to prod this girl into standing firm.

Anne-Marie's animal fright had swept her beyond conventional sentiments of gratitude.

"Will you? Will you for once do something not for your career or the satisfaction of your balls?" she exclaimed. The coarseness was meant to shock. "You always want to feel one-up on everybody. Now is your chance—"

Levanon swung about, muttering. "Whatever your plan happens to be, why should she trust you? For that matter, why should I?" To Anne-Marie he said, "We are making a mistake. Their Service cannot jeopardize its interests here for three non-Americans who are an embarrassment—"

Preston's temper snapped. "Does one more mistake bother you? You've already made so many." His face was stiff and undecipherable. "Would you prefer to trust someone else? Did I come to you in the first place or was it the other way around? I could do nothing at all; *that* would be in the Agency's interest. Whatever I do, if I do it, don't put it down to altruism—am I the type?"

Preston felt delivered of an ambiguous burden. In spite of his outburst, he had chosen sides. Wasn't it Mills who had said, "There's no place for Hamlets in this business, friend?" The feelings he had just expressed were honest, but there were other, equally important feelings he had passed over because they could not easily or decently be translated into words. He had left unspoken, for example, his concern about Kheli's probable fate. Nor had he stated explicitly that he was acting for Anne-Marie's sake, since this explanation appeared to him self-evident as the most natural of the lot.

Committed, Preston had only one basic doubt: Would Mills buy his idea? To succeed, it depended on will power, impudence and a born ability to bluff. Its only merit, from the Agency's point of view, lay in the prospect of sapping Fawzi's position. But was this advantage compelling enough? If the plan backfired, it would bring spectacular retaliation and Fawzi would emerge more powerful than ever. The temptation existed to patch up a working relationship with the Committee; Mills had made this blindingly clear. After hearing out the plan, he might say, "I have a lot of respect for the Israelis, granted, but we're under no obligation to haul their chestnuts out of the fire." He would glide over Anne-Marie's problem, not out of lack of sympathy with her, but because it was a matter he could not officially take into account; the personal problem was simultaneously more or less urgent, depending on your vantage point.

Stubbornly, Levanon continued to address Anne-Marie. "This is as sincere an answer as this man is going to give. Who knows? Maybe my instinct is wrong and he is a miracle worker." Appeased, he sat down and asked, "Did you receive any news about my agent Marston?"

"Yes."

"I cannot forgive myself for what happened to him. I was ready to drive through the checkpoint in our car but he insisted on taking my place. Was it very bad news?"

"He's dead—suicide or murder, according to whom you believe." Preston's voice was neutral.

Max hoisted himself stiffly out of the chair, went to the window and stared out in silence, then, conscious that they were watching him, he turned around and said, "Marston was always an unrelenting bastard. I'm sure he told them very

338

little. He was an excellent driver and a hard-working fellow."

"How could it happen so fast?" Anne-Marie demanded, outraged. "Alex said there was a safety margin—"

"The Tunisian Secret Police are pretty spry when they want to be on a matter like that. They probably didn't leave him much choice." Preston put on a gabardine topcoat and found his car keys. He did not want to alarm her further, but before departing for Mills's house he felt that she must be made aware of the grimness of the situation. "A purge is coming. Fawzi made this clear, and he won't spare enemies—so there isn't much time, not enough, at any rate, to move you to another place. We'll have to run a risk and keep you here. This is the plan—this is what you must do . . ."

Never before in her life had Anne-Marie listened so attentively.

An hour later, telephoning from the cottage, she asked for a number Preston had given her at the Interior Ministry; then she identified herself.

"I would like an appointment with Captain Fawzi on an urgent matter," she said in a tremorless voice.

There was a silence. Then a man's gruff voice replied, "This is Fawzi. Come to my office at once."

## CHAPTER TWENTY-THREE

# The Deal

Fawzi distrusted European women; this one who sat in his office, more than most. His eye fastened on the gold clip in her blond hair, the cashmere sweater and skirt, the crocodile handbag in her lap. To fabricate a woman like this cost a shocking sum. Save for an insignificant minority, Arab women were not so recklessly spoiled, certainly his own young wife and sisters were not. The world Fawzi wanted to construct and defend contained no place for a woman like this; industrialization, standardization, purification—these were the key concepts of the new era, his era, when his countrymen could begin to vie with the extravagant, domineering West.

He looked at her with loathing. "You are not Jewish but married to a Jew."

"My husband is a French citizen," Anne-Marie replied staunchly.

"Does this entitle him to violate Tunisian law? Besides, his allegiance is not to France . . . of this we have proof." Suddenly he was seized by a compulsive desire to make her squirm; she reminded him uncomfortably of a youthful, condescending schoolmistress who had filled his days with rage when he was a fidgety pupil at the French *lycée*. "We are judging our enemies—profiteers, venal ministers, rapacious landowners, all the lice from the old regime which have to be plucked out before we can make progress. Your husband throve in this breeding ground of corruption. Think of it! For eight years, if not more, he and you duped us, every time we gave him information, every time you entered our homes! I can think of nothing more vile or brazen since Cohen in Damascus. For your information, Alex Gauthier, or whatever his real name happens to be, is charged with espionage on behalf of the Zionist usurper State, organization of a kidnapping, illegal wireless transmissions, bribery of a government official . . . many evil things. If found guilty, he faces a similar fate as that other scoundrel."

Fawzi watched with interest a peach flush mount to her fair skin; however, try as he might to stare her down, her eyes did not waver.

Enraged, he went on. "Your husband for years was the ringleader of a network of vicious and dangerous spies. We are in the course of identifying and neutralizing them. I have issued a warrant for your arrest as an accomplice. By coming here, you saved me a certain amount of trouble, but abandon any illusion that this will gain you leniency."

Anne-Marie was disconcerted by Fawzi's earnest, voluble indignation, but his aggressive maneuvering to throw her off balance and instill in her a sense of shame came as no surprise. He had been thoroughly coached by Preston.

She addressed herself to this corpulent would-be reformer. "You accuse my husband of Al Houaranni's kidnapping, but the man who actually committed this crime under the noses of

341

your police—and made them a laughingstock throughout the Arab world—is still at large. Do you want to capture him?"

"At this stage what should I do with him?" Fawzi gave way to a curt, scornful Mediterranean shrug. "We hold your husband, who was the Israeli Resident! This is an unprecedented catch! Who would have hoped for it two days ago? Neither the Libyans nor the Algerians have ever managed to achieve as much. Two of your husband's slimy agents are liquidated. Of what importance is one more frightened subordinate? Besides"—his smile was patronizing and all-encompassing—"you may decide to tell us where he is hiding."

Anne-Marie's hands were deathly cold on her bag. She was intensely impressed by her surroundings. The lake was acting up this evening; the acid aroma of excrement wafted, cloying and overpowering, into the Ministry. The captain's office bore a dingy look of hard use and frugality, the air itself smelled of dust, steel and brown soap; it was bathed in human viciousness and errors. Like police premises everywhere, the captain's quarters suggested the gloomy antechamber of a prison; in this office the threat of torture stirred, still no clearly stated, dissimulated behind a hint, but present.

"You don't have to threaten me," Anne-Marie said in her clear, forthright voice. "I will tell you right now who I am talking about. His real name is Kaleb Levanon, but he entered Tunisia under a German passport delivered to Hans Konrad Stoerchler of Saarbrücken. Contrary to what you believe, he is no 'frightened subordinate.' He is a captain in Israeli Intelligence—that is, he holds the same rank as you." She added these last words in a hurry but audibly. If the call on the captain was a hair-raising gamble in its own right, this ap roach was even riskier: Fawzi's vanity must be scratched without ruffling his temper too far.

He blinked at the slur but did not retort. He watched her closely as she searched in her handbag and removed a pack of French cigarettes. With a frown he refused when she proffered a Gitane.

"It is not authorized to smoke here," he observed. "No, go ahead since you have begun." He made no attempt to light her cigarette. "What are you proposing exactly?"

Anne-Marie was approaching a part of the conversation that was critical. Never had she been so aware of the lightness of her voice, which seemed too insubstantial for the weight of each momentous word she had to utter.

"I will turn over Levanon to you as well as one hundred thousand dollars in return for my husband's freedom. The money will be made available to the Coordinating Committee to disburse as it chooses—a donation to the Revolution, if you like."

Fawzi sat back and shook his head. He was visibly relieved; attempted subornation was an offense he could deal with more expertly than a young woman's insinuations about his rank. "Your proposal does not interest me in the slightest. I expected this sort of maneuver. It is a clumsy attempt at bribery, no matter what you choose to call it." He reached for the intercom. "Let's waste no further time. You are under arrest. My aide has some questions to ask you. We can obtain information concerning Levanon's whereabouts without entering into putrid deals. That was the old regime's habit and the major reason for its fall."

"Please listen to me for a moment," she said sharply.

"Levanon is an experienced field agent. If you jail me, he will vanish and you will be no more successful than before in tracking him down. I can be made to tell where he *was*; it will not enable you to discover where he *is*. The money, of course, is safely out of Tunis, except for this." She placed an oblong plain envelope on the desk. "I brought the equivalent of ten thousand dollars in Swiss francs."

Fawzi recoiled as swiftly as though the envelope contained a scorpion. Anne-Marie pursued. "It was the only way I could prove my good faith."

Fawzi said angrily, "Where does this money come from?" She noticed that his hand had strayed from the intercom.

"These are my husband's operational funds. He kept them at the house. I removed every franc before your police arrived, thank God."

Fawzi's dark, suspicious eyes rose and scanned her face for what seemed an eternity. He was seething with repressed fury. Finally, with intense distaste, he took a letter cutter, slit open the envelope and glanced inside at the contents.

"You claim these are Israeli Intelligence funds?"

Anne-Marie nodded affirmatively. The skin around her mouth was bloodless, an unhealthy dingy white, as when she was menstruating. It wasn't true. But if he ever learned that was CIA money, his anger would be far more dangerous. As it was, he was eying the envelope in the way a rodent does when it sniffs alien fingermarks on a piece of cheese.

"Is this your idea? I think you may be quick but not that quick. Who put you up to it?"

"Who would come to my assistance? Would Ha Mossad instruct me to turn over Levanon?" She had been briefed in painstaking detail by Preston.

Fawzi had removed the dull-colored bank notes and piled them on his desk. "The total is correct," he said. "I am confiscating this sum. This is foreign currency imported illegally into Tunisia."

"It represents only one-tenth of what I am offering," Anne-Marie interjected hurriedly. "The rest of the money is deposited in an escrow account in a Beirut bank that is used as a funding mechanism for making payments to Arab agents working for Israel. My husband and I have signatory powers. As soon as outgoing telephone calls are authorized tomorrow morning, I will contact the bank and give instructions to deposit ninety thousand dollars to a new account in your name and mine. Lebanese banks are still willing to open new accounts sight unseen, which is no longer the case in Switzerland. There will be no problem about the transfer, as I shall use a prearranged code my husband has resorted to in the past. The bank will then send you an advice of credit, but you will be unable to withdraw funds without my consent. When my husband receives an exit visa, I will confirm my agreement to the withdrawal of forty thousand dollars. Once we are out of the country, I will advise the bank that I am relinquishing my interest in the account. It will then be in your sole custody and you can withdraw the remaining fifty thousand dollars whenever you please. For this final transaction, you will have to trust me. Of course you're thinking, What is to prevent us from defaulting once we are out of your reach? If this happened, you would still hold Levanon and be fifty thousand dollars richer."

Would he buy it? Anne-Marie saw his deep-set brown eyes grow deceptively dull. "Your plan is foolish. After acquiring fifty thousand dollars, I can change my mind, invalidate the visa and prevent you both from flying out. Have you thought about this?"

"Yes, but it is in your interest to receive the balance. You must trust me to transfer it to your custody, while I must trust you to let us leave."

"Obviously." He could not quite smooth out the derision in his voice.

"Permit me to leave now and I promise to turn Levanon over to you at my house tonight. He will be disarmed and drugged; there will be no danger of a gun battle—my husband had pentobarbital tablets that he planned to administer to Al Houaranni if necessary." Anne-Marie paused, taut and out of breath, then she asked desperately, "Have you publicly announced my husband's arrest yet?"

"We are about to."

"Suppose that you don't? Don't you see what I am getting at? People know an Israeli spy has been captured, but they aren't sure of his identity. It's just as easy for you to announce at the press conference that it is Kaleb Levanon. Later, if any questions are raised about Alex, the police can state that he was temporarily held in connection with a misleading story he tried to send about the Revolution; his name does not have to be linked at all to an espionage charge."

Fawzi reflected for a moment, deliberately avoiding her tense stare and tracing with the tip of one fat forefinger an abstract design on the polished desk.

"You propose to do all this—betraying this man Levanon, cheating Ha Mossad of so much money—to save your husband?"

"Yes."

"It was my understanding that you were not on close terms."

346

"Perhaps, but he is nevertheless my husband."

Involuntarily Fawzi glanced at the neat pile of bank notes on the desk. His cupidity had been aroused all right, she thought.

Instead of mentioning the money, Fawzi asked, "Do you realize what will happen to Levanon once he is in our hands?"

Anne-Marie glanced down at her lap and nodded very swiftly.

"The allegiance you feel to your husband's cause—is it that superficial?" When she said nothing, he insisted. "I am asking you a serious question."

To her astonishment Anne-Marie discovered the answer within herself, unhesitatingly.

"Captain, I am not Jewish. Furthermore, contrary to what you think, I am not a Mossad agent; my sole responsibility is to my husband and son."

There had been prompting by Preston to furnish this reply too, but she had found a tone of stony and bottomless distress that was hers alone.

She waited. The delay seemed interminable. She dared not stare into the smug gleaming face across the desk. Anne-Marie recalled Preston's cautionary preamble: "The man you'll be coming up against is stupid, obstinate and hard." But was he so stupid? It was not her impression. If Fawzi said, "I shall take this matter up with the Committee," then the gamble had failed. The odds were in favor of such a negative reaction, but Fawzi did not react as she feared. He said softly, "In the event that I agreed—this is theoretical, of course—your husband has many more things to tell us of interest. How can I release him prematurely?"

"I cannot deliver Levanon to you for another two hours,"

she said cold-bloodedly. "He is obviously not in my house at present."

Fawzi stared at her hard. Was she suggesting that he put the time to profit and torture her husband? It was inconceivable, but she seemed to understand that they would in any event prize loose a maximum of information before relinquishing Gauthier. In short, she was assessing the situation with utter worldly realism. She seemed a woman who could, in defense of her vital interests, be simultaneously flexible and obstinate, that was, simple to bend but impossible to break. The suppleness was misleading; beneath lay basalt. He was beginning to admire her courage; it had required courage in the first place to venture into his office. No other worried foreigner in memory had ever dared do so.

Fawzi was in something of a quandary. He had spotted a flaw in her plan that he could exploit, but was there another, undiscovered, that she could exploit against him?

"Show me your handbag," he asked suddenly.

She opened the bag and handed it over. He rummaged through the contents and returned it.

Anne-Marie watched him and a sarcastic smile played fleetingly on her lips.

"Did you expect to find something dangerous? I have no gun."

"I was not looking for a gun," he muttered without further amplification. "To get back to your plan—purely for the sake of argument, let me stress—why not transfer the second installment of forty thousand dollars directly here without opening a new account in Beirut? You could do it in your name so that the money would be safe."

Under other circumstances, Anne-Marie would have

laughed aloud; the question was so evidently a trap—like those that clumsy teachers put in the hope of catching pupils unawares.

"Captain, once the money arrived in a local bank, would you feel any pressure whatever to let us go? Besides," she replied evenly, "I cannot transfer funds to Tunisia since the Committee blocked *virements* in both directions."

"I am glad that you are not trying to side-step that regulation too. Then how would the second and third payments be of use to me, exactly?"

He was really new to this game, Anne-Marie thought; power had come to him only within the past twenty-four hours; he was not acquainted with the elementary mechanics of manipulating large sums of money. Nor am I, she reminded herself.

"Until funds can be repatriated, the ninety thousand dollars, once withdrawn, will remain in a Beirut account solely in your name or," she added blandly, "another Committee member's. But this seems unnecessarily complicated, as I am dealing with you." She had to tread carefully here, for his artlessness might conceal another trap. "How do I know someone else will honor our agreement?"

"I have entered into no agreement so far," he rebuked her quickly, and tried another gambit. "How do I know the man you want to deliver is really an Israeli agent?"

"The police who were on duty outside Al Houaranni's suite at the Hotel Africa two nights ago can identify him."

The door opened and a thickset man with a drooping walrus mustache glanced in. Fawzi impatiently waved him away and rose. "Perhaps we can work something out. Understand me: all depends on whether you are able to deliver Levanon.

349

The money is really of secondary importance. Your husband is a valuable prize and I am not especially desirous to exchange him for lesser goods." This was his indirect Arab way of expressing assent. "However, we are a poor movement and the money may do some good. There is something gratifying about allowing Ha Mossad to finance one or two of our projects." He sized her up with dispassionate curiosity. "Let us hope that you are not a stupid woman who is trying to outwit me. There is nothing more disastrous than a stupid woman."

Anne-Marie felt no compulsion to reply. Her heart again was beating very fast. It had worked; the trap was about to spring.

"If, for any reason, someone were to follow me when I leave here"—she continued to recite in her lucid, honest voice the provocative remarks that Preston had supplied—"you run the risk of automatically sabotaging the entire arrangement. Levanon is high-strung; I'm not sure how far he trusts me— not very far, at any rate. While I may not realize that I am being followed, he surely will. What I mean is, if he's scared off, there won't be a second chance of catching him off guard."

"One chance should be enough. There will be no blundering on my part. Good! The rendezvous is at nine P.M. at your house. I'll be there on time, and meanwhile the policeman stationed outside will be removed. Don't keep me waiting; I am sure that you want to recover your husband safe and sound before something goes wrong," Fawzi concluded, and the words smacked of unmatched ugliness.

## CHAPTER TWENTY-FOUR

# The Central Prison

Fᴵᴸᴹʏ clouds, black scum in a gray liquid sky, obscured a crescent moon. The beacon from Sidi Bou Said winked over the houses of the rich in Gammarth and Carthage. Then the charcoal smudges of cloud dispersed and the moon shone down on a sea as gray, trackless and dangerous as the desert.

Preston peered through the small, barred window in the vestibule of the Gauthiers' house at the empty steep road gouged out of the hillside. He could see the shadowy crown of an umbrella pine stirring in the wind off the bay. The sea breeze blew and filtered eddies of sand with a sinister, scraping sound around the eaves of the house. At infrequent intervals a car swept down the road, its beam dancing in the windy dark long before the car itself tore past the gate and vanished down the grade on the way to Hamilcar. At this season, almost no one came out from town. Now a car was coming up the road. Preston saw a glow of headlights hesitate and stop before the garden, then go out soundlessly. Fawzi had parked his car a little way from the house. He was starting up the stairs amid the rustling pungent bushes. The gate lamp was extinguished.

"How many men are in the car?" Anne-Marie asked.

"At least two. He may have fallen for it—we'll know in a moment."

Breathing heavily, Fawzi appeared in the doorway. He frowned when Anne-Marie motioned to him to enter.

"Where is Levanon?" he demanded testily.

"In the living room. The tablets knocked him out at once."

As soon as Anne-Marie had shut the door on the captain's large back, Preston stepped into sight from the study.

Fawzi glared at him. "I am not altogether surprised to see you. More American-Israeli collaboration? The Agency ought to select officers with less obvious prejudices." His lips were pressed into a tight clamp. "Just the same, I do not suppose that *you* are Al Houaranni's kidnapper. He is the man I am interested in. Where is he?"

Preston watched Fawzi's gestures with minute care. "Levanon is here, as promised, but there is a new factor in the equation. I want you to listen to this, Captain."

He went to the stereo tape deck and switched it on. Through the two loudspeakers could be heard clearly the conversation between Fawzi and Anne-Marie.

Fawzi listened without visible emotion to his voice saying, "It is a clumsy attempt at bribery, no matter what you choose to call it," then, at the end, Anne-Marie's voice specifying, ". . . a Beirut account solely in your name," and his concluding agreement.

Anne-Marie was staring at him, spellbound.

He shrugged. "It's not much." But uneasiness was embedded in his features like a soft tooth mark.

Preston shut the stereo off. "It's enough. The Committee may take a negative view of its Intelligence Chief accepting Israeli funds *in his own name* against the release of a top-ranking 'illegal.' "

Fawzi made a movement toward the door.

"If you're thinking of calling in your people to confiscate this too, wait just one minute. This tape is a dub; the original is in my office at the Embassy."

The captain paused and faced Anne-Marie. His eyes were as flat and dirty as mud pies. "I see. This is why you needed two hours' time: to get the recording to the Embassy and make a copy. I wondered why you were unable to turn Levanon over earlier this evening. I searched your handbag. Where was the tape recorder?"

"In her pack of cigarettes," Preston replied for Anne-Marie.

"I see," Fawzi repeated. "And of course you never intended really to produce Levanon," he added with sulky, profound disappointment.

"Oh, he is here as I told you—but the situation is reversed. Captain, we have a question too. Where is Gauthier?"

Fawzi described an impatient gesture with his arm. A basically fat man, when he pivoted on his heels, his hips had trouble catching up. In only a few years, Preston thought, he would boast a quartermaster general's paunch.

"If you take the trouble to look, you can just make him out seated in the back of my car beside a police officer."

"Why didn't you bring him into the house as arranged?"

"From what has happened, it seems that I was wise not to."

Max entered from the study. His black curls were combed and matted down, a residue of fever glittered in his alert eyes.

"Have you taken away this Arab's gun?" he grunted.

"We don't have to worry about guns tonight," Preston retorted. "The tape is a weapon."

"That's what you think. Never trust these Secret Police gangsters."

"So this is what you mean by 'disarmed and drugged'!" Tensely, Fawzi stared at his quarry, disgusted and fascinated. Finally, with a noticeable effort, he turned away and said to Preston, "This is evidently an amateurish trap set on your orders. I admit that I did not foresee the tape's existence. What do you want from me?"

"Seats for two—Gauthier and Levanon—on the ten o'clock flight tonight."

"This is impossible. The plane is full."

"Off-load two passengers—this is your prerogative. In return, you obtain the tape."

Fawzi shook his head. "No."

"Then the tape will be brought to the Committee's attention. Think about it—and the effect on your career. Suspect elements are being 'plucked out,' I think this is how you put it."

Fawzi's smooth-shaven complexion had turned yellow, like the color of unripe dates. It did not become a fat man to look so pale and slick.

"Suppose that I were mad enough to do this? As you pointed out, the master tape is at your Embassy; even if you were to hand it over together with the dub—which you have not proposed doing—how could I be sure that more copies were not made? An indefinite number of dubs can be produced from an original; their existence will lead to endless blackmail." He was breathing stertorously. "Your offer is not good

354

enough. Besides, I think the Committee will strongly doubt the tape's authenticity; hasn't your Agency peddled notoriously forged documents to other governments in the past?"

"The voice prints don't lend themselves easily to falsification. As for copies, there are just the master tape and this one dub. You'll have to accept my word for that. I don't believe you have a choice."

"The tape makes it clear that I am acting on the Committee's behalf, not my own."

"It can be interpreted otherwise . . . and the Committee is in no mood for complicated explanations."

"Why are you mounting this plot"—Fawzi's voice grated with repressed fury—"and ruining your chances of ever obtaining my cooperation again?"

"The aim is to get these people away from your hangmen," Preston said stonily, "not to put the tape into the Committee's possession."

"That is a lie. Your Agency hopes to control me in future. Blackmail is the only fitting description—"

"We're not so optimistic as to think you won't find a way of wriggling free, Captain."

"Perhaps. I don't believe your smug chatter about disinterested motives. At any rate, no matter what your objectives are—and provided that I were to agree to a bargain—I cannot immediately fulfill all the terms. Gauthier is being held at the Tunis Central Prison; it takes time and red tape to release an inmate. Even I cannot speed the process up beyond a certain point."

Anne-Marie's low, smothered exclamation of disappointment jarred them. "Then he's not in your car!"

Preston said to Fawzi, "You were supposed to bring him

355

here tonight. That was the bargain. Who is in the car?"

"Be grown up. Would I walk into an obvious trap like this without taking precautions? Until further notice her husband is securely incarcerated under heavy guard. The two men who accompanied me are police officers. There are others outside, more than you think. Have a look for yourself." He gestured in the direction of the garden gate.

Preston went to the window and looked out. The hill was silvered by moonlight; up and down the street he made out small, shadowy groups of men.

"Two more cars just turned their lights off beyond the streetlamp," Max muttered, coming away from the door.

Fawzi trembled with rage. "So it seems I do have a choice after all! Do you think I ever put the slightest faith in your absurd plan, that nonsensical, elaborate bait of a Beirut account, joint signatures, cable transfers, who knows what else? Whom do you take me for—a degenerate American politician? The money never interested me in the least, not one crooked franc. That is what is so tragic about this affair." The captain's youthful face looked bleak and careworn for the first time. "When she came to my office and claimed to be sheltering the commando leader, I decided that I must capture him at all cost and smash once and for all this whole unclean gang of murderers and spies. I came here for that sole purpose after pretending to enter into a dishonest deal. As soon as you had produced Levanon, I was going to signal my ment to storm this house by lifting my cap so." He simulated the gesture, stopping short of actually removing it. "To hell with the money!"

"In short, Captain, you were the one who organized a double-cross."

Fawzi swung about ponderously in his crisp khakis and confronted Preston with a mirthless snarl that drew his lips back over his pale gums. "No one in this house has told the truth for so long that he can recall when it was—especially you, Mr. Preston! Therefore, why preach? You had better listen instead to *my* proposal. I do not want the tape to reach the Committee, that is true, for it could prove embarrassing. In consequence, I shall dismiss the police stationed around the house immediately, then I shall put this *moujrimeen*, this murderer"—he indicated Max—"on tonight's flight. Let us get him out of the way. He is no use to anyone but he complicates the situation. Take-off time is in less than one hour. As I told you, it is utterly unthinkable to discharge her husband in time to board the plane. After we leave the airport, we shall drive to the Embassy, you will retrieve the master tape, and then you will both come with me to the Tunis Central Prison, where the exchange—Gauthier against the tape—will be made correctly, allowing time for formalities. If you fear that once the tape comes into my possession I will detain her husband or try to prevent his departure from the country, bear in mind that for all I know another dub exists. If anyone is acting on trust in this thieves' game, it is I—"

Anne-Marie at once went up to Preston. "You can't agree. Alex's freedom comes first; that's why I did exactly as you suggested and made the tape—"

"Let's listen to the rest of his plan, at least."

"Why can't he first release Alex? Then we'll worry about who boards the plane, Alex or Levanon."

"Do you expect me to conceal this wanted kidnapper on Tunisian soil indefinitely?" Fawzi's voice broke in, curt and irritable. "Either he flies out now or he faces the consequences

357

of his bloody acts. And let me assure you that if I throw him into prison he will rot there longer than is good for his health."

"You just said that he was of no use to you," Preston objected.

"Certainly. You notice that I have not even inquired how he sneaked into Tunis while we thought that he was bottled up on Cap Bon? It is of no real interest. But this is not the point. If we wait too long, word of his presence will reach the Committee; they will begin asking questions and then the whole matter will be in their hands, not mine."

Preston glanced at Anne-Marie but found no consent on her face. He checked his watch. "I think we should come to an agreement and get moving."

"I don't believe him," Anne-Marie said. "It's a trick to keep Alex and get hold of the tape."

"I'm not so sure we can do otherwise at this point than what the captain proposes."

"Then from the prison we'll bring Alex straight back here?" Anne-Marie's question was directed at both men.

Fawzi nodded in somber silence.

"All right, we agree to your plan," Preston said abruptly.

Throughout, eyes darting from one secretive face to another, Max had not uttered a single word.

They stood outdoors, gathered into a small, taut group in the gusty dark. Fawzi had dismissed the policemen and sent them back to Tunis in the two cars parked down the street. He moved briskly around Max. "I don't want this swine seated near me, but I shall need his passport. Let him get in back with Madame. Occupy the place beside me," he said to Preston.

As they drove onto the main Tunis highway, Fawzi spoke again.

"The Swiss francs in the envelope were not Israeli funds. This was another lie, wasn't it? The money came from your Agency's *caisse noire*, I suppose. Who else is rich enough to afford such whims?"

Preston shrugged.

"Am I not right?"

"If it consoles you, we had a hard time rounding up the sum on short notice."

"This complete breakdown of cooperation would never have occurred if the United States government had not insisted on infiltrating Israeli terrorists into this country."

"That is entirely untrue."

"Then why were you present tonight where you had no business?" Fawzi snapped. "Because of the woman, naturally —I have seen the confidential report on your private life. She is your mistress; let's hope that she will show gratitude."

In the dark, Anne-Marie's hand gripped Preston's shoulder, commanding him to keep his temper.


By the time they arrived, the overhead clock in the airport hall marked nine-forty-five and outbound passengers were being summoned onto the field. Relatives and visitors and police milled about the departure gate; the arrival gate was deserted.

Fawzi proceeded hurriedly to the Airport Police Office and motioned to Preston, Anne-Marie and Max to wait while he disappeared behind the door inscribed ENTRÉE INTERDITE. The outer office was staffed by three young policemen who had saluted when Fawzi strode in. They stared without friendliness at the foreign group. The office was equipped with a bulletin board, stamps and inking pads, and a well-thumbed, dog-eared card index in a steel file box. After a few seconds the captain re-emerged from the inner office, unsmiling, and led them down the corridor.

Taking them aside, he said in an undertone, "It is arranged; the Jew can leave."

Then for the first time he addressed Max directly. "Here is your passport—you will be leaving with the same forged document on which you were admitted. We have taken note of the number and notched each page; it is worthless after this trip. Keep it; we don't want your trashy property. I am communicating the details to the West German Embassy, and naturally your full description goes to the police in all Arab and European countries. Your filthy career as a terrorist is over."

"*Ain Davar!* It doesn't matter," Max grunted as he pocketed the green passport in the name of Hans Konrad Stoerchler, real-estate agent.

Fawzi's somber eyes shone with malicious vengefulness. "Before you escape, I have one piece of news for you. Kol Israel has just reported one hundred cases of water poisoning in the Emek Hefer region. Bacteria have been found in wells and streams and the Israeli Cabinet is holding an emergency session. Al Houaranni's front claims credit for the attack."

Max nodded as though he had been smacked in the face and his bull head rolled from side to side.

"Go to the devil," he muttered thickly and turned to Preston. "You see? By capturing Al Houaranni we wanted to stamp out this barbarism. Perhaps the means were wrong, but the intention was defensible. I am more persuaded of that than ever. I think that should it be necessary—and for the moment it is—we will try again to put an end to this sickness."

"I'm skeptical of moral justifications for Intelligence operations," Preston said.

"You are not in our place; remember this. For us there is not so much choice." Max said to Anne-Marie, "I want to thank you for saving my life. You are a courageous woman; please never change. Fortunately I don't think you will. I hope that all goes well for your husband and son. If it had been in my power, perhaps I would not be leaving first."

"Before you go," Preston intervened, "there's one thing I'd like to know."

"It is of no interest—" Fawzi burst in.

"It is to me. How did you manage to make your way back to Tunis?" Out of the corner of his eye Preston saw that Fawzi, who had been too proud to ask, was paying close attention.

Levanon studied each of them with mild contempt and took his time about answering. "On a mission you must be lucky and in good health; this is no secret. A little indisposition did not put me out of business. You know that I stopped at a village café to call Gauthier? When I came out, I found a bus filled with teachers and students preparing to drive into Tunis to demonstrate their support of the Revolution. I jumped on and became a demonstrator. The troops waved us through all the checkpoints. So what was so wonderful about that?"

He waved to them with what might have been disdain or revulsion and ran after the last of the embarking passengers

361

who were hurrying down the departure corridor with the taut expression of people who mistrusted the Committee's benevolence and feared that it might abruptly cease.

Fawzi's face worked queerly as he watched Max exit on the far side of the Passport Control booth unchallenged, but the captain had a good grip on himself and said nothing.

Past the gate Max trotted toward the waiting Caravelle. He sweat in the night as the winter breeze blew over the airfield. So this was the way out he had so ardently sought. It led through a narrow gate, alone and in discomfiture. He could not escape the thought of Marston and Black, who had not found a similar way, and those he was leaving behind who were still seeking it; of the commandos' deceptively uneventful landing at this airport three days ago; and of the two-story, blue-shuttered summer retreat on Cap Bon which, during thirty-six hours of their lives, had become a safe-house, a staging area and a sort of home. What was it the General had said? "There will come times when you wonder whether what you are doing is right."

He was the last to turn in his boarding pass, and this was their last vision of him—a stout, middle-aged, obstreperous member of the Israeli Secret Service, citrus farmer and father of two, who was returning to ten acres of lemon groves near Natanya, a man who throughout various scourges and wanderings had never lost altogether the quality of belief.

He clambered up the passenger ladder without deigning to cast a single glance behind.


Anne-Marie sat in silence beside Preston, hands touching conspiratorially without cheer, as they sped through darkened

Tunis (they had revised the seating arrangements after stopping off at the American Embassy). Fawzi concentrated on the road ahead, bent on ending this despicable day. Although it was all settled and they were on their way to release her husband, Anne-Marie could not overcome a foreboding of evil.

They plunged down Avenue Hedi Cheker, past the Porte du Miel, along Boulevard Hedi Saidi. The little acacia trees rustled in the wind. A stuffy smell of cooking oil permeated the air. At one major intersection—Bab Sadoun—parked command cars and weapons carriers formed shadowy disturbing masses. They passed blind reeking staircases and slummy cafés festooned with loops of red and white electric bulbs, the national colors, which went out abruptly as they flew past; from a few villainous-looking rooms naked lemon light peeped out behind wooden shutters. The curfew would come into force at 11 P.M. but traffic was already sparse. Except for a few cyclists, they encountered no one; then two minicabs swept hell-bent down the street like bats, their yellow headlights turned up full, swinging wildly into the curves, and the beams turned up a pack of cats in an empty lot scavenging an overturned garbage can.

Straight up a divided highway and then Fawzi braked with a lurch before the Central Prison's thick towering walls. Around this compound, Preston had seen the families of inmates lining up humbly to be admitted during afternoon visiting hours; but there was no life here at night. Before the sturdy Moorish doors they waited. Then one portal swung open on oiled hinges, an unkempt guard peered at them from the darkness within and with a mutter stepped aside as he spied Fawzi's khaki uniform.

Following the captain, they passed under a broad stone arch and entered the forecourt. Palms swayed in the moist breeze with a dry, nervous click and incantation. In the moonlit night a watchtower designed in the incongruous form of a minaret rose ghostly and sinister. The guard scurried to bring up the rear as Fawzi snapped an order and struck off down a passageway.

The spartan room to which he introduced them was the warden's office. A fluorescent tube lit the corners mercilessly in hideous green. Here, too, the President's portrait had been removed, leaving a telltale blank space on the wall. While the guard took up a position beside the door, Fawzi deposited himself with a soft murmur of satisfaction in a leather chair behind a massive, ugly walnut desk.

He looked at them with a mixture of resentment and wariness and cunning. There are few men past thirty who can feed and toast throughout a dinner, as he apparently had, and not show it before midnight. He sat at the desk, flushed and buttoned up, his features settling into an attitude of replete complacence.

"Good! So now I have carried out my promise and in return you will turn over the tape."

"Where is Gauthier?" Preston asked sharply. "Where is the warden?"

"All in good time. I shall do no more until I have the tape—and the dub too."

Preston began to speak, then thought better of it and placed the tape box on the desk. It contained the master tape and rewound dub on the same spool.

Fawzi did not pick the box up. He was scrutinizing Preston dispassionately. "There is one more condition—"

"There are no other conditions, Captain."

Anne-Marie sat erect, green eyes large and attentive.

"You will sign a statement that I shall dictate declaring that this tape is a CIA forgery from start to finish, intended, for base purposes, to confuse and mislead the Committee. Have you a pen? I want this written, signed and dated in your hand."

A vein was throbbing with angry excitement in Preston's eye, but Fawzi fortunately could not spot that. The deal with this fox had been perilous to begin with; now, visibly, it had boomeranged. How? "Yes, I have a pen"—Preston tapped his shirt pocket—"but I plan to sign nothing. You know the tape is genuine."

"I know it, but that is beside the point." Fawzi shifted his large bottom in the leather seat. They suddenly realized that he was altogether, possessively at home here, secure in his bailiwick, his power buttressed by the stone walls, the barred windows, the unseen but hinted presence of other guards prowling within call. "The tape is useless to me, as you well know," he continued. "Am I an uneducated street Arab to accept your meaningless promise to refrain from blackmail? For all I know, dozens of dubs besides this one have already been made and are being distributed by your busy Agency. And as long as one dub remains in existence outside my control, you—or someone—can be tempted to use it to destroy me. The statement you are going to sign neutralizes this danger. It constitutes a solid guarantee, unlike an Intelligence officer's trivial word of honor. The statement will remain locked up in my personal safe—this is my promise to *you*— unless, of course, your people foolishly try to pressure me. Fortunately, I had time during the drive from the airport to sort out matters in my mind and decide what to do about your fancy mousetrap."

Preston had cast a glance around the office.

"The guard does not understand a word of what we are saying, if that is a hope you are entertaining." Fawzi leaned forward. "Unless you sign the statement, this woman will not leave the prison. Remember that I have issued a valid warrant for her arrest. It can be delivered right now. On the other hand, she can walk out of here tonight as freely as she entered; I have no special interest in detaining her. You are her lover and claim to be concerned about her well-being; now is the time to prove it."

"What sort of fantastic extortion is this, Fawzi? Is this why you were so eager to bring us here? Are you going to jail her on trumped-up espionage charges after letting Levanon escape?"

"The two cases are very different. When I saw Levanon board the plane, I honestly thought, Good riddance! What was I to do with the fat pig? His operation had failed miserably; the network was smashed. But she is important to me as a means of forcing you to sign the statement—as a hostage, if you like." He sat back, talked out, with a grunt of exhaustion, but continued to eye Preston speculatively.

"You plan to make me sign this under duress?"

"If you put it that way, yes."

"What is wrong with both of you?" Anne-Marie blurted. "Do you remember why we came here in the first place? When will you release Alex? I no longer believe in your deals." She was unnerved by the prison's deep neutral silence. It seemed no place for keeping commitments; indifference to the future was rubbed into its smooth walls and haunted its

366

long corridors; it was as unpromising as a stagnant pond.

Fawzi wheeled on her at once, his eyes flashing. "Nothing more can be done for your husband, I am afraid. Within an hour of his arrest he appeared before a special military court at Le Bardo fortress. He was tried on the charges I described to you. On the basis of overwhelming evidence he was found guilty on all counts and he was sentenced to be hanged. Under our law there is no provision for appeal in such cases; the President can grant a pardon, but since he quit office this power has reverted to the Committee, which decided not to accord mercy. The sentence was carried out without further delay at six P.M."

Anne-Marie had shuddered and emitted a single, low involuntary cry and was clutching Preston's hand in a brittle death grip. She had brought her other hand up to her mouth and was biting on it savagely.

"You filthy killer!" Preston shouted at Fawzi. "He was already dead when she came to see you. You could never deliver on that deal! That's Tunisian justice and Arab honor."

Anne-Marie was undergoing shock to a degree that appalled Preston. It would have reassured him to have her break out in a sustained moan of despair or a cold dizzy sweat and collapse to the floor—any reaction, in short, but this immobile, soundless horror.

Fawzi was not so easily discomfited. "Be careful of the language you use, though I am taking into account that you are overwrought. You are supposed to be a professional diplomat who measures his words under stress. You are forgetting that Gauthier was for years this country's most dangerous enemy. How many Arab deaths do you think he indirectly caused through information he wormed out of this government? Control your temper, please, and take care of her."

"Where is he?" Anne-Marie asked in an almost inaudible, throaty voice.

"We are not Syrians who display the executed in public under spotlights before television cameras. He is at the morgue; decent arrangements have been made for his burial."

Anne-Marie rose. "I am going to be sick," she said weakly.

"No, don't you go," Fawzi told Preston and motioned to the guard to escort the woman from the office.

As soon as she was out of earshot, Preston began to shout again. "He was a French citizen. Paris is going to make your life miserable—"

"It will protest just enough for the press's benefit," Fawzi said with scorn, "but the French government knows better than to make an issue of this affair. Privately it has already indicated as much. Through reliable channels we are transmitting to Paris a detailed file about Gauthier's activities on behalf of Israel. It is unbelievable, you know, what he got away with. He confessed to a great deal. However, in the first instance, I suppose that we have only our own corruptibility and gullibility to blame."

"Don't hand out that sanctimonious vomit to justify what you did. What 'overwhelming evidence' did you have—and why the hurry?"

"Listen, before Gauthier appeared for sentencing we managed to extract the shortwave frequency and time schedule from him and there was some thought of hoodwinking Ha Mossad with a series of signals. But we could not raise his people; apparently they had broken contact with him, anticipating the worst. Does this mean they won't infiltrate other agents? Of course not! But Gauthier's death will cause them to think twice. That's the reason why we proceeded so quickly." Fawzi paused, pale cheeks gleaming.

"As for evidence, when I say 'overwhelming,' I am hardly exaggerating the facts. For the past two years Gauthier ran an agent named Ali Ben Larbi, a minor civil servant who penetrated the Inner Committee. He played an essential role in Al Houaranni's kidnapping. Although we knew nothing of this, it was obvious that an Israeli agent existed in the government and that he was employed at the Interior Ministry. Through a process of elimination Ben Larbi and a number of his colleagues fell under suspicion. Accordingly they were placed under surveillance. It was, in fact, Kheli's last official act before the coup, and I must admit that the colonel had a certain flair. When I assumed his functions last night, I simply renewed the order to maintain surveillance without thinking much about it one way or another.

"Now from the way we have reconstituted the sequence of events, Gauthier this morning learned from Levanon of the kidnap commando's collapse. He concluded rightly that his own cover was dangerously jeopardized. This conclusion was reinforced when he heard official confirmation on the radio of one agent's arrest on Cap Bon. I can take credit for that broadcast, which was made deliberately for the purpose of stampeding whoever was masterminding the operation. Ha Mossad may also have tipped Gauthier off and given him orders to clear out, although this is not certain. At any rate, he went to Ben Larbi to obtain a priority travel order for the evening flight because he was the only person Gauthier could turn to in the confused situation following the coup. It was an ultimate gamble—or perhaps, considering the depressed

369

state he was in after the botched kidnapping, a disguised form of suicide. I suppose that a nervous crisis was overdue; fourteen years is a long time to hide your true personality. There is no doubt he blamed himself for the kidnapping's failure and that this weighed on his action. He told us as much.

"The significant thing is that he might have gotten away with the gamble, but as it happened my men saw a European enter Ben Larbi's building. They promptly informed me and I told them to check the foreigner's papers when he emerged. Gauthier took alarm, made a dash for his car, opened fire and was overpowered. I had simply ordered my men to carry out a routine *vérification d'identité*. You see, we had no firm proof whatever of Ben Larbi's guilt. Oh, it would have come to the same in the end, for once we had an inkling that Gauthier the journalist was in contact with Ben Larbi the civil servant we would have put two and two together. There is no doubt at all that Gauthier's time had run out."

"And you're pleased with yourself?"

"In a way, yes. I performed my duty."

Fawzi paused again and stared pensively at Preston. "One curious aspect is that he went to his death persuaded that he had stepped into a trap laid by Ben Larbi. This wasn't true at all. I am sure that we could in the end have turned Ben Larbi around, but this is not what actually happened. Ben Larbi had never come to us with the truth. After the gun battle on Rue Ibn Khaldoun we rounded him up and interrogated him. For a fairy boy he managed to muster some pluck; I am afraid we had to be rough with him. He ended up by giving all the information he could give. After that, Gauthier could deny whatever he pleased, the case against him was airtight.

"I want to see him," Anne-Marie said. She had returned t

the office, looking pale and inhumanly composed. "Can I go to the morgue?"

"Naturally. In due time." Fawzi reached into the warden's desk drawer. "Your husband left this letter for you."

Anne-Marie sat down, accepted the oblong white envelope and broke it open. Visibly she had not wept. It seemed to Preston that this struggle to bolster up her self-control was so solitary and profound and inward-directed that it afforded no hold with which to save her. In the room's crude light her face wavered a bit, as though Time had moved across the curved planes of her oval cheeks and taken up a stalking position.

"Can't you see that she's had enough?" he railed furiously at Fawzi. "Why don't you ease up on her?"

"It's all right," she interrupted. "I won't break down again."

Anne-Marie read the letter without quite comprehending its message. It was two pages long. She recognized her husband's even script at the start, but succeeding passages were crawled and, it seemed, not altogether coherent. Later, she promised herself, she would read it with complete application. Anne-Marie had lost all notion of time in this austere office where the fluorescent overhead light bathed the men's faces in a hideous green tint. It might have been midnight or noon; they were as isolated as in a cavern.

She recalled her last glimpse of her husband from the terrace on Rue Didon. What had it all amounted to? Her husband was a man who had sailed a boat in the bay of Carthage, believed wholeheartedly in a cause and come to grief because he had taken his sick son to the doctor. Her husband had been brave, but courage wasn't enough. Morbidly she wondered how the intervening hours had altered him, and especially she

371

speculated about that transcendent moment in a foul cell when he had realized that he was going to be marched out to the gallows without assistance or comfort. Her imagination was not particularly rich, but she thought that she caught the moment's smell and substance. One ends as one fears—her husband had dreaded solitude; he had died alone. In a cruel abstract way it was perhaps fitting that he had died in this country. She knew that he had been receptive to the chill purity of Islam rubbed smooth by fervor as a rock is by tides, the chilliness that was not indifference but humility in the presence of grandeur.

"What have you decided?" Fawzi asked glacially.

"She can't be allowed to go to jail," Preston said. "I never entered my mind. Start dictating."

"You'll be perjuring yourself." Anne-Marie made a gesture to restrain him. "He can use the statement to wreck your career. I no longer care what happens to me—"

Preston firmly set her hand aside and placed on the desk a ball-point pen he had unclipped from his shirt pocket.

It was Fawzi's greatest triumph to date. He watched the European woman who sat upright and tearless and the proud American who was cursing coldly and helplessly but who accepted the sheet of paper and began to write compliantly as he was told.

# An Incomplete Puzzle

"THE President's death," Mills said a week later, "has settled numerous problems for the Committee and rendered it almost respectable. People are already forgetting how it came to power. A smooth transition helps. And I can't help but admire the way in which the loose ends of the Al Houaranni affair have been tied up. For example, the rumor that the third kidnapper died of fever on Cap Bon and was secretly buried. No one is going to challenge *that*. Have you grasped that Al Houaranni's main purpose in flying here was to pressure the Committee—if and when it overthrew the government —to cancel Western oil concessions in the desert? That's what had me in an uproar, since the Committee was ready at that point to make romantic commitments. Now it's being more realistic. I think we can look forward to what the French call 'correct relationship' with them—all the more so as a result of your hocus-pocus." He picked up the ball-point pen that Preston had unclipped in the warden's office and re-examined it casually. The interior contained a miniaturized tape recorder of U.S. Army Signal Corps manufacture. "In this business I don't normally put much faith in gadgetry, but this item performed in the crunch."

"It might not have worked in a more sophisticated country."

"I can imagine Fawzi's reaction when he hears the playback. That's unmistakably his voice acknowledging that the original tape is genuine. It certainly renders worthless the statement you signed at the prison. This recording ought to keep him in order for a while to come. It could be that eventually we recruit him, in which case those ten thousand dollars—for which I was personally accountable; it gave me a sleepless night—would make him the cheapest agent we've ever taken on at Cabinet level."

"I would never trust him."

"Of course he did try to put over a specially dirty one on you. But admit that you never hit it off with him. That's why you'll be more useful elsewhere; future liaison between you two could be sticky." Mills looked down upon the broad avenue, the bawling noises and ragged traffic of workaday Tunis. "You'll go and present Fawzi with this memento of his carelessness, and it will be your last contact with him. Wait until she's clear out of the country—we don't need any further hitches. Are you going to see her off?"

"Yes."

"How is she now?"

"About as could be expected."

Mills nodded. "At least Fawzi has granted her an exit visa. You know, her husband must have driven her to distraction. He was a complex man with a neurotic side; that type is sometimes capable of achieving brilliant offbeat results. I'm sorry I had no opportunity to know him better." Mills added with all of a propertied Philadelphian's blandness

"Until he went to pieces he was certainly one of Ha Mossad's best men."

The large house on Rue Didon already had a forsaken air. Furniture stood crated outdoors on the pavement watched over by a glum Arab.

Anne-Marie stood in the dismantled living room overseeing the packing by two workmen. She smiled at Preston, but it was a lukewarm, strained smile, perfunctory and devoid of warmth.

"Are there any books or records you want? I've already given away so much, but as it is the movers' bill is going to be enormous."

"You're in such a damned hurry to leave."

"If it weren't for all the clothes, I'd be flying." She was sailing on the *Kairouan* at three o'clock that afternoon.

"They're transferring me so that I won't be PNG-d," he told her. "The orders arrived this morning."

"What is PNG-d?"

"Being declared *persona non grata*. Fawzi would surely sign the order with pleasure."

She said nothing.

People always end up alone, of course, Preston thought, one way or the other, but in Anne-Marie's case the moment had overtaken her with indecent haste.

"I don't want you to go away like this, alone. I want you to come with me. Otherwise, it all seems such a waste."

"How can you believe that? I loved you." She touched his creased, chilly face, then let her hand fall. "I have a good memory, and I'll always remember what you tried to do. Why

375

did you? You knew that if it succeeded I was going to leave with him."

"I did it for us. Don't think I was being noble or altruistic, for God's sake." He bristled promptly; no unjust accusation could have drawn a more hostile reaction. "If I had saved him, you would be flying out with me."

"You came to this city at the wrong time, Michael."

Anne-Marie seldom uttered his first name. She said distractedly, "I left the garage keys on the terrace. Do you want to come with me?"

He followed her. He could have wrung her slender, uncooperative neck in bitter frustration.

"Listen, how is it possible? How can it have lasted so short a time? How can Time play such tricks?" Preston was thinking with rage: It must have been happiness because it had lasted no longer than a heartbeat; happiness didn't have the stubborn, rooted-in longevity of deprival and loss.

"It wasn't a trick. We reacted to each other . . . for the worse. Supposedly, to do things to one another is a form of love."

"Then why is it over?"

"It just is. Do you remember? I was afraid it could never work out."

"I think back often and feel that my best chance of keeping you was not to have been with you that afternoon at my cottage."

Anne-Marie wheeled on him. "I have no choice. You understand that, don't you? I have a son to think about. What do you do exactly, what do you tell a boy whose father has been hanged as a spy?" She was slipping out of control again as she had a number of times during the past week. "Do you know what he wrote in his letter? 'I regret nothing of my action; it was done to repay a great debt.' He also said, 'I hope that Marc will be loved and that you will be happy.' No one else was mentioned, no relative or friend."

"Don't start thinking about it again, Anne-Marie."

"Do you realize that I'm not even sure where he came from? Depending on his mood, he told me different things. Once he said he was born in a village in Sudetenland; then he contradicted himself and said he was born and grew up in a poor district of Vienna."

"Does it matter all that much?"

"Yes, it does matter to me." She tossed back her hair in thwarted freedom. "So now we'll never know. Perhaps he made it all up."

Preston saw no point in remarking that on the streets of Europe today walked hundreds of Gauthiers whose real names were obliterated, their birthplaces a blank and their early careers a mystery. He shook his head. A week before, it had seemed unlikely, but now he missed and felt a sad fellowship with that blond man who had been beating with such single-minded willfulness toward an awful goal he would not acknowledge.

"Spying can be as intoxicating as, say, taking dope," he said.

"What are you driving at?" she asked, annoyed.

"From time to time it provides the satisfaction of being one step ahead of everybody else."

"Doesn't this apply to you too?"

"It could," Preston said unbendingly.

"Yet you want me to begin again?"

He heard the scrape of tires in the street but Anne-Marie

377

gave no indication that she was aware of the sound. She was watching him wide-eyed and curious. He knew that in her view he was already identified with the unhealthy mangy past; the present belonged to those who hadn't harmed her.

"You ought to come with me," he said. "It's as simple as that."

"You know it's never as simple as that."

"For just one moment admit that the past is over. Don't you think we ought to take advantage of the opportunity?"

"Yes, but not together."

"If you leave alone, you'll be running out on everything."

A vein in her neck trembled. "I know." It was no expression of assent. She was studying him like a stranger. It was the same stubbornness that had led her to refuse to stay longer at his cottage that afternoon.

"Will you at least give it a chance?"

"I couldn't be any good to you now. He'd always be there standing alongside and judging me."

Preston looked down coldly upon Gauthier's untended garden. How often in one short, adult life does a man find a woman he feels it would be a mortal error to part from, to go onward without? Preston had felt this way about two women only, who, instead of anchoring his life, drove it toward the open sea. Whether there would be time and enthusiasm for a third, he strongly doubted. When he had arrived in Tunisia his motto had been: "Just take life as it comes . . ."; it had prevented him from appreciating Anne-Marie, the significance of that summer, and the uniqueness of each moment. And above all, he had always misjudged the rapidity with which his stay here was approaching a close.

"Your taxi is here," he said in anger directed mostly at himself.

"Don't feel offended by the way I'm behaving. I'm not being very nice with you."

"I'm coming with you to the port."

"No."

All that subsisted of the affair now was rancor, he thought, but this would diminish with time, then fondness and an intermittent dizzy, urgent, sickening want would replace it, only to falter, to be succeeded by haphazard stabs of remembrance, which would also flag. If love was a disease, why couldn't it last, be incurable, recur when you believed that you were forever healed? He was sure that far too soon the day would come when he would look forward to another woman's attractions.

Preston made an abrupt, choppy gesture of surrender. Suddenly time had sped up; he realized that Tunisia and his life, at least the last year, were one and the same, woven together inseparably into an austere pattern; that it was impossible to repudiate one without the other; that both were lodged irrecoverably in a period of time from which he was hurtling off at tremendous speed into a tunnel of middle age; and he foresaw that soon—far too soon, no matter what he did to check the onward rush—he would enter the tunnel and, worse, consider it a blessing and call it peace of mind.


The white Cathedral towers stand out more distinctly than ever they did before the detail of the coast is clear it is *grand beau temps* over the land a breeze blowing up the

bay stirs the thorny broom on the uninhabited point    there's
the yacht club dwarfed under the red eroded cliffs of Sidi
Bou Said where mansion and minaret are assembled in an artful jumble like gleaming pieces of an incomplete puzzle    the
puny cliffs recede quickly    the whole intrepid scheme of bay
and smudged hills and pagan ruins slides into view, glistens
and diminishes    a bell buoy tolls and lurches    a mess
steward hurries aft to the first-class dining room    the water
is Mediterranean blue, that royal blue so intense that it daz-
zles you time and time again    why am I leaving?    I
want to be with him, feel his breath    I needed him once    the
waves dash up tossing steely blue-black manes; the sea rises to
the deck and falls off in defeat    once upon a time I thought
I would be leaving with relief; instead—    I struggled so hard
to escape    it's unfair    I love each palm, each particle of
sand; I never want to lose this country for a fraction of a second
again    the sea is no ally of the coast; it is no platform for
memory    a white cube—house or marabout?—catches the
light on the sunniest bluff    you can still see a neutral line
Tunisia has drawn across the present, formed of arid eleva-
tions here and there whose inhabitants are a question mark
then suddenly it's gone too, below the horizon    drowned
overcome lost unfulfilled    and that's the end of Africa!

If you would like a complete list of Arrow books
please send a postcard to
P.O. Box 29, Douglas, Isle of Man, Great Britain.

*Other Arrow Books of interest:*

# Robert Rostand

## THE KILLER ELITE

Locken was the best agent SYOPS had – till Hansen crippled him with three methodically placed bullets.

Now almost a year later, Locken's old boss offers him a fresh assignment – and a chance to settle the score with the man who maimed him.

The job – to shield a deposed African premier – is strictly unofficial.

And, with the world's top three assassins hired to kill him first, very nearly impossible. . . .

# Austin Ferguson

# JETSTREAM

As Transcon Flight 602 leaves San Francisco for New York, the bad weather reports start to come in.

And there are personal worries for the men flying the plane - for Captain Peter Douglas, whose wife is undergoing a life-or-death operation, for co-pilot Stan Burkhardt, faced with a rediscovered love which jeopardizes his carefully laid plans.

Among the passengers, too, there are those who stand at crossroads in their lives. But soon private fears and sorrows are to be overwhelmed by sudden – and horrifying – violence.

For as the Boeing 727 heads into one of the worst blizzards in memory it carries a human time-bomb, a desperate man determined to seize freedom – even if it costs the lives of everybody on board.

**Richard Haley**

## SAXBY FOR GOD

Bob Saxby hasn't done badly for a working-class lad. With money, power and a beautiful wife he's got everything a charming ambitious bastard could hope for.

Or nearly everything. He's within striking distance of becoming the local MP – and he doesn't intend to miss his chance.

Then into the Saxby stronghold walks Esther Moore. Too attractive – and too clever – to be anything but a threat.